D1033111

COMPUTER GAME-PLAYING: Theory and Practice

ELLIS HORWOOD SERIES IN ARTIFICIAL INTELLIGENCE

Series Editor: **Professor John Campbell,** University of Exeter

COMPUTER GAME PLAYING: Theory and Practice
Edited by M. A. BRAMER, The Open University, Milton Keynes

MACHINE INTELLIGENCE 8: Machine Representations of Knowledge
Edited by E. W. ELCOCK, University of Western Ontario, and D. MICHIE, University of Edinburgh

MACHINE INTELLIGENCE 9
Edited by J. E. HAYES, D. MICHIE, University of Edinburgh, and L. I. MIKULICH, Academy of Sciences, USSR

MACHINE INTELLIGENCE 10: Intelligent Systems: Practice and Perspective
Edited by J. E. HAYES and D. MICHIE, University of Edinburgh, and Y-H. PAO, Case Western Reserve University, Cleveland, Ohio

IMPLICATIONS OF COMPUTER INTELLIGENCE
Edited by M. YAZDANI and A. NARAYANAN, University of Exeter

AUTOMATIC NATURAL LANGUAGE PARSING
K. SPARCK JONES, University of Cambridge, and Y. WILKS, University of Exeter

COMMUNICATING WITH DATA BASES IN NATURAL LANGUAGE
M. WALLACE, ICL, Bracknell, Berks

COMPUTER GAME-PLAYING: Theory and Practice

Edited by
M. A. BRAMER, Ph.D. (Computer Science), MBCS
Faculty of Mathematics
The Open University

ELLIS HORWOOD LIMITED
Publishers · Chichester

Halsted Press: a division of
JOHN WILEY & SONS
New York · Brisbane · Chichester · Ontario

First published in 1983 by
ELLIS HORWOOD LIMITED
Market Cross House, Cooper Street, Chichester, West Sussex, PO19 1EB, England

The publisher's colophon is reproduced from James Gillison's drawing of the ancient Market Cross, Chichester.

Distributors:

Australia, New Zealand, South-east Asia:
Jacaranda-Wiley Ltd., Jacaranda Press,
JOHN WILEY & SONS INC.,
G.P.O. Box 859, Brisbane, Queensland 40001, Australia

Canada:
JOHN WILEY & SONS CANADA LIMITED
22 Worcester Road, Rexdale, Ontario, Canada.

Europe, Africa:
JOHN WILEY & SONS LIMITED
Baffins Lane, Chichester, West Sussex, England.

North and South America and the rest of the world:
Halsted Press: a division of
JOHN WILEY & SONS
605 Third Avenue, New York, N.Y. 10016, U.S.A.

British Library Cataloguing in Publication Data
Bramer, M. A.
Computer game-playing. – (Ellis Horwood series in artificial intelligence).
1. Electronic Games 2. Artificial Intelligence
I. Title
794 GV1469.2

Library of Congress Card No. 83–10678
ISBN 0-85312-488-4 (Ellis Horwood Ltd.)
ISBN 0-470-27466-2 (Halsted Press)

Typeset in Press Roman by Ellis Horwood Ltd.
Printed in Great Britain by R. J. Acford, Chichester.

Table of Contents

Foreword

This collection of articles has been brought together to provide an overview of Artificial Intelligence approaches to constructing game-playing programs. Papers on both theory and practice are included.

Game-playing can claim to be not only one of the oldest task areas for Artificial Intelligence research but also the best-known and arguably the most successful. Chess-playing programs regularly perform well in tournaments against human opposition and are approaching (some would say they have reached) master standard. A Checkers program is said to perform at around world championship level and a Backgammon program has beaten the reigning world champion in a match. A number of strong programs for a variety of games are available at low cost for the hobbyist microcomputer owner and purpose-built game-playing machines are now on sale in many department stores.

The modern history of game-playing programs goes back to Claude Shannon's classic paper 'Programming a digital computer for playing Chess', which was published in 1950 (*Philosophical Magazine,* **41**(314), pp. 256–275), but an electromechanical device for playing the chess endgame King and Rook against King was built by a Spanish inventor Torres y Quevedo in the 1890s and demonstrated at the Paris World Fair of 1900. Newell, Shaw and Simon, in their 1958 paper 'Chess-playing programs and the problem of complexity' (reprinted in *Computers and Thought,* edited by E. A. Feigenbaum and J. Feldman, McGraw-Hill, 1963, pp. 39–70) justified their interest in chess from the Artificial Intelligence viewpoint in the following way:

> *Chess is the intellectual game* par excellence. *Without a chance device to obscure the contest, it pits two intellects against each other in a situation so complex that neither can hope to understand it completely, but sufficiently amenable to analysis that each can hope to outthink his opponent. The game is sufficiently deep and subtle in its implications to have supported the rise of professional players, and to have allowed a deepening analysis through 200 years of intensive study and play without becoming exhausted*

or barren. Such characteristics mark chess as a natural area for attempts at mechanization. If one could devise a successful chess machine, one would seem to have penetrated to the core of human intellectual endeavor.

Although chess has remained the major area of interest – and is the topic of seven papers in this collection – a number of other games have attracted attention. There are four papers here on Go, a game which because of the large number of moves available at every stage is not amenable to the conventional method of 'brute-force search plus evaluation function' in more than a very limited way. There are two papers on Scrabble, two on Reversi and its near-relative Othello, one on Poker, one on the 'problem-solving' card game New Eleusis and even one on Three-cushion Billiards, a game that might seem at first glance to require more manual dexterity than analytical judgement.

In addition to the papers which deal predominantly with particular games, which themselves raise many of the issues central to Artificial Intelligence (such as representation of knowledge, knowledge-based problem solving, planning and machine learning), there are three papers which give a detailed account of various aspects of the general theory of searching game trees and an initial 'overview' paper by Professor Donald Michie which places some recent work on game-playing in a broader context.

The depth of treatment of each game reflects the amount of previous work in that area and the likely familiarity of the reader with the game itself. Thus for Reversi, the full rules are given together with a fairly detailed account of a general playing strategy, whereas for chess the reader is assumed to be aware of the rules and there are a number of detailed accounts of quite specialised aspects of the overall problem.

This collection is a revised and extended version of one which first appeared as a special issue of the newsletter of the Special Interest Group on Artificial Intelligence of the Association for Computing Machinery.

PART I – OVERVIEW

1

Game-playing programs and the conceptual interface†

Donald Michie
Machine Intelligence Research Unit,
University of Edinburgh, UK

ABSTRACT

Continuing decline in the cost of computer memories encourages use of tabular representations. Their main drawback is user-inscrutability, which also afflicts, for a complementary reason, conventional calculation intensive representations. Representations employed in expert systems fall between the two extremes.

INTRODUCTION

Numerous scientifically and socially important functions are too complex to evaluate by hand. Many are too complex to evaluate even by machine. Examples abound in large combinatorial domains – route-finding, network design, scheduling and allocation problems, chemical inference, game-playing and many more. The infeasibility problem has been popularised by Knuth (1976).

The interest of some infeasible computations is so great that trained human specialists consume their lives obtaining inaccurate and unreliable hand solutions on the basis that these are better than nothing. The skilled approximators are called experts and are paid highly either in cash or (in the case of chess-masters) in fame.

†Abridged from a lecture entitled 'Problems of the conceptual interface' delivered at the 'Prospects for Man' Symposium at York University, Toronto, 1980, under the auspices of the Royal Society of Canada.

Machine methods enter the picture in a number of ways:

1. Interactive programs for generating candidate solutions within constraints enable experts to make better informed and better researched guesses. An example is CONGEN (see Carhart, 1977a and b) developed at Edinburgh for assisting industrial chemists to identify unknown compounds.
2. Machine representations of expert knowledge can have a lower consultation cost than the expert, while being smart enough to out-guess him most of the time. Expert systems (Michie, 1979a) can advantageously be originated stepwise from (1).
3. Evasion of the whole problem may be possible by a trick. The trick requires a large memory and has been tested only in chess (Michie, 1979b). But there are no technical reasons for not trying it more widely.

THE LOOKUP MACHINE

We start with the following question.

Given that algorithmic evaluation of some function is hard, is there any reason why its inverse should also be hard?

'Let me see', says the reader, '*square* is the inverse of *square-root,* and *square* is easy; *square-root* is not so easy, otherwise Newton would not have troubled to find a good method. What about chess? The function which maps from chess-positions to their best-move successor-sets is notoriously hard, perhaps intractable in general. But for positions of known value at a given level it is easy to find for each of them a best-move predecessor. So complexity is not invariant with respect to direction.'

How can we apply this insight?

First find a scientifically or commercially interesting function, *f*, whose domain has no more than, say, a billion problem states and which for reasons of computational complexity cannot reliably be evaluated by machine. We are required to design a cheap device to embody *f*. The device must cost next to nothing to use and must answer all questions infallibly and immediately. So we build a lookup table for *f* by entering the *right*-hand values ('answers') first. From these we construct the corresponding left-hand values ('questions'). Certain props are needed (Fig. 1), as follows.

1. A fast efficient routine, G, to generate exhaustively and irredundantly all the elements of *f*'s co-domain or 'answer-space'.
2. A routine, H, also fast and economical, to derive from each answer the corresponding question. The question–answer pair so obtained is added to the list (by routine I, see diagram).
3. A memory large enough to hold a table of a billion question–answer pairs.
4. Indexing and accessing routines.

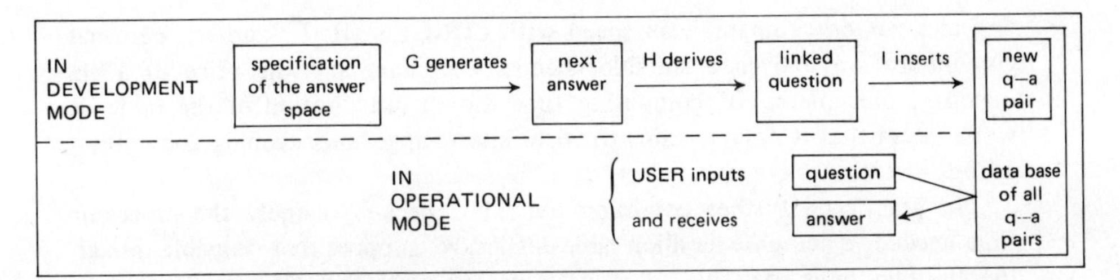

Upper diagram shows construction and use of a lookup table for a function which cannot feasibly be evaluated by an algorithmic computation (true of many AI functions)

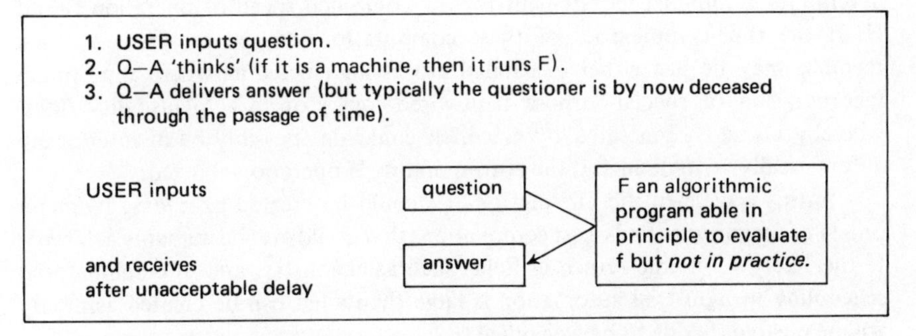

In the traditional scheme, shown in the lower diagram, F is pre-fabricated by some labour-intensive process and represents Q–A's 'understanding' of the domain

Fig. 1 – Proposed scheme (top) contrasted with conventional style (bottom).

CHEMISTRY ILLUSTRATION

To illustrate, consider a potential chemistry application. Mass spectrogram patterns are used by experts to infer likely molecular structures for unknown organic compounds. For this domain reliable computation of *f* is not feasible. There exists a program corresponding to F in the diagram, namely DENDRAL (Buchanan and Feigenbaum, 1978), but it is sufficiently limited and fallible to motivate a search for other methods.

Carhart's CONGEN, which within user-supplied constraints enumerates the 'answer set' (all possible molecular structures within the defined space), is fast and exact. Up to 100 structures are generated per second on a DEC system 10/KL10 computer. CONGEN corresponds to G in the diagram. Stanford's PREDICTOR routine corresponds to H. From a molecular structure as input it infers the expected mass spectrogram pattern, essentially by simulating the action of the mass spectrometer. An improved version for acyclic structures is expected to be comparable in speed with CONGEN (R. E. Carhart, personal communication). Given a suitable chemistry domain and the price of a big memory, plus plenty of computing time during initialisation of the table, it would seem that it only remains to write interfacing, housekeeping and input–output software.

In practice a further condition must be checked, namely the processor time needed to compute a billion table-entries. We suppose that, valuable though the finished table may be, its value is not so great that we are prepared to dedicate more than say, a year's continuous processing to its construction. Since there are only some 32 million seconds in a year, if follows that no more than a thirtieth of a second of processor time can be allowed per table entry, and this determines a minimal requirement for the combined speed of operation G and H. If the time-complexities of these computations exceed requirement, then recourse may be had either to parallel processing (including where appropriate incorporation of special-purpose hard-wired logic) or to a 'plausibility filter' whereby elements generated by G which could not possibly be of interest are automatically recognised and the corresponding H-operation aborted.

In this way scientific fact-dictionaries could be created exceeding by many orders of magnitude the largest compilations that could ever be humanly achieved. If the likely economic return in fields such as chemistry, and in combinatorial scheduling in industrial automation is large then what can be created assuredly will be created. Is this to be welcomed?

THE STRANGE CASE OF THOMPSON'S TABLE

There are reasons for fearing that such a development may be attended by dangers. These arise from the inscrutable face which a purely lookup representation presents to those who have to monitor and respond to the events which it controls. In computer chess, where these phenomena can conveniently be isolated for study on a laboratory scale, a cloud no bigger than a man's hand has been sighted.

An illustrative incident was witnessed at the 1977 Toronto meeting of the International Federation of Information Processing. Kenneth Thompson of Bell Telephone Laboratories had computed a giant lookup table giving optimal play for either side of the chess ending King and Queen against King and Rook. This ending is known to be a theoretical win for the Queen's side, except for a few special positions. It is therefore necessary to qualify rather carefully what one means by saying that the table's strategy for the defending side was optimal, since against a faultless opponent the defence loses anyway. In Thompson's table the move entered for the Rook's side always maximally delays the Queen's side's progress to victory. The method for constructing this dictionary of some three million entries was precisely similar to that illustrated earlier for chemical structure identification.

Thompson invited two International Masters who were present in the hall to demonstrate winning play for the Queen's side. Secure in the knowledge that a Master can ordinarily demonstrate the win against defending play by any other Master, Hans Berliner, former World Correspondence Chess Champion, and Lawrence Day, Chess Champion of Canada, accepted the invitation. To their embarrassment they found that they could make no progress against the machine. Yet every position with which they were confronted in the entire course of play was a winning position from which at least one continuation shortened the path to their goal of checkmate or Rook-capture.

They found the experience upsetting. So also do process-control operators who have responsibility for understanding machine decisions sufficiently to intervene in case of malfunction (Voysey, 1977).

A VERY SHALLOW MENTALITY

The chess-masters soon concentrated on trying to discover what had been happening. They earnestly wished to ask the machine certain questions. This proved impossible, since the chess mentality with which they were confronted was *powerful* in the sense that it knew more than they, but so *shallow* as scarcely to deserve the name (see Fig. 2).

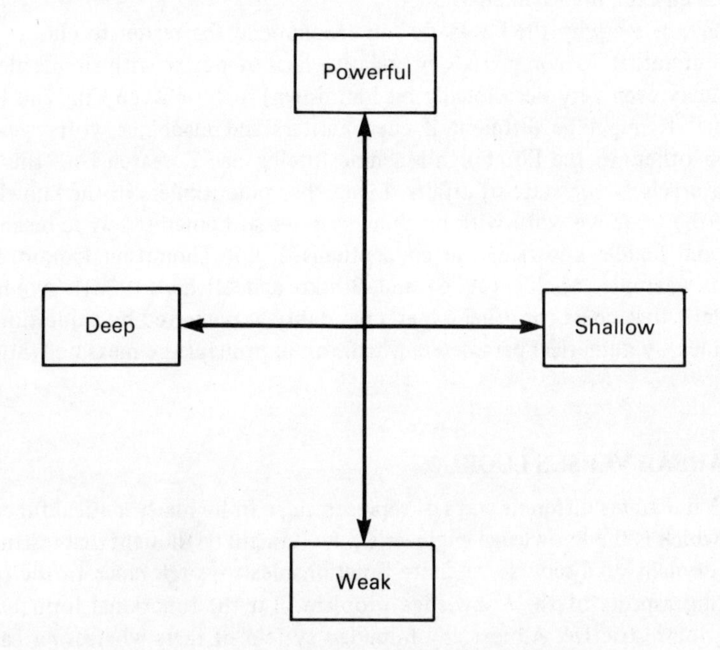

Fig. 2 – Two dimensions for the computational representation of an intellectual skill.

The reasons for its decisions were of course uniformly 'It's in the table'. Totally lacking was any representation of its knowledge in terms of goals, opportunities, constraints, risks, themes, tactical ideas and the rest of the rich conceptual structure in terms of which chess-masters frame questions and receive answers. The system with which they had grappled presented to their eyes a new morphology with bizarre features to which their chess experience was unaccustomed. The machine repeatedly conducted the defence in ways which to them were so counter-intuitive that they were left grasping air, time and again missing the best continuation. Thus it is a cardinal principle as expounded in the treatises of the masters that care must be taken to ensure that King and Rook do not become separated from each other. The assumption is that fatally dangerous territory is entered. The Queen's side is likely to find a forcing series of checks by which the Rook can eventually be pinned on the King, or the King caught in a skewer attack on the Rook, with the result in each case that the Rook falls. The program does not trouble itself with reasoning in these terms. If some path, however narrow and convoluted, can be threaded through a region of the problem space in which King and Rook are separated, there is nothing in the program's design to prevent it taking that path. However far beyond his capacity it would be for a human player to pick his way without error along the path, the program need not be deterred. It will know the way, for it has all been pre-calculated.

One can see why the books do not recommend the reader to choose such paths, but rather to compensate his relative lack of power with simple slogans (which may even very occasionally let him down) such as 'Keep King and Rook together!' It might be different if chess-masters and machines wrote treatises for each other. In the Edinburgh Machine Intelligence Research Unit this is in embryo precisely the state of affairs. Like other practitioners of the knowledge engineering trade we work with machine systems so humanised as to be able to accept and handle knowledge in conceptualised, not Thompson lookup, form (see, for example, Michie (1976) and Bratko and Michie (1980)). A guiding principle is that chess (or other expert) mentality as perceived by a questioner is determined by numerical parameters which can in principle be measured (Michie, 1977).

LOOKAHEAD VERSUS LOOKUP

Figure 3 illustrates different ways of representing a finite mathematical function, one of which is the knowledge engineer's way. It might be thought that restriction of the domain of discourse to finite functions destroys relevance to the really interesting aspects of the knowledge problem. But the functional formalism is in fact not restrictive. Almost any bounded system of facts whatsoever can be expressed as an ordered set of questions paired with their answers, i.e. as a function. 'What is the square of 31?' . . . '961'; 'What is the right thing to do

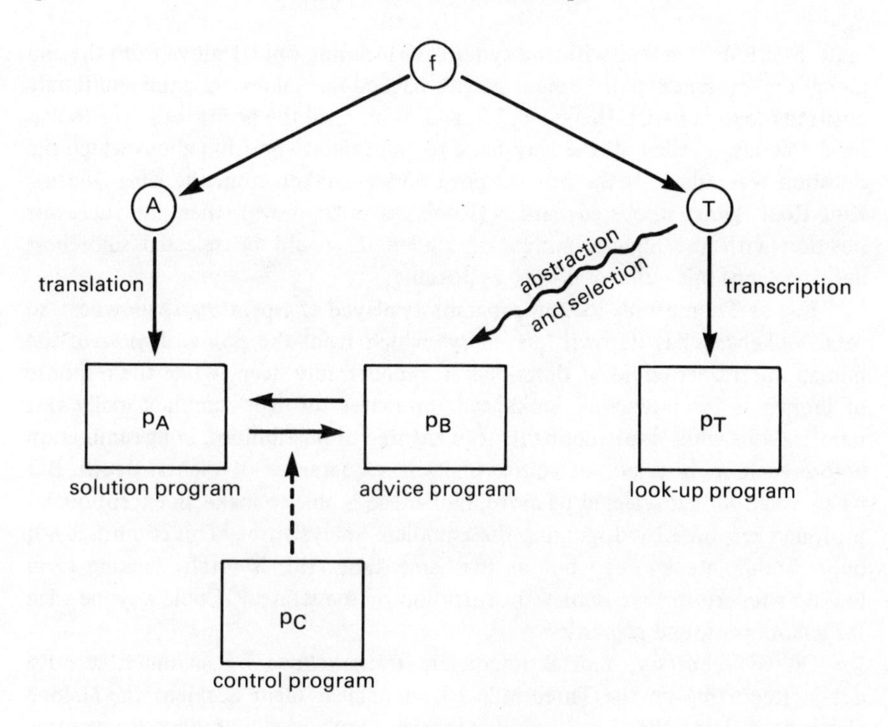

Fig. 3 – Relations among various kinds of mathematical and computational objects. Abstract objects are ringed, concrete are boxed. A and T denote two contrasted abstract representations of the function f, namely as an evaluation algorithm and as a function table (ordered set of pairs) respectively.

when lost?' . . . 'Ask a policeman'; 'What is the freezing point of the seas?' . . . '–4°C'; 'What is the truth-value of Fermat's conjecture?' . . . 'Unknown'. Knowledge which cannot be expressed in question-answer form may be important, but it is hard to pin down and will not concern us here.

The diagram displays two contrasted ways of representing a finite function in a device which is to be questioned about it. In the King-Queen–King-Rook case we have an example of a device whose knowledge of *f* belongs to one of the two extremal forms shown, namely the tabular representation. The corresponding mentality was characterised as shallow. The device could say nothing about *how* it knew what it knew.

At the opposite extreme is the compact algorithmic representation. For chess and similar games it operates as follows. On receipt of the question 'What is your move in this position?', the device looks ahead along all possible branches to the end of the game, labels these terminal positions 'Won', 'Drawn' or 'Lost' in each case, and then by the minimax rule assigns outcome values to the penultimate positions together with the symbol 1 (meaning only 1 move from the end along the minimax path), then assigns backed-up values to antepenultimate positions together with the symbol 2, and so on until the positions of the lookahead tree are labelled all the way back to the original position about which the question was asked. If the original position were taken from the King-Queen–King-Rook game discussed earlier (Rook's side to move), then the successor position with the highest minimax path-length would be selected since best defence keeps this number as large as possible.

Just as Thompson's lookup program displayed exasperating shallowness, so total lookahead has its own 'mentality' which from the point of view of the human questioner could be described as impenetrably deep. While the response of lookup is instantaneous, lookahead ruminates through combinatorially vast ramifications while constructing its forward tree of possibilities. Long rumination before each reply is not of course in itself a guarantee of mental depth. But when asked *how* it selected its move, lookahead is able to make an exceptionally profound response by disgorging the complete analysis tree. This comprises not only a complete strategy but at the same time (this is totally lacking from lookup's repertoire) a complete justification of the strategy. Could anyone wish for a more profound response?

On the contrary, mortal minds are overwhelmed by so much reactive detail. Reporting on the Three Mile Island nuclear plant accident the Malone Committee stated that '. . . the operator was bombarded with displays, warning lights, print-outs and so on to the point where the detection of any error condition and the assessment of the right action to correct the condition was impossible'. So lookahead, with a quite opposite mentality from lookup, has its own reasons for inability to interact helpfully with a human. Of what help is an analysis tree containing a million nodes?

The Three Mile Island software was at least of human authorship. How long in general will this situation last? As long (one may conjecture), and only as long, as it takes to develop methods of synthesising by machine software modules which are cheaper to make and cheaper to run than the best hand-coded versions.

J. R. Quinlan (personal communication, 1979) has demonstrated machine synthesis in a few processor-seconds of a descriptive concept in the King-Rook–King-Knight ending ('Lost-3-ply') which requires months of work for human programmers to code efficiently, when they can do it at all. Moreover at run time the machine-made representation executes 5 times faster then the most efficient program which Quinlan himself can write. But the synthetic representation, taking the form of a 177-node decision tree, defies human power to grasp, memorise, or understand in any reasonable sense. Yet a master can evaluate the concept for a given board position in less than half a minute. Hence efficient human representations of the concept can it seems be constructed. Clearly, though, between the human and machine representations is a gulf which at present we do not know how to bridge.

ADVICE TEXTS AND KNOWLEDGE REFINING

Whether specialised for chess or any other combinatorial problem-solving domain, for a machine to respond helpfully in conditions of partial or suspected malfunction a mentality not too different from our own must be constructed. The key box in Fig. 3 is labelled 'Advice program'. The role of this package of conceptualised information is twofold. First it aborts most of the unnecessary combinatorial explorations of the lookahead program, and thus introduces speed and economy into responses to *questions of the first kind* ('What is the value of $f(x)$?'). Second it allows answers to be computed to *questions of the second kind* ('How did you arrive at that value?'). Advice provides an intellectual entrepot where man and machine can exchange concepts at a level precisely placed between deep and shallow.

Bratko (1978) and Niblett (1982) have shown how to exploit this correspondence to generate endgame micro-manuals or 'advice texts'. They derive them from what we call Advice Tables. These have a different character from the Thompson table, being designed to correspond to the terms in which a master conceptualises the task. Having checked out an Advice Table on the machine by the exacting criterion that it must display the skill which the chess books purport to describe, the table is then translated back into English. At first we believed that we would get back something like the original textbook formulation. Instead, greatly improved representations of expert knowledge emerge, with the knowledge itself corrected, extended and refined.

Figure 4 shows an advice text obtained by Ivan Bratko for the elementary King-Rook–King ending. Unlike the page or two of diffuse text and diagrams

Provided always that stalemate is not created nor the Rook left exposed:

'MATE' 1. look for a way to mate the opponent's King in two moves;

'SQUEEZE' 2. if the above is not possible, then look for a way to further constrain the area on the chess-board to which the opponent's King is confined by our Rook;

'APPROACH' 3. if the above is not possible, then look for a way to move our King closer to the opponent's King (so as to help the Rook in squeezing the opponent's King) ;

'KEEPROOM' 4. if none of the above pieces of advice 1, 2, 3, works, then look for a way of maintaining present achievements in the sense of 2 and 3 (i.e. make a waiting move);

'DIVIDE' 5. if none of 1, 2, 3, or 4 is attainable then look for a way of obtaining a position in which our Rook divides the two Kings either vertically or horizontally.

Fig. 4 – Bratko's advice text for the King-Rook–King ending.

which the standard books devote to this ending, the new rules are so few and compact that anyone can memorise them in a few minutes, thus becoming effectively move-perfect. Moreover they come with a certificate, partly derived from machine-testing and partly from formal proof, that they are complete and correct.

A necessary condition for the trick to work is that the machine representations of knowledge (packed in the 'advice' box of Fig. 3) must be expressed at approximately the same point on the deep–shallow spectrum as that employed by expert human practitioners. A representation placed at a significantly lower level of abstraction, however faithful and operationally efficient, overburdens the mind with ad hoc detail. Figure 5 places on the deep–shallow scale four representations of correct play of the King-Pawn–King ending due respectively to Harris (1976), Bramer (1980), Beal (1980), and Clarke (1977). US National Master D. Kopec is working at Edinburgh on the translation of these representations into advice texts and their testing as micro-manuals for chess beginners. Any of the four, if there were no time limits set, could in principle be used to guide play under 'open-book' conditions.

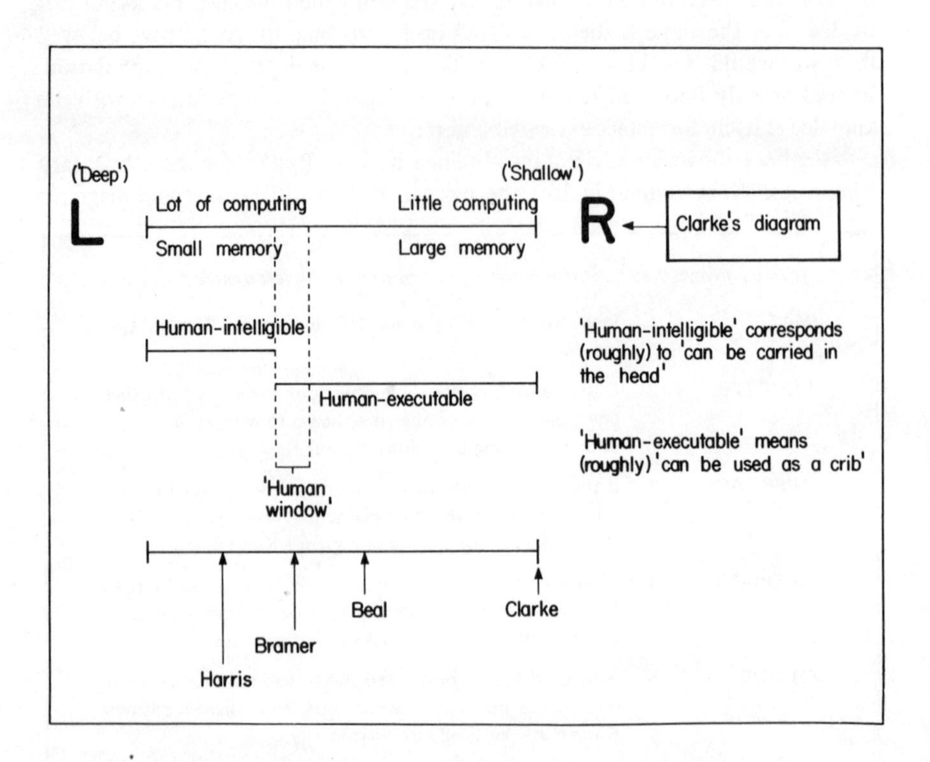

Fig. 5 – Four King-Pawn–King representations to be treated as 'cribs'.

Obviously, however, Clarke's lookup representation consisting of 98,304 table entries would be ungraspable by the human understanding and impossible to memorise for closed-book use. Beal's program, although based (as is human chess knowledge) on typifying patterns, is also ungraspable. Segmenting as he does the problem space into some fifty descriptive patterns as compared with twenty or so used by the expert, Beal's 'grain size' is too small. Even though the difference represents a tiny step in the lookup direction, away from the deep–shallow spectrum's 'human window', it is sufficient to render the corresponding advice text completely opaque to chess-masters. Only Bramer's program puts its knowledge in a nutshell of human dimensions. Its ordered list of twenty patterns specifying optimal (not just 'correct') play, is immediately intelligible and readily memorisable. As such it constitutes a significant contribution to the published corpus of endgame theory.

A step in the opposite (lookahead) direction away from the human window takes us to Harris's program. This results in an advice text which is too deep for faultless mental execution by the chess beginner. The Bramer representation, then, is the humanised one, refined by successive bouts of checking and modification, just as was Bratko's advice text for King-Rook–King.

KNOWLEDGE REFINING

E. A. Feigenbaum (personal communication, 1979) has noted an unexpected reaction to expert systems. Chemists write requesting not copies of the DENDRAL program itself, but the rules about molecular stability and mass spectrometry in which the program's knowledge is codified. In 1976 a paper appeared in the Journal of the American Chemical Society describing a set of rules constituting a new spectroscopic theory for the mono- and poly-androstanes (Buchanan *et al.* 1976). The paper's seven authors were distinguished chemists and computer scientists. But in the conceptual sense the author was the Meta-DENDRAL program, developed at Stanford to generalise over DENDRAL's experience and thus to propose new descriptive rules. Figure 6 lists this case among other well-attested examples of the use of expert systems for the refinement of human knowledge.

There is promise here of the use of knowledge-processing techniques to re-forge parts of our accumulated technical culture. A new kind of industrial plant, the 'knowledge refinery', will bear a similar relation to man's existing codifications as oil refineries bear to crude oil.

CONCLUDING REMARKS

The following three different machine mentalities will confront the information society.

1. Tabular representations: fast, too shallow for helpful interaction.

Domain	Previous Codification	Refining Instrument	Desired end-product
Chess: spotting mates 'at a glance'	No nontrivial classifications published	PL1 tournament program MASTER	Reference text of mating patterns
Chess: how to mate with king and rook against king	Chess primers by Capablanca, Fine, etc.	AL1 'Advice Taker' program	Six sufficient rules, formally proved correct
Chess: how to defend with king and knight against king and rook	Chess primers by Fine and Keres	AL1 'Advice Taker' program	Micro-manual of pattern-based rules
Internal medicine: diagnosis and treatment	Medical texts	INTERNIST knowledge-based program	Improved medical texts
Chemical synthesis planning	Textbooks on synthesis	SECS program with data-base of chemical 'transforms'	Improved source of synthesis-relevant knowledge for chemists
Planning robotic assembly sequences	Toy car assembly scheme for Edinburgh versatile assembly program	WARPLAN predicate-calculus-based program	Improved assembly sequence
Plant pathology	Pathologist's diagnostic classification of soybean diseases	AQVAL program for inductive inference	Improved set of classificatory rules
Mass spectral information on mono- and poly-ketoandrostanes	No satisfactory pre-existing explanation of spectroscopic behaviour	Meta-DENDRAL module of DENDRAL program	Substructures defining main cleavages, yielding predictive theory for new ketoandrostanes

Fig. 6 – Representative cases where knowledge-based programs have been used to improve previous codifications of human knowledge, a phenomenon termed 'knowledge refining'.

2. Compact algorithmic representations: slow, too deep for helpful interaction.
3. Rule-based 'advice' representations: human in style, perfectible to super-human completeness, accuracy and reliability. Just right for interaction.

It is a provable fact that for many complex combinatorial domains no device with either of the first two pure morphologies can perform within terrestrial limits of space and time (Knuth, 1976). Number 1 would need to be too big, while number 2 would calculate too long before answering. But this design consideration only tends to push commercial computing a little way towards the middle ground. In realms such as nuclear power, air traffic control, industrial automation and medicine, the evidence is that these super-powerful but alien mentalities may be hard to handle. Lighthill (1973) has suggested that the aspect of artificial intelligence concerned with 'bridge' representations (i.e. located within the human window) is misconceived and should not be undertaken. Such an embargo, if unopposed, would certainly engender hazards to human life and property of a magnitude which cannot yet be fully foreseen. If legislation for complex systems of computer decision and control is to follow the same protective paths as it has for the automobile, then human-window representations should be the only ones permitted.

Even aside from technological hazards, tractability and appeal to the human mind is a legitimate consideration. On theories in physics Hermann Bondi has said: 'We have had, mainly in the last 50 years, but probably earlier too, various attempts to come to ultimate equations, to come to ultimate final and complete statements, to theories unifying all we know; and it does seem to me that this is a very dangerous tendency in the search for depth. And I say it is dangerous, not only because it has proved fruitless, but also because I find it personally repugnant' (Bondi, 1967). In a related context I have contrasted 'top down' with 'bottom up' theories in science (Michie, 1979c). My conclusions, based on the properties needed for effective machine implementation, are in harmony with Bondi's.

Science, in which 'questions of the second kind' dominate, must by its nature adjust its representations to the human window. In technology, on the other hand, cost-effective performance rather than transparency holds sway. Hence information engineers will increasingly thrust towards us lookup representations of great shallowness and algorithmic representations of great depth. Such embodiments should be resisted, and certificates of humanoid morphology should be demanded before responsible tasks of high complexity are entrusted to machines.

ACKNOWLEDGEMENTS

The substance of this paper was delivered to the 1980 Symposium 'Prospects for Man – Computers and Society' held by York University, Toronto, and the Royal

Society of Canada. The author's thanks are due for permission to reproduce it here.

REFERENCES

Beal, D. F. (1980), Discriminating wins from draws in KPK. Appendix 5 of Beal, D. F. and Clarke, M. R. B. (1980). The construction of economical and correct algorithms for king and pawn against king, in Clarke, M. R. B. (ed.), *Advances in Computer Chess 2,* Edinburgh: Edinburgh University Press, 1–30.

Bondi, H. (1967), *Assumption and Myth in Physical Theory,* Cambridge: Cambridge University Press. 8.

Bramer, M. (1980), Representing pattern-knowledge for chess endgames: an optimal algorithm for king and pawn against king, in Clarke, M. R. B. (ed.), *Advances in Computer Chess 2,* Edinburgh: Edinburgh University Press, 82–96.

Bratko, I. (1978), Proving correctness of strategies in the AL1 assertional language, *Inf. Proc. Letters,* **7**, 223–230.

Bratko, I. and Michie, D. (1980), An advice program for a complex chess programming task, *Computer Journal,* **23**, 353–359.

Buchanan, B. G. and Feigenbaum, E. A. (1978), Dendral and Meta-Dendral: their applications dimension, *Artificial Intelligence,* **11**, 5–24.

Buchanan, B. G., Smith, D. H., White, W. C., Gritter, R. J., Feigenbaum, E. A., Lederberg, J. and Djerassi, C. (1976), Applications of artificial intelligence for chemical inference. XXII Automatic rule formation in mass spectrometry by means of the Meta-DENDRAL program, *J. Amer. Chem. Soc.,* **98**, 6168–6178.

Carhart, R. E. (1977a), A simple approach to the computer generation of chemical structures. Research Memorandum MIP–R–118, Edinburgh, Machine Intelligence Research Unit.

Carhart, R. E. (1977b), Reprogramming DENDRAL, *AISB Quarterly,* **28**, 20–22.

Clarke, M. R. B. (1977), A quantitative study of King and Pawn against King, in Clarke, M. R. B. (ed.), *Advances in Computer Chess 1,* Edinburgh: Edinburgh University Press, 108–118.

Harris, L. (1976), described by J. Bitner and B. Hansche in : Topics concerning KPK end-games. Research Report, Urbana-Champaign: Dept. of Computer Science, University of Illinois.

Knuth, D. E. (1976), Mathematics and computer science: coping with finiteness, *Science,* **194**, 1235–1242.

Lighthill, J. (1973), Artificial intelligence: a general survey, in *Artificial Intelligence: a Paper Symposium,* London: Science Research Council. 1–21.

Michie, D. (1976), An advice-taking system for computer chess, *Computer Bulletin,* **10**, 12–14.

Michie, D. (1977), A theory of advice, in Elcock, E. W. and Michie, D. (eds), *Machine Intelligence* **8**, Chichester: Ellis Horwood, and New York: Halsted Press (John Wiley), 151–168.

Michie, D. (ed), (1979a), *Expert Systems in the Micro-electronic Age,* Edinburgh: Edinburgh University Press.

Michie, D. (1979b), Feasibly computable sub-games of chess. Unpublished report.

Michie, D. (1979c), Machine models of perceptual and intellectual skills, in Harris, H. (ed.), *Scientific Models and Man: The Herbert Spencer Lectures 1976,* Oxford: Oxford University Press. 56–79.

Niblett, T. B. (1982), A provably correct advice strategy for the end-game of king and pawn versus king, in *Machine Intelligence 10,* Chichester: Ellis Horwood, and New York: Halsted Press.

Voysey, H. (1977), Problems of mingling men and machines, *New Scientist,* 18 Aug., 416–417.

PART II – CHESS

INTRODUCTION

Chess as an area for Artificial Intelligence research has a long and distinguished history going back over 30 years.

Many leading Artificial Intelligence researchers have worked on the problem at one time or another, as have an increasing number of strong chess-players including the former world champion, Mikhail Botvinnik, whose interests have moved almost entirely from over-the-board play to computer chess in the last ten years.

Early chess programs had no pre-stored opening 'book' and performed abysmally badly. It seems that good opening moves are too difficult to find by general principles alone. Rather, they have become established after centuries of detailed experiment by human players.

Adding an opening book improved the programs' play to a respectable level, at least in terms of the occasional or club player. The first tournament program appeared in the mid-sixties, but it took another ten years for the first tournament successes to arrive. Today the strongest programs, together with the purpose-built chess-playing machine BELLE, frequently win tournaments against human opposition and are claimed to be approaching master standard. Although such claims should be interpreted with caution, there is no doubt that the best programs perform at a level far above that of the vast majority of the human race on a task generally held to require a high degree of intellectual skill.

Most of this success has been achieved with programs that do not differ much in principle from those of the 1950s and 1960s. The basic method employed is that of 'brute-force search plus simple evaluation function' or, in chess-players' terms, deep analysis using a rudimentary knowledge of what constitutes a good position taking account of such factors as material advantage, mobility and centre occupancy.

Were it not for the existence of an extensive 'chess culture' and literature, today's programs would be hailed as a major achievement in mechanising human thinking. Instead, the success of BELLE and its strongest rivals is profoundly dissatisfying. Human chess skill does not depend on deep analysis (although that is part of it); rather, it requires an ability to form plans, generalise from examples, learn from experience etc., and to recognise the important features of a position such as a 'strong' square or a weak Pawn structure. A good discussion of this topic is given by Frey (1977). It is remarkable that programs without these features can perform as well as they do, but it is virtually impossible to believe that progress to grandmaster level could ever be made, whatever advances in processing speed or memory size might occur, without incorporating human-like reasoning skills.

The fact that attempts to incorporate, say, planning into chess-playing programs have only been partially successful so far is an indication that the game of chess provides a serious and complex – yet well-defined and self-contained – testbed for Artificial Intelligence theories of planning, particularly in comparison with the 'toy' domains in which such theories are often developed such as the 'blocks world'.

The first paper in this section is concerned with the development of basic 'chess software' built on top of Lisp. Others are concerned with such fundamental topics as planning, machine learning, knowledge-based problem solving and 'quiescence search', to determine when a position becomes stable enough to be statically evaluated.

Five of the seven papers focus on endgames. This is an accurate reflection of the major centre of attention in the field in recent years. Endgames retain much of the complexity of the full game but in a much simplified setting. Even three- and four-piece endgames are surprisingly complex and unamenable to conventional techniques based on deep searching.

As a side-effect, studies of endgames have led to an extension of the theory of certain endgames and the discovery of errors in standard textbooks even in apparently elementary endgames such as King and Rook against King. Even the most successful chess-playing programs are notably weak in the endgame, where deep analysis is much less important than pattern recognition and planning.

In this context the well-known observation that it is the endgame which most reliably differentiates the grandmaster from the master, the master from the strong amateur, etc. is both significant and challenging.

REFERENCE

Frey, P. W. (ed.) (1977), *Chess Skill in Man and Machine,* New York: Springer-Verlag.

2

Chess knowledge representation and fast tree searching

Peter van Diepen
AI-IOP, Hoogovens, IJmuiden, Holland

ABSTRACT

This paper presents IGM/Lisp, a system especially designed for experiments in computer chess. The goals of the system are to support chess knowledge engineering and to provide fast basic chess software such as: legal move generators, attack/defence predicates and path generators. The system can also act as the supervisor of multiple chess programs and chess data bases.

The relation of this work to some other work in artificial intelligence research and computer chess is discussed briefly and extensions to a Lisp 1.5 interpreter, which make it an IGM/Lisp interpreter are described. The use of IGM/Lisp is illustrated by a few examples of minor applications.

A version of IGM/Lisp and a simple compiler are implemented on a microcomputer system.

INTRODUCTION TO ARTIFICIAL INTELLIGENCE AND COMPUTER CHESS

The game of chess has been the subject of artificial intelligence (AI) research for as long as artificial intelligence research has existed.

AI is concerned with chess playing machines which try to (1) achieve a level comparable to the level of a chess grandmaster; (2) act like a human chess-player. Machines of the second type do not necessarily play very well, but that is not the object. The aim is to gain some insight into human intelligence by developing a machine which 'thinks' like a human chess-player. For the first type of machine it is not necessary that it 'thinks' like a grandmaster, but that it plays a move which a grandmaster would play. In any case, it is the author's belief that some knowledge of the second type is needed in order to build a machine of the first type. It is also believed that the first type is the easier to build.

Early AI research was concentrated on general programs such as the General Problem Solver of Newell and Simon (1963) and chess programs which play the full game. Nowadays most AI research is being carried out in specific domains, in which it is possible to achieve expert level performance (see Michie, 1980), such as in elementary chess end games (Bramer, 1980 a and b; Bratko and Michie, 1980 a and b; van den Herik, 1980). The general programs do a large amount of searching among alternatives, while the so-called expert systems direct their search by using specific knowledge.

CONVENTIONAL CHESS PROGRAMS

The majority of existing chess programs, including the most successful ones, use the Shannon-A strategy, which means that they build huge game trees, comprising moves as branches and positions as nodes. Such chess programs evaluate the terminal nodes and back up the resulting values on to lower levels (plies) of the tree. At the lowest level (ply 1) the chess program chooses the move with the highest value as its choice in the current position (Shannon 1950). Programs of this kind will be referred to as 'conventional' chess programs.

The chess knowledge of conventional chess programs is located in the evaluation function and is usually simple to compute (Gillogly, 1972; Birmingham and Kent, 1977). Evaluation functions have to be simple and fast because these programs wish to examine as many positions and moves as possible. Even if the evaluation function is arbitrarily complicated the amount of chess knowledge will remain small. Taking this into account the playing strength of conventional chess programs is surprising. The best programs beat 95% of human chessplayers.

The high playing level of conventional chess programs is based on efficient search methods and fast hardware. Thompson (1982) gives an example of extremely fast hardware. Important search methods are the alpha-beta algorithm (Knuth and Moore, 1975) and its derivative, the iterative alpha-beta algorithm (Slate and Atkin, 1977). The main feature of the alpha-beta algorithm is that it avoids building parts of the game tree which are not logically necessary.

IGM/LISP

AI research has always led to the invention of new programming languages. Recent developments deal with new notations for representing knowledge (Bobrow and Raphael, 1974; Mylopoulos, 1981). The list processing and symbol manipulation language Lisp 1.5 is, however, fairly old and still in use. It has become the traditional tool of AI researchers and has often been used to implement new notations as embedded languages. To the reader who needs more information about Lisp than is given in this paper, the following books are recommended: McCarthy *et al.* (1962), van der Poel (1972), Siklossy (1976), Allen (1978) and Winston and Horn (1981).

IGM/Lisp is a dialect of Lisp. IGM/Lisp is upward compatible with Lisp. 1.5 and has some extensions especially made for chess. It was designed primarily as a tool to make chess programming easier. According to Slate and Mittman (1978) and to the author's own experience with the Dutch chess program IGM, it is known that such a tool is needed. Because IGM/Lisp has interactive testing facilities, ideas can be implemented (and thrown away) very fast. Thanks to Lisp, higher level chess-knowledge notations can be embedded, running programs can be written or rewritten automatically, etc. Of course, such an idea is not new: Newell, Shaw and Simon (1958) used IPL–IV, a predecessor of Lisp 1.5, to implement their chess program. In addition to chess-knowledge engineering, IGM/Lisp is also suitable for fast tree-searching, because it is equipped with fast legal move generators, fast attack/defence predicates and fast path generators, all of them written in machine language. The IGM/Lisp programmer is not aware of the machine language routines. Most IGM/Lisp functions behave as lists, the usual data structures in Lisp, which are higher level notations than the machine language routines hidden behind them.

In summary: IGM/Lisp is a tool to build chess programs, as well as a language to express chess knowledge and is able to perform a tree search fast.

CHESS ATOMS

The chess atoms, which are the chess-oriented words of the IGM/Lisp language, are now presented. There are two groups: those which are only necessary for purposes of description and those which have other functions. The IGM/Lisp interpreter will not be described here in detail, because it is very much the same as an ordinary Lisp 1.5 interpreter. Details of the Lisp 1.5 interpreter are given by McCarthy *et al.* (1962).

The primary data structure in Lisp is the list. Every element of a list is either an atom or another list. An atom is a primitive named object, the name being an arbitrary string of characters. The entire set of objects (atoms) existing in a Lisp system is kept on the so-called OBLIST. The IGM/Lisp system has some additional atoms on its initial OBLIST compared with an ordinary Lisp 1.5 system. Among them are atoms that look familiar to chessplayers: A1, B1, C1, . . . , F8, G8, H8, KING, QUEEN, BISHOP, KNIGHT, ROOK, PAWN, MATE, STALEMATE, BLACK and WHITE.

An important feature of Lisp is that atoms can be carriers of properties. A single atom may carry any number of properties, distinguished by indicators. The chess atoms mentioned above have no special properties; only a name. So the user can assign values to them and build complex data structures on them. The chess atoms as shown in Table 1 have SUBR indicators with a pointer to a machine language routine. This means that the IGM/Lisp interpreter must call that machine language routine when it interprets a list headed by such an atom. In general, a Lisp interpreter evaluates a single atom or a list. When a single atom is evaluated, the value of that atom is the result. When a list is evaluated,

Table 1

Function	Argument	Value/effect
MOVES	–	List of legal moves, or MATE or STALEMATE.
PLAY	a move	If T then plays the move.
TAKE-BACK	–	If T then takes back the last move.
COLOUR	–	WHITE or BLACK depending on which colour is to move.
COLOUR	a square	NIL when empty, otherwise WHITE or BLACK depending on the colour of the piece.
PIECE	a square	NIL when empty, otherwise the piece.
ATTACK	a square	T if the square is attacked by a piece of the side which is not to move, otherwise NIL.
ATTACK	a move	T if it is an attacking move, otherwise NIL.
DEFEND	a square	T if the square is defended by a piece of the side which is to move, otherwise NIL.
DEFEND	a move	T if it is a defending move, otherwise NIL.
CHECK	a move	T if it is a checking move, otherwise NIL.
TAKES	a move	NIL when nothing is taken, otherwise the piece that is taken.
CASTLE	a move	T if it is a castling move, otherwise NIL.
EP	a move	T if it is an *en passant* capture, otherwise NIL.
PROMOTION	a move	NIL when it is not a promotion, otherwise the promotion piece.
PATH	a starting square and a goal square and a list of limitations (maximum search depth, dangerous squares)	NIL when the starting square is empty, otherwise a list of squares along which the piece on the starting square moves legally to the goal square.

the first elements of the list are the arguments of the function, and these arguments will also, in general, be evaluated. The final result will be the value of the function applied to its arguments. This list of chess atoms may be made arbitrarily longer by compiling functions written in IGM/Lisp or by programming more machine language routines. These are the basic ones.

Squares are identified by the usual algebraic notation written as chess atoms: A1, B1, etc. If a function expects a square and its argument is not a square, IGM/Lisp aborts the running functions and gives an error message. A move is a list with a '(*n* from to)' format, in which '*n*' is an integer, which contains information about the move in a binary pattern, and 'from' and 'to' represent the from-square and the to-square of the move. Castling moves are treated as king moves. Only a promotion needs some additional information. TAKES, CASTLE, EP and PROMOTION trigger their values from '*n*'. PLAY and TAKEBACK are able to do their job because of '*n*'. If a function expects a move and its argument is not a move, IGM/Lisp aborts the running functions and gives an error message. If a function expects a square, a move or nothing, IGM/Lisp determines whether the argument is a square, a move or NIL.

A SAMPLE CHESS PROGRAM

Although only a small set of IGM/Lisp functions is presented in this paper, it is nevertheless easy to define a conventional chess program with functions of this set combined with the standard Lisp 1.5 set, as given by McCarthy *et al.* (1962). The main functions of such a program are the search function and the evaluation function. In this sample chess program they are called ANALYSE and EVALUATE-POSITION. ANALYSE performs an alpha-beta search ending at a given depth, see Knuth and Moore (1975).

```
ANALYSE
(LAMBDA (LIS DEPTH ALPHA BETA)
   (COND
    ( (EQ LIS MATE) –999999)
    ( (EQ LIS STALEMATE) 0)
    ( (EQ DEPTH 0) (EVALUATE-POSITION))
    (T (PROG
           (MOVE BEST-MOVE)
           (SETQ BEST-MOVE ALPHA)
        L  (PLAY (CAR LIS))
           (SETQ MOVE
                  (MINUS
                     (ANALYSE  (MOVES)
                               (DIFFERENCE DEPTH 1)
                               (MINUS BETA)
                               (MINUS BEST-MOVE) ) ) )
```

```
        (TAKE-BACK)
        (COND ( (GREATERP MOVE BEST-MOVE)
                (SETQ BEST-MOVE MOVE) ) )
        (COND ( (LESSP BETA BEST-MOVE)
                (RETURN BEST-MOVE) ) )
        (SETQ LIS (CDR LIS) )
        (COND ( (NULL LIS) (RETURN BEST-MOVE) )
              (T (GO L) ) ) ) ) ) )
```

This version of ANALYSE is not very efficient, but a good arrangement of the moves will make it much faster. TAKES, PROMOTION and other IGM/Lisp functions may be useful to arrange the moves. Another refinement, which also can be useful to arrange the moves, is to store the moves that cause alpha-beta cut-offs (Birmingham and Kent, 1977).

In order to build EVALUATE-POSITION the IGM/Lisp programmer may use IGM/Lisp functions and take advantage of the possibility in Lisp that atoms may also carry properties. The chess atoms, which represent squares and pieces, may each carry a single value or a complex function to compute a value. For example when the IGM/Lisp interpreter evaluates the list:

```
(EVAL (CONS SQUARE (PIECE (SQUARE) ) ) )
```

1. it constructs a list consisting of the given square and the piece on that square,
2. it passes this list to EVAL.

EVAL is the Lisp interpreter itself. So, a function attached to the given square will be applied to the piece on that square. The result of this evaluation will be the value of the entire list.

OPENING AND ENDGAME KNOWLEDGE

The sample chess program given here is a conventional one where all chess knowledge is concentrated in the evaluation function. If the evaluation function is fixed, that knowledge must be applicable to every position. Hence, it must contain a large amount of general chess knowledge and at the same time as much information as possible about exceptions. However, certain positions demand very specific knowledge. Especially in the endgame and in some opening lines general chess knowledge is almost worthless.

It is the author's opinion that a chess system must have neither a fixed evaluation function nor a fixed chess program. In IGM/Lisp a supervisor routine may reprogram evaluation functions or complete chess programs at run time. The supervisor gets its input from a data base on mass storage (device 2 in the example below). The Lisp reader (READ) takes care of the input data and the interpreter itself (EVAL) evaluates it, whatever it is: a single move or a complete redefinition of the current chess program together with a call to the new-defined chess program.

```
SUPERVISOR
    (PLAY (COND ( ( EXPERT-NEEDED) (EVAL (READ 2) ) )
                ( T (CURRENT-CHESS-PROGRAM) ) ) )
```

Through the supervisor all expert chess knowledge is potentially available to the IGM/Lisp system. Here we shall mention only opening and endgame expert chess programs, because other expert chess programs do not yet exist.

Chess-knowledge representation of opening lines is straightforward. Besides, the program can be restricted to a repertoire (Marovic and Parma, 1978). Obviously opening knowledge is declarative, but a retrieval function is also needed if, for example, the opening lines are structured as a tree.

```
WHITE
   (D2 D4
     (D7 D5 C2 C4 QUEENS-GAMBIT)
     (G8 F6 C2 C4
              (E7 E6 B1 C3 F8 B4 NIMZO-INDIAN)
              (G7 G6 KINGS-INDIAN) )
     (F7 F5 DUTCH) )
```

Here WHITE is the label of this tree and QUEENS-GAMBIT, NIMZO-INDIAN, KINGS-INDIAN and DUTCH are the labels of successor trees. In order to make engineering of opening knowledge possible by an ordinary chess-player, the moves in this data base do not have the usual IGM/Lisp format.

In endgames there are no lines like those in the openings. The issue is handling plans and trying to reach favourable positions. For human chess-players many books are written on this topic, but even the most elementary endgames (Averbakh, 1966) are hard to program. The main problem is how to describe a chess position in such a way that a computer can do something with it. Known expert chess programs for endgames (Bramer, 1980 a and b; Bratko and Michie, 1980 a and b; van den Herik, 1980) are based on pattern recognition. They compare certain conditions of the given position with patterns in their knowledge bases. When a match is found the program 'knows' how to proceed.

In the future it will be desirable for expert chess-players to create chess-knowledge bases. However, as a first step, programmers should create the appropriate chess functions. To define high-level chess functions IGM/Lisp offers the descriptive power of Lisp 1.5 together with some chess-oriented descriptive functions as presented in this paper. For example: PATH can be used to define a function which 'sees' whether or not a Pawn can run in a given position.

Fig. 1

In the position illustrated in Fig. 1 it is essential to know if the Pawn on g2 can run. Thus paths to square g8 are generated for both the Black King on b3 and the White Pawn on g2.

(PATH (QUOTE G2) (QUOTE G8)) generates:
(G2 G4 G5 G6 G7 G8)

(PATH (QUOTE B3) (QUOTE G8)) generates:
(B3 C4 D5 E6 F7 G8)

Both lists contain six elements, so both paths are equally long and thus the Black King can catch the Pawn. Hence White tries the preliminary sequence e5–e6, d7Xe6 and now

(PATH (QUOTE B3) (QUOTE G8)) generates:
(B3 C4 D5 E5 F6 F7 G8)

This time the list is longer than that for the Pawn on g2. This implies that the Pawn on g2 can now run. Another remarkable list for illustrating the PATH function is generated by:

(PATH (QUOTE G2) (QUOTE G1))
(G2 G4 G5 G6 G7 G8 G1)

IMPLEMENTATION

IGM/Lisp is implemented on a Maxboard, a microcomputer system with a Motorola 6802 processor (Manudax, 1979). A simple IGM/Lisp compiler is also available.

The IGM part of IGM/Lisp includes legal move generators, attack/defence predicates, path generators, etc. in the form of machine language routines. These routines have been written to execute as fast as possible. 2000 legal moves per second are generated on a 6802 microprocessor with a 1 megahertz clock speed. The IGM part of IGM/Lisp is independent of the Lisp part. IGM/Lisp is, in fact, an interface between IGM and a Lisp 1.5 interpreter. The interface itself is naturally constrained into Lisp. From the point of view of an IGM/Lisp programmer, most IGM/Lisp functions behave as lists.

FINAL REMARKS

In the author's opinion, a really 'intelligent' chess system looks like a hierarchical structure of layers, where IGM/Lisp is just one layer, but an indispensable one. Beneath the IGM/Lisp layer the 6802 microprocessor could be replaced by some VLSI chips for chess (Thompson, 1982) and for list processing (Steele and Sussman, 1979). It is not yet known how many layers the whole system will need. However, it is evident that human chess-players must be able to communicate with some of the layers; in order not only to play a game against the system, but also to improve the system by means of chess-knowledge acquisition. Communication here means communication at chess-player's level, using their jargon and 'talking' about nothing else but chess. Chess-players should not be programmers. Even if they are programmers it may be more sound not to confuse chess and programming. Programmers are asked to use another layer of the chess system, for example: IGM/Lisp.

ACKNOWLEDGEMENTS

The work on IGM/Lisp is supported by Manudax B. V. Holland. Frits van den Wateren wrote the Lisp 1.5 interpreter for the 6800 microprocessor. I wish to thank Gerrit Slot for his help in implementing IGM/Lisp, Jaap van den Herik for his encouragement in writing this paper, Max Bramer for his invitation to submit a paper and Maria Schulten for her help with the translation. I also wish to thank Jaap van den Herik (again), S. Kooi, Professor H. J. M. Lombaers and J. J. van Oosterwijk Bruyn, who made useful comments on earlier versions of this paper.

REFERENCES

Allen, J. (1978), *Anatomy of Lisp,* New York: McGraw-Hill.

Averbakh, Y. (1966), *Chess Endings: Essential Knowledge,* Oxford: Pergamon Press.

Birmingham, J. A. and Kent, P. (1977), Tree-searching and tree-pruning techniques, in Clarke, M. R. B. (ed.), *Advances in Computer Chess 1,* Edinburgh: Edinburgh University Press, 89–97.

Bobrow, D. G. and Raphael, B. (1974), New programming languages for artificial intelligence research, *Computing Surveys,* **6** (3), 153–174.

Bramer, M. A. (1980a), Pattern-based representations of knowledge in the game of chess. Proceedings of the AISB-80 Conference on Artificial Intelligence, Amsterdam.

Bramer, M. A. (1980b), An optimal algorithm for King and Pawn against King using pattern knowledge, in Clarke, M. R. B. (ed.), *Advances in Computer Chess 2,* Edinburgh: Edinburgh University Press, 82–96.

Bratko, I. and Michie, D. (1980a), A representation for pattern-knowledge in chess end-games, in Clarke, M. R. B. (ed.) *Advances in Computer Chess 2,* Edinburgh: Edinburgh University Press, 31–56.

Bratko, I. and Michie, D. (1980b), An advice program for a complex chess programming task, *Computer Journal,* **23** (4), 353–359.

Gillogly, J. J. (1972), The technology chess program, *Artificial Intelligence,* **3** (3), 145–163.

van den Herik, H. J. (1980), Goal-directed search in chess end games, *Delft Progress Report 5* (4), 253–279.

Knuth, D. E. and Moore, R. E. (1975), An analysis of alpha-beta pruning, *Artificial Intelligence,* **6**, 293–326.

McCarthy, J., Abrahams, P. W., Edwards, D. J., Hart, T. P. and Levin, M. I. (1962), *Lisp 1.5 Programmers Manual,* Cambridge, Massachusetts: MIT Press.

Manudax Nederland B. V. (1979), Maxboard, Stand-Alone Micro-Processor Board for Application and/or Development, 5473 ZG Heeswijk (N.B.) Holland.

Marovic, D. and Parma, B. (1978), *An Opening Repertoire for Black,* London. Batsford.

Michie, D. (1980), Expert systems, *Computer Journal,* **23** (4), 369–393.

Mylopoulos, J. (1981), An overview of knowledge representation. Proceedings of the Workshop on Data Abstractions, Databases and Conceptual Modelling, Pingree Park, Colorado 1980. *SIGART Newsletter,* **74**, 5–12.

Newell, A., Shaw, J. C. and Simon, H. A. (1958), Chess-playing programs and the problem of complexity, in Feigenbaum, E. A. and Feldman, J. (eds.), *Computers and Thought,* New York: McGraw-Hill, 39–70.

Newell, A. and Simon, H. A. (1963), GPS, a program that simulates human thought, in Feigenbaum, E. A. and Feldman, J. (eds.), *Computers and Thought,* New York: McGraw-Hill, 279–293.

van der Poel, W. L. (1972), *The Programming Languages Lisp and Trac,* Third edition. Aug. TH Delft, Holland.

Shannon, C. E. (1950), Programming a computer for playing chess, *Philosophical Magazine,* **41**, 256–275.

Siklossy, L. (1976), *Let's Talk Lisp,* Englewood Cliffs, New Jersey: Prentice-Hall.

Slate, D. J. and Atkin, L. R. (1977), Chess 4.5– the Northwestern University chess program, in Frey P. W. (ed.), *Chess Skill in Man and Machine,* New York: Springer Verlag, 82–118.

Slate, D. J. and Mittman, B. (1978), Chess 4.6 – Where do we go from here? in Moneta, J. (ed.), *Proceedings of the 3rd Jerusalem Conference on Information Technology,* 193–198.

Steele, G. L. and Sussman, G. J. (1979), Design of Lisp-based processors. MIT Artificial Intelligence Laboratory Memo 514.

Thompson, K. (1982), Belle chess hardware, in Clarke, M. R. B. (ed.), *Advances in Computer Chess 3,* Oxford: Pergamon Press.

Winston, P. H. and Horn, B. K. P. (1981), *Lisp,* New York: Addison-Wesley.

3

Quiescence search in computer chess

Hermann Kaindl
Marxergasse 18/2/1, 1030 Wien, Austria

ABSTRACT

This paper discusses the problem of which chess positions are quiescent enough for static evaluation by a program. Both tactical and positional aspects of quiescence are considered here.

Some of today's chess programs restrict themselves to static evaluation at fixed depth. However, static evaluation of tactical aspects in chess is rather inaccurate and a lot of blunders can occur. Other programs employ a quiscence search which looks at most or even all captures, checks and promotion moves. This search requires a lot of time, even though it seriously lacks the possibility of investigating other chess aspects not statically measurable with sufficient accuracy. Thus it is the author's opinion that static analysis of tactics should be performed by a program, but with the aim of guiding a more selective quiescence search rather than computing static values that cannot be accurate.

A fact often disregarded is that the so-called horizon effect can arise when cutting positional moves as well as tactical ones. Thus special knowledge about positional long-range plans also needs to be used for feeding moves to the quiescence search.

Every move selected for quiescence search should represent an idea. Thus it is necessary to give the program enough chess knowledge for having the right ideas.

INTRODUCTION

From the beginning of chess programming the necessity of search beyond fixed limits for reaching a quiescent position has been demonstrated (see Shannon (1950), Turing (1953), etc.). However, up to now it has not been clear which chess positions are quiescent, in the sense that they can be evaluated accurately by a program. Only a few very crude criteria have been implemented, e.g. 'search until no capture moves are possible for the side to move'.

A very interesting idea of Beal (1980) is the so-called consistency search. ('A node is consistent if its heuristic value is the same as the backed-up value from a 1-ply search over its descendants.') But apart from difficulties in controlling such a tree search there is a distinct problem. If it is necessary to generate the descendants of a position to decide whether the position is quiescent or the search has to continue, then this search has already been performed, at least in part! This is the same reason why, for example, Adelson-Velskiy *et al.* (1975) have rejected the use of the static evaluation of a position as a preliminary estimate of a move which leads to the position.

Thus it is necessary for a chess program to decide statically whether or not a position is quiescent. A lot of chess knowledge for both tactics and positional play must be available to the program in order for it to make such a decision.

TACTICAL ASPECTS OF QUIESCENCE

Conventional chess programs of today play rather good tactical chess by looking at most or even all possible continuations up to a fixed depth. However, because of this fixed limit a lot of blunders can occur. If the static evaluation functions and the quiescence search beyond this limit cannot recognize a threat, the program tries to push this threat out of its generated search tree. This phenomenon is called the horizon effect (see Berliner, 1974). Thus the program needs to be able to recognize every such threat by its static evaluation function or by a quiescence search.

Some attempts have been made to build special chess automata for analysing tactics and finding combinations without performing a full width search. The following works are of special interest here.

Berliner (1974) has developed a program which searches a relatively small tree, performing relatively little computation at each generated node. This computation even includes an analysis of causality of events in the tree search. The program can find impressively deep combinations but also ignores more simple threats it does not have knowledge about. (In this sense there is a great similarity with the strengths and weaknesses of a human chess-player.)

Pitrat (1977) has created a chess combination program which performs a goal-oriented search using plans in a tactical sense.

Coplen (1981) has built a special-purpose machine which searches for so-called Cycle i Threats ($i = 1, 2, 3$).

Although the tactical abilities of such special automata are rather impressive they cannot play a complete game of chess very well. There are many positions which have no possibility of a concrete combination; and in such positions these automata do not know how to proceed successfully.

But why not combine conventional programs and use such special algorithms to perform the quiescence search? From a logical point of view this would be a solution to most of the problems involving tactical aspects of quiescence. However, considering the practicability of such a program, doubts arise because of the time needed for such a quiescence search. The number of terminal nodes of a full width search at plies 5 to 8, even when using alpha-beta pruning, can be estimated (see Knuth and Moore, 1975) as well as counted by most of the good chess programs of today. The application of one of the algorithms referenced before to every such node clearly would lead to an explosion of the search time. Moreover, the goal of these alogorithms is to find a chess combination whereas the goal of a quiescence search should be to search for a quiescent position. Admittedly these goals cannot be distinguished in many cases.

The algorithms actually implemented in the good chess programs of today differ across a wide range. For example, the Canadian program L'EXCENTRIQUE employs neither a quiescence search nor a static analysis or evaluation of tactics at the terminal nodes of its fixed-depth search (this information was given in a personal conversation with the author of this program, C. Jerry, at the 3rd World Computer Chess Championship in Linz 1980). Most of the microcomputer programs restrict themselves to static evaluation and do not search for quiescent positions at all. Programs like CHESS 4.5 (see Slate and Atkin, 1977) or KAISSA (see Adleson-Velskiy *et al.* 1975) conduct a limited quiescence search of captures, checks and promotion moves beyond the fixed depth. The selective program MASTER (see Kent and Birmingham, 1980) employs static evaluation of tactics by computing values of swapping off on the squares of each of the pieces. Additionally MASTER uses the static evaluation function of a position for ordering the moves, by making each move in turn. However, despite this, all captures and checks are forced into the tree search, no matter how low their static evaluation is.

To finish search at a fixed limit without static analysis or quiescence search is very dangerous because of the horizon effect. Because L'EXCENTRIQUE is a very fast program running on a very fast computer it can perform a full depth search of 6 to 8 ply in middle game positions under tournament conditions, and thus play is stronger than that of many other programs of today. In master chess far deeper combinations occur frequently and hence this method seems to be capable of extension.

Assigning a single static value to a highly tactical position is a very hard problem. In master chess very often positions occur where several hung pieces of both sides exist; nevertheless most of these positions are dynamically balanced. However, at today's state of the art it is impossible for a program to recognize this statically. (It is not even clear how accurate a 'static analysis' by a human chess master can be.) Even when assuming that the error in such an evaluation is small enough to be negligible for the pure evaluation of material (let us say about half the value of a Pawn), another problem arises: every attempt to give a program more positional knowledge must fail as the positional evaluation is superposed by such tactical errors!

The method of looking at captures, checks etc. seems to be the most promising, although the existing realisations are rather crude. Static analysis of tactics should be performed by a program and the results of such an analysis should be used for guiding a rather selective quiescence search. Such a search could be a good compromise between doing nothing and thoroughly searching for a combination.

Now let us assume we have a special routine called EXCHANGE-ANALYSIS which can compute the true value of every capture move that is possible in a given legal position and the true value of every square in this position with respect to its safety. Thus its output can be represented using the following variables (capturing the King or leaving it in check is not considered here):

EGAIN. . . . . estimated gain of material (capture move);
EGAIN $\leqslant$ value of Queen;
EGAIN $\geqslant -$(value of Queen $-$ value of Pawn)
ELOSS. . . . . estimated loss of material (square);
ELOSS $\geqslant 0$;
ELOSS $\leqslant$ value of Queen

A real routine of this type has been built for experiment and gives good approximations to these values in most cases. This routine is a development of one given by Schreier (1979), and the basic idea is the computation of so-called swap-off values (see Levy (1976) and Kent and Birmingham (1980)). Pins to the King and the ordering of captures considering the transparency of Queen, Rook and Bishop are taken into account. Positions with the King in check are an exception and they are not input to this routine.

Now let us look at the capture quiescence. The most important idea of a capture move is to win material. Thus it does not make sense to try capture moves which lose material unless there is another reason for doing so. For the formulation of this simple criterion the output of EXCHANGE-ANALYSIS can be used. Additionally, a variable for regulating the search is included.

CBIAS. . . . . bias for selecting captures

$$\text{(C.1)} \quad \text{EGAIN(move)} + \text{CBIAS} > 0$$

CBIAS $-> -$ infinite. . . . . no capture at all
CBIAS $-> +$ infinite. . . . . all capture moves

A subtler criterion is only to look at those captures that probably give a better value than the best value reached so far. This new value is estimated by adding the actual material value and the estimated gain of the move in question and the maximum positional score; thus it is an optimistic estimate.

MATBAL. . . . . material balance of the position before move
MAXPS. . . . . maximum positional score
BSTVL. . . . . best value so far
(ALPHA or backed-up value or static value)

(C.2) EGAIN(move) + MATBAL + MAXPS + CBIAS > BSTVL

(Such a criterion is in fact used in CHESS 4.5, but the estimation of the capture's value is rather crude and is not computed by an analysis of exchanges.) The resulting statement for the selection of a capture move runs as follows:

```
(S.1) FORALL moves : (capture) DO
          IF (C.i) THEN SELMOV(move);
              i = 1 or 2
```

The most important deficiency of today's programs when considering quiescence is hung pieces that are subject to capture by the side not on move. Some programs punish their existence by subtracting a constant value when evaluating statically, others ignore them completely. Looking for safe escape squares is also suggested but there remain the problems of tempo and of positional evaluation.

Taking the premise that static evaluation of positions with hung pieces is too inaccurate, the conclusion is that no such evaluation is computed and used for minimax at all. For a criterion, if hung pieces are to be considered the output of EXCHANGE-ANALYSIS can be used. The maximum estimated loss is a function of all the estimated losses of material on the squares of piece location. An approximation of this function is to take the maximum value. Additionally a bias variable is included.

MAXELOSS. . . . . . maximum estimated loss;
(≈ max ELOSS (squares of piece-location))
HBIAS. . . . . bias for considering hung pieces

(H.1) ELOSS(square) + HBIAS > 0

HBIAS −> − infinite. . . . . no consideration of hung pieces
HBIAS −> + infinite. . . . . panic of hung pieces

One of the principal methods of quiescence search performed by programs like CHESS 4.5 is the following (see Slate and Atkin, 1977): 'At each node in the capture search, the side to move is given the choice of accepting the evaluation score or of trying to better it by trying capture moves.'

When the criterion (H.1) is fulfilled this method cannot be applied directly (as argued before). However, a pessimistic estimate of the static value (including the results of EXCHANGE-ANALYSIS) can be used; and if this estimate is better than BETA after all, then heuristically a cut-off is rectified, too. The resulting statement can be formulated as follows:

PESSVL . . . . pessimistic value (estimate of the static evaluation)

```
(S.2)   PESSVL := MATBAL − MAXPS − MAXELOSS − HBIAS;
        IF PESSVL > BSTVL THEN
          BEGIN
            BSTVL := PESSVL;
            IF BSTVL ≥ BETA THEN
              EXIT (BETA-cut-off);

          END;
```

If this cut-off is not performed the moves of hung pieces should be selected:

```
(H.2)   ELOSS(square) + HBIAS > 0.

(S.3)   FORALL squares DO
          IF (H.2) THEN
              FORALL moves : (move. from = square) DO
                  SELMOV(move);
```

The importance of ordering moves to achieve as many alpha-beta cut-offs as possible is well known. Thus 'sorting values' for the moves should be computed:

SVAL. . . . . sorting value (move)

Considering only captures, the estimated gain achieved by a move can be used for sorting:

```
(S.4)   SVAL := EGAIN(move);
```

Considering moves of hung pieces, the maximum estimated loss of material associated with a move can be used for sorting. Thus for moves from the square with the value MAXELOSS the value MBELOSS is taken into account:

MBELOSS. . . . . 'highest but one' estimated loss

Additionally the estimated loss when moving to an empty square should be considered. (If such a square is safe this value is 0.)

```
(S.5)   IF ELOSS(move.from) = MAXELOSS THEN
            SVAL(move) := − ELOSS(move.to) − MBELOSS
        ELSE
            SVAL(move) := − ELOSS(move.to) − MAXELOSS;
```

In practice, it is not clear if the computation of the estimated loss for the to-square is worth its cost; thus a simpler estimate of this value is actually used.

As a capture move can also be a move of a hung piece, and as sometimes a saving move can be much better than all the possible capture moves, it is convenient to sort these moves together.

```
(S.6)   FORALL moves : (capture) DO
          IF (ELOSS(move.from) = MAXELOSS) THEN
            SVAL(move) := EGAIN(move) − MBELOSS
          ELSE
            SVAL(move) := EGAIN(move) − MAXELOSS;
(S.7)   FORALL moves : (no capture) DO
          (S.5)
```

Looking at these moves in decreasing order of their associated SVAL, captures with big estimated gains and moves of the pieces on squares with biggest value threatened are selected first.

If all these moves are already searched and if nevertheless BSTVL is equal to PESSVL (that means no move has given a new best value), other moves should be tried. Clearly promotion and checking moves could give good values in such situations. Furthermore, moves that attack pieces of the opponent or defend pieces attacked should be worth considering. But in principle it is necessary to try all remaining moves, as any move could give a better value.

Thus the resulting algorithm could run as follows:

```
EXCHANGE–ANALYSIS(position, EGAIN, ELOSS, MAXELOSS, MBELOSS);
BSTVL := ALPHA;
IF MAXELOSS + HBIAS ⩽ 0 THEN (*not (H.1)*)
  BEGIN
    EVALUATE(STATVL); (* static evaluation *)
    IF STATVL > BSTVL THEN (* new best value *)
      BEGIN
        BSTVL := STATVL;
        IF BSTVL ⩾ BETA THEN
          EXIT (BETA-cut-off);
      END;
  GENCAP; (* generate captures *)
  FORALL moves : (capture) DO
    IF EGAIN(move) + MATBAL + MAXPS + CBIAS > BSTVL THEN
                          (* (C.2) *)
      SELMOV(move); (* (S.1) *)
  END
ELSE
```

```
BEGIN
  PESSVL := MATBAL − MAXPS − MAXELOSS − HBIAS;
  IF PESSVL > BSTVL THEN
    BEGIN
      BSTVL := PESSVL;
      IF BSTVL ⩾ BETA THEN
        EXIT (BETA-cut-off);
    END;
  GENCAP;                (* generate captures *)
  GENFROM(squares : (ELOSS(square) + HBIAS > 0))
                         (* generate moves of hung pieces. *)
  FORALL moves : (capture) DO (* (S.6) *)
    IF (ELOSS(move.from) = MAXELOSS) THEN
      SVAL(move) := EGAIN(move) − MBELOSS
    ELSE
      SVAL(move) := EGAIN(move) − MAXELOSS;
  FORALL moves : (no capture) DO (* (S.7) *)
    IF (ELOSS(move.from) = MAXELOSS) THEN
      SVAL(move) := − ELOSS(move.to) − MBELOSS
    ELSE
      SVAL(move) := − ELOSS(move.to) − MAXELOSS;
  FORALL moves : (already generated) DO
      SELMOV(move : (SVAL(move) = max (SVAL(moves) ) ) );
      (* moves with biggest SVAL first *)
  IF BSTVL = PESSVL THEN (* no best value found *)
    BEGIN
      GENALL;
      (* generate and select remaining moves *)
      FORALL moves DO
        SELMOV;
    END
  END;
```

This algorithm is only a theoretical framework for managing the problem of hung pieces. It has been developed under the severe premise that static evaluation of such situations is too inaccurate to use at all. However, it is not hard to imagine such a quiescence search blowing up, mainly because there is no mechanism for controlling the selection of more and more moves. Moreover, most of the positions generated during a full-width search are rather strange from a human chess-player's point of view; and when such a position is fed to this quiescence search it can take a big search to reach positions which are quiescent only.

These considerations have been confirmed by experiments with the conventional chess program MERLIN which is of the same type as CHESS 4.5. (The data-base and some basic routines are taken from Frey and Atkin (1978).) Thus some extensions have to be built in to make this method practicable.

- If no best value has been found during the search of captures and of moves of hung pieces, the chance of finding a good move simply by searching all the remaining moves is not worth its cost. Again, only those moves that represent a distinct idea should be selected.
- Also it makes no sense to select moves of hung pieces to squares which are themselves not safe either.
- A depth limitation can be made in relation to the full depth limit for the consideration of moves of hung pieces as well as for other remaining moves.
- The static value of such a position can also be estimated optimistically; and if even this optimistic value is smaller than ALPHA a restriction to static evaluation can be admitted as this value will not become important.
- In criterion (H.1) MAXELOSS can be replaced by MBELOSS. This means that only situations with more than one hung piece are considered in such a way. There it is necessary to confirm that this piece is not pinned and that it has a safe escape square. Nevertheless problems with positional evaluation remain, as for example the piece has to retreat to a worse position. Also the value of the tempo has to be estimated.
- The quiescence search can be made 'staged' in the sense that there are different limitations for different methods.

Finally, the search can be regulated by setting the parameters CBIAS and HBIAS.

Another important subject is that of checking moves. For example, the selective program MASTER looks at all possible checks. CHESS 4.5 employs only a limited check-quiescence search.

Looking at all checks during quiescence search really does not seem to make sense, as (especially in the strange positions arising from a full-width search) an 'explosion' of the search tree can occur. However, there are certain types of checking moves which are dangerous for the opponent in nearly every case. For example, double checks are of special interest here. Discovered checks are also highly tactical, especially when they are combined with captures. It is important to note that programs like CHESS 4.5 have to perform extra computations to know if a move gives check (before building the resulting position), but for recognising such important threats it must be worth its cost.

More difficult problems arise when considering simple checks, as there should be a distinct idea for selecting them. A very important criterion for selecting simple checks must be that the opponent's King is threatened with checkmate. Clearly such a criterion is rather complex and cannot easily be formulated for use by a program. Consider the partial problem of back-rank mate. Here the King cannot get out of check by a Queen or a Rook as it has no square to move to on the second rank which is not attacked by any enemy pieces and not occupied by a friendly piece (especially a Pawn); thus checks by Queen or Rook on the first rank are worth selecting, if the checking piece cannot be captured. This criterion can be generalized in such a way that the King is in danger if it only has escape squares either on a diagonal or on a rank or file, and if a sweep piece can give check there safely. Further criteria can be derived from the definition of 'pseudo' mate by Birmingham and Kent (1980).

To summarise, it can be stated that tactical aspects of quiescence are very complex and manifold. Many other important features could be discussed (see also Harris (1977)), but first of all the simpler aspects should be solved. The practical realisation of a quiescence search for chess programs always has to be a good compromise between 'being blind' and 'blowing up'.

POSITIONAL ASPECTS OF QUIESCENCE

For programs which purely evaluate material, positional aspects clearly are not of interest when considering the quiescence of a given position. However for programs which compute a positional evaluation, the horizon effect can also arise when cutting positional moves. As most of today's programs have only little knowledge about positional chess and as positional values are rather small compared with the value of material, this effect is not so striking here. It is not even an easy task to give a general example. However, if one knows the static evaluation function of a program rather well, occasionally the following can be observed: the program worsens its position slightly as a means of pushing another deterioration with a bigger value out of its horizon, but the latter cannot be avoided anyway at a later stage.

Thus strong positional moves should be fed to the quiescence search, too. The main problem for chess programs evaluating positions rather than moves is to recognise a strong positional move. Again it seems not to be a convenient solution to build the position first and then to evaluate the move. Shaffer (1980) has described a program which gives positional scores to moves. These scores are added to the values of the chess program TREEFROG. The moves can be sorted according to their resulting value and only the best ones are examined. This method solves the problem given before; but as TREEFROG uses only these move values for evaluation and does not evaluate the resulting positions at terminal nodes, the backed-up values seem to be susceptible to inaccuracy. Thus the most convenient way seems to be to evaluate terminal positions statically and to use the same knowledge for preliminary evaluation of a move as well, but not by building the resulting positions during the tree search.

Kaindl (1981) has developed a model for positional long-range planning. There special evaluations using pawn patterns are added to the usual evaluation of a position. In the following it will be described how such pattern knowledge can be used for efficient selection of strong positional moves. For the reader not familiar with this model a short description of the main features is given now for a better understanding of the following.

A description of a positional long-range plan can be given to a computer using a formal descriptive language called PPDL. Such a description is mainly oriented to the pawn structure of a position and uses pawn-to-pawn relations defined by Tan (1977) according to the terminology of Kmoch (1967). Additionally the position of non-pawn pieces in relation to the pawn structure is taken into account. This description is parsed by a special program called PPGEN which generates all the described pawn patterns. These patterns and the associated descriptions including relative evaluations are written to files. Any chess program which can read these files can use the patterns following up a positional long-range plan by including the extra value in its static evaluation.

When a chess program using such patterns should select a good positional move with regard to the given plan for quiescence, it would have to build the descendants of the position for look-up in the patterns table. Why not extend the model in such a way that these moves are already stored?

In the model given by Kaindl (1981) a pawn pattern entry points to a list of non-pawn descriptions. These contain information about the value of a certain piece standing on a certain square (in relation to pawn structure). Now this representation is extended in such a way that the pawn pattern entry additionally points to a list of moves (see Fig. 1).

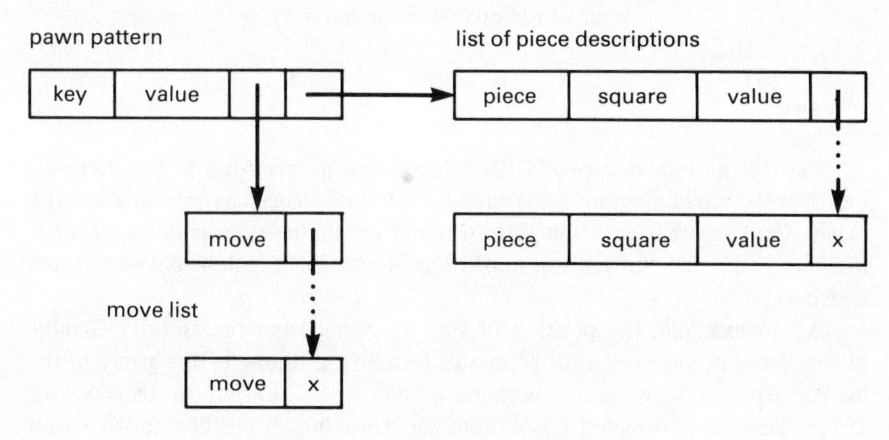

Fig. 1

Now the question arises when and how these moves should be generated. It seems to be convenient for the program PPGEN to generate these moves after the generation of the patterns. As the whole model is totally oriented to pawn structure a restriction to pawn moves has been made. Thus PPGEN stores those pawn moves that give an increase of the values of pawn patterns for White and Black respectively. The generation of these moves can be performed using the following algorithm:

```
FORALL pawn patterns DO
  BEGIN
    IVAL := VALUE; (* of this pattern *)
    FOR ITM : = LIGHT TO DARK DO
     BEGIN
      GENPWN(pawn configuration, ITM);
                (* generate all pawn moves for ITM *)
      FORALL pawn moves DO
        BEGIN
          MAKE(pawn move);
          LOOKUP(resulting pawn configuration);
          IF pawn pattern found THEN
            IF ( (ITM = LIGHT) AND
                (VALUE > IVAL) )
               OR
               ( (ITM = DARK) AND
                (VALUE < IVAL) ) THEN
            STORE(pawn move);
                   (* value of resulting pawn pattern better than
                   value of old one —> good move *)
        END;
     END;
  END;
```

Clearly the interface of PPGEN to any chess program has to be extended, but then the chess program using such pattern knowledge has only to select the moves listed together with the pattern found for the position in question. Thus it is important that the generation of these moves has been done before the tree search.

As an example, the position of Fig. 2, arising from the Queen's Gambit Declined has occurred in a lot of master games (e.g. in one of the games of the human World Championship between Korchnoi and Karpov in Baguio City 1978). There are two good possibilities for White in this position following up the positional long-range plan called the minority attack:

- Ra1–b1 with the idea of playing b2–b4 on the next move
- Bg5*Nf6 virtually forces Be7*f6; and now b2–b4 can be played. (This way was chosen by Korchnoi against Karpov.)

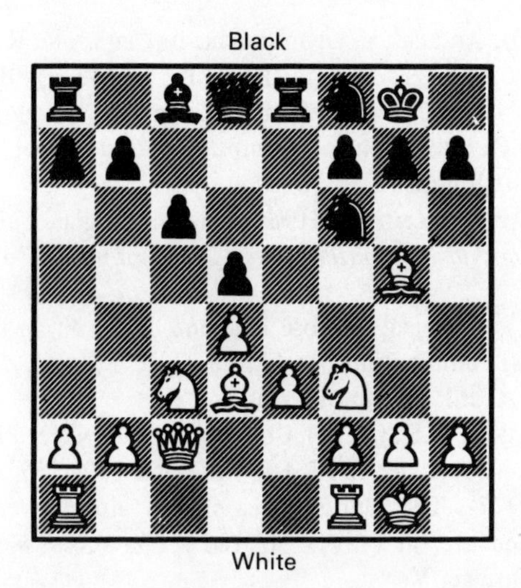

Fig. 2 – White to move.

Without feeding positional moves to the quiescence search, MERLIN using pattern knowledge of the minority attack selected the second way, performing a 3-ply search (see Kaindl, 1981). Using additional knowledge about good pawn moves following up the given plan, the whole variation can be found completely during quiescence search.

CONCLUDING REMARKS

To summarise, it must be admitted that most of the problems of quiescence in computer chess are not solved at today's state of the art, at least from a good chess-player's point of view. The most obvious explanation is that the programs do not know enough about the game they play, and consequently cannot distinguish really promising moves from all the 'ordinary' alternative possible moves.

Most of the considerations given here concerned brute-force programs, but it seems that they are also valid for programs which perform selective search as the problem of quiescence arises for any chess program. Moreover, sophisticated quiescence search seems to be a necessary condition for the development of a chess program performing selective search without a high probability of blunders.

REFERENCES

Adelson-Velskiy, G. M., Arlazarov, V. L. and Donskoy, M. V. (1975), Some methods of controlling the tree search in chess programs, *Artificial Intelligence,* **6**, 361–371.

Beal, D. F. (1980), An analysis of minimax, in Clarke, M. R. B. (ed.), *Advances in Computer Chess 2,* Edinburgh: Edinburgh University Press.

Berliner, H. (1974), Chess as problem solving: the development of a tactics analyser. Ph.D. Dissertation, Computer Science Dept., Carnegie-Mellon University, Pittsburgh.

Birmingham, J. A. and Kent, P. (1980), Mate at a glance, in Clarke, M. R. B. (ed.), *Advances in Computer Chess 2,* Edinburgh: Edinburgh University Press.

Coplen, K. (1981), A special purpose machine based on an improved algorithm for deep chess combinations, in Clarke, M. R. B. (ed.), *Advances in Computer Chess 3,* Oxford: Pergamon Press.

Frey, P. W. and Atkin, L. R. (1978), Creating a chess player Parts 2 and 3, *BYTE,* November and December 1978, 162–181 and 140–157.

Harris, L. R. (1977), The heuristic search: an alternative to the alpha-beta minimax procedure, in Frey, P. W. (ed.), *Chess Skill in Man and Machine,* New York: Springer Verlag.

Kaindl, H. (1981), Positional long-range planning in computer chess, in Clarke, M. R. B. (ed.), *Advances in Computer Chess 3,* Oxford: Pergamon Press.

Kent, P. and Birmingham, J. A. (1980), The MASTER chess program, in Clarke, M. R. B. (ed.), *Advances in Computer Chess 2,* Edinburgh: Edinburgh University Press.

Kmoch, H. (1967), Die Kunst der Bauernfuehrung. Siegfried Engelhardt Verlag.

Knuth, D. E. and Moore, R. W. (1975), An analysis of alpha-beta pruning, *Artificial Intelligence,* **6**, 293–326.

Levy, D. N. L. (1976), *Chess and Computers.* London: Batsford.

Pitrat, J. (1977), A chess combination program which uses plans, *Artificial Intelligence,* **8**, 275–321.

Schreier, R. (1979), Dialog- und Optimierungs-probleme am Beispiel eines Schachprogrammes. M. thesis, Technische Universitaet Wien.

Shaffer, J. (1980), Long-range planning in computer chess. M. thesis, Waterloo University, Ontario.

Shannon, C. (1950), Programming a computer for playing chess, *Phil. Mag.*, **41**, 256–275.

Slate, D. J. and Atkin, L. R. (1977), Chess 4.5 – The Northwestern University chess program, in Frey, P. W. (ed.), *Chess skill in Man and Machine,* New York: Springer Verlag.

Tan, S. T. (1977), Describing pawn structures, in Clarke, M. R. B. (ed.), *Advances in Computer Chess 1,* Edinburgh: Edinburgh University Press.

Turing, A. M. (1953), Digital computers applied to games, in Bowden, B. V. (ed.), *Faster than Thought,* London: Pitman, 286–295.

4

Machine learning and chess

H. J. Messerschmidt
IBM S.A., Johannesburg, South Africa

INTRODUCTION

The game of chess has provided a good testbed for quite a few AI experiments. It provides a typical problem-solving environment with the added incentive of competition against humans and other computer programs. With respect to computer chess, the author agrees with Berliner (1974) and others, that further significant advances are likely to be knowledge-based. The various knowledge-based approaches (Huberman, 1968; Tan, 1973; etc.) have all indicated the enormous amount of knowledge needed and the difficulty of transcribing it into machine-usable form.

Machine learning is a concept of tremendous potential, but currently lacks sufficient efficiency to be of general practical use. The pattern classification approach (Nilsson, 1965) seems to be the most appropriate for problem-solving. However, empirical evidence suggests (Banerji, 1976) that more complex patterns than Nilsson's ϕ-functions are needed. Quite apart from the knowledge base itself, an efficient system for its application is of course needed.

APPROACH

The work described in this paper starts from the premise that the knowledge contained in the knowledge base need not be perfect. This makes the learning task considerably easier, since machine learning and most other complex computing tasks are subject to the 80–20 rule. This means that 80 per cent of the result can be obtained by 20 per cent of the effort, but the remaining 20 per cent is subject to heavy diminishing returns penalties. The premise of imperfect knowledge is empirically acceptable; after all most human beings live perfectly acceptable lives using imperfect and sometimes even downright false knowledge. This acceptable behaviour stems from three reasons.

(a) The error in the knowledge has no direct bearing on the problem at hand or does not materially affect the actions taken. (A car driver's faulty knowledge of the detailed construction of the internal combustion engine does not affect his driving capability.)

(b) The errors introduced by faulty knowledge, while detrimental to performance, are such that the overall result is still worthwhile. (Even chess grandmasters occasionally play the wrong move; anyone who could predict stock market movements with 80 per cent accuracy would still be very rich.)

(c) Some other way of verifying the intended action exists, before it leads to disastrous consequences due to errors in the knowledge base. (This fact is used in this work by using tree searching to verify the correctness of plausible moves.)

The knowledge base is constructed completely automatically through machine learning. To increase the speed and efficiency of the learning process a 'teacher' component is used to guide it. The knowledge is stored as a tree structure of discriminant functions. Using a stack these functions can be applied to chess positions effectively. This application process results in the recognition of the various salient characteristics of a chess position and results in a plausible move being proposed. In effect this gives a Shannon type B chess-playing program. Tree searching is then used for move verification. Berliner's recent B* algorithm (Berliner, 1979) is used. Because the plausible moves have been selected on the basis of a plan, an interesting by-product of this method is the availability of an optimistic node value which is needed for Berliner's algorithm and which greatly increases searching efficiency.

Whatever method is chosen, the amount of knowledge needed to play reasonable chess is vast. In order not to extend the project indefinitely and to be able to test its effectiveness on a subset of chess, the KRK (King and Rook versus lone King) endgame was chosen. Since this endgame is very simple, the objective of perfect play was added. After all, if the method cannot succeed in playing the KRK endgame perfectly, there is not much hope for the full game of chess.

IMPLEMENTATION – THE KNOWLEDGE BASE

The knowledge base consists of a number of sets of patterns, arranged in a tree structure such that every path from the root of the tree to any leaf node represents a complete pattern. The nodes of the tree represent discriminant functions to be applied to chess positions. While checking a pattern for applicability by applying the discriminant functions, a plan is set up. Should any discriminant function fail, this signifies that the pattern does not apply to the particular position under consideration and the pattern, as well as the plan, is abandoned. Finally the plan is used in conjunction with the last pattern node to generate one or more plausible moves. A plan is a set of location vectors, each vector containing the locations on the board of a set of squares that conform to a certain set of criteria, e.g. all squares next to the enemy king.

There are currently three types of discriminant or node-function. *Set-up functions* check the chess position for the presence (or absence) of certain pieces and set up plan vectors containing their locations, e.g.

OCCUP 1,Q

checks the position for the presence of friendly Queens and marks their positions in plan vector 1. If there are no Queens on the board the pattern fails and the plan is abandoned. Any piece type or combination of piece types, as well as empty squares, can be located in this way.

Condition functions verify the relative position of a piece or square with respect to the board or with respect to other pieces or squares. In general, these functions remove occurrences from the plan vectors and both pattern and plan are abandoned if an empty plan vector occurs. For example,

CORNER 2

checks the occurrences in plan vector 2 for a corner condition; all non-corner occurrences are removed. Not only board geometry, but also relative positions of pieces can be checked. Thus,

GEO 2,3 VOPP

checks the occurrences in plan vectors 2 and 3 pairwise for vertical opposition and

GOTO 2,3

checks if the pieces noted in plan vector 2 can move to at least one square in plan vector 3.

A third type of node is the *utility node.* These nodes are used for debugging purposes, to convey sundry information to other parts of the system (e.g. optimistic plan value), identifying patterns and to generate the plausible moves. An example of a simple pattern is found in Fig. 1. It generates a plausible move to capture an enemy piece that is totally or partially *en prise.*

```
OCCUP  0,E     locate all enemy pieces
OCCUP  1,F     locate all friendly pieces
DATT   1,0     keep only direct attacks
CAPG   1,0     that gain material
NUM    0,0,0   this is pattern zero
GEN    1,0,0   move piece from vector 1 to 0 with relative plan value
               from 0
```

Fig. 1 – A simple pattern.

The patterns are grouped together in strategy sets, each strategy set being a distinct pattern tree. A general tactics set, containing such patterns as 'take piece *en prise*', 'fork', 'skewer' etc. is applied to all positions, but patterns such as 'promote pawn' and 'seek a draw' are only used if the strategy selection module dictates it.

IMPLEMENTATION – THE LEARNING PROCESS

From the description of the knowledge base it should be clear that it is fairly easy to take any endgame position and with the necessary chess knowledge manually formulate a pattern. There are, however, several obstacles to automating the process.

It serves no purpose to end up with a unique pattern for every endgame position. If pattern synthesis takes place using single endgame positions, it is very difficult to distinguish between real and accidental characteristics of the position. To increase the utility of the patterns, each pattern must apply to as large a group of positions as possible. On the other hand a pattern that applies to the KRK endgame with black to move that simply states 'Move the King to any safe square', is of no value. To overcome these two difficulties, two new devices were designed, i.e. the use of multiple positions in parallel and synthetic position verification.

The system does not construct new patterns from single positions, but rather from sets of similar endgame positions called learning sets. Conditional nodes are only included in the pattern if they apply to all members of the learning set. This simple device ensures the exclusion of most accidental characteristics of single positions. The learning set can be selected iteratively as will be described later. The problem of selecting the minimum number of necessary conditional nodes can be solved by using the plan vectors slightly differently. Starting with the hypothesis that the plan will work for any position with pieces currently under consideration, the conditional nodes can be used to restrict the plan more and more till it matches the learning set. In fact, a synthetic position is built up in the plan vectors representing the positions in the learning set. As soon as the synthetic position more or less (allowing for imperfect knowledge) matches the learning set, the pattern is finished.

The purpose of the selection of the learning sets is to select set with the highest degree of homogeneity. The teacher component initially selects all the positions with a certain constant depth (number of moves to mate) and the same piece to move from a complete enumeration table (Clarke, 1977; Messerschmidt, 1980). This initial set is passed to the learning component, which tries to construct a pattern that fits all members of the set. Any positive conditional functions that are tried and found not to be universally applicable are noted, together with their applicability vectors, which indicate to which members of the learning set the condition applies. When the learning component now fails to find a pattern applicable to the whole learning set, it reports this fact

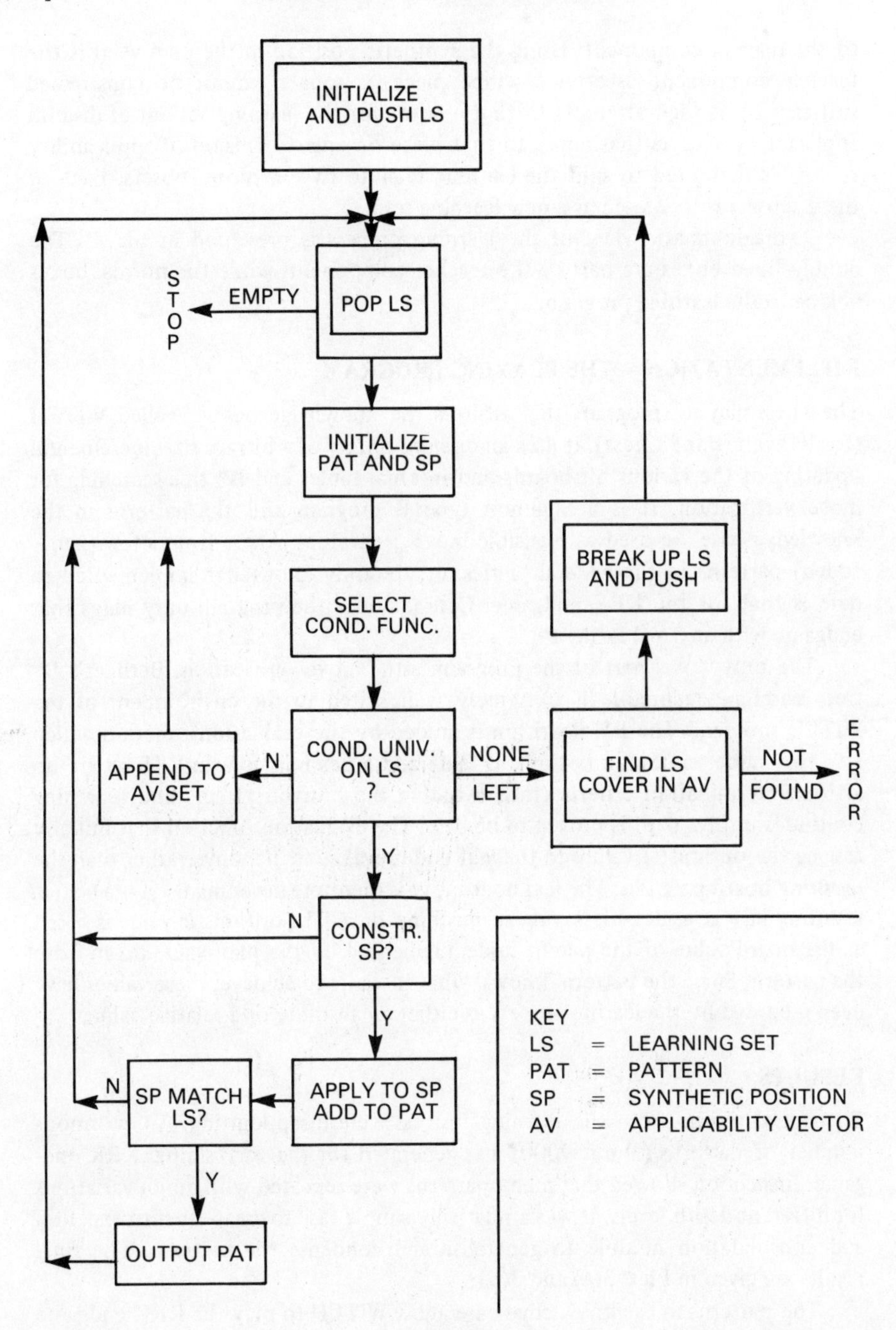
INITIALIZE AND PUSH LS
POP LS
EMPTY
STOP
INITIALIZE PAT AND SP
SELECT COND. FUNC.
COND. UNIV. ON LS ?
N
APPEND TO AV SET
NONE LEFT
FIND LS COVER IN AV
NOT FOUND
ERROR
BREAK UP LS AND PUSH
Y
CONSTR. SP?
N
Y
APPLY TO SP ADD TO PAT
SP MATCH LS?
N
Y
OUTPUT PAT
KEY
LS = LEARNING SET
PAT = PATTERN
SP = SYNTHETIC POSITION
AV = APPLICABILITY VECTOR

Fig. 2

to the teacher component. Using the synthetic position in the plan vectors the teacher component ascertains which piece or square cannot be constrained sufficiently. It then attempts to find a cover for the learning set out of disjoint applicability vectors that apply to that piece or square. This set of applicability vectors is then used to split the learning set into two or more subsets. Each of these subsets is then used as a new learning set.

A diagrammatic view of the learning process is presented in Fig. 2. The doubly lined boxes are part of the teacher component, while the normal boxes belong to the learning program.

IMPLEMENTATION – THE PLAYING PROGRAM

The chess-playing program that utilizes the knowledge base is called WITCH (for *Wit*watersrand *Ch*ess). It uses an opening library of arbitrary size, incremental updating of the various bit boards and internal tables and B* tree searching for move verification. It is a Shannon type B program and the patterns in the knowledge base are used as plausible move generators. Apart from a few (hand-coded) patterns in the general tactics set, the only knowledge implemented to date is that for the KRK endgame. Consequently the program only plays that endgame with any real skill.

The only novel part of the program is the move verification. Berliner's B* tree searching technique is extremely well suited to the environment of the WITCH program. The B* algorithm is guided by the evaluation function which sets two node values, an optimistic value and a pessimistic value. There are no artificial termination criteria (thus avoiding the horizon effect) and searching continues until a path is proven to be best. The evaluation function that initially assigns the optimistic values to the leaf nodes evaluates the move rather than the resulting board position. The leaf node move is therefore never made on the board, resulting in a considerable saving of machine time. The optimistic value is taken as the board value of the parent node augmented by the plan value taken from the pattern. Since the pattern 'knows' what it wants to achieve, these values have been recorded by the learing process as either an absolute or a relative value.

RESULTS

The initial results from the learning process were disappointing. An enormous number of patterns (about 9000) was generated for the very simple KRK endgame. Inspection showed that many patterns were repeated with minor variations for different depth levels. It was a relatively simple task to create an introspection and consolidation module to generalise and condense the patterns. The final results are given in Figs. 3(a) and 3(b).

The patterns in the knowledge base allow WITCH to play the KRK endgame perfectly. A small number of plausible moves is generated and tree-searching never extends to more than 3-ply. An example of play is given below.

DEPTH	POS	PATTERNS
0	189	2
1	587	31
2	484	10
3	238	23
4	607	24
5	1091	40
6	1418	72
7	2149	109
8	2514	142
9	2382	105
10	2565	121
11	2691	146
12	2234	82
13	2027	75
14	662	24
15	121	7
	TOTAL:	1013

Fig. 3(a) – Pattern numbers for White to move.

DEPTH	POS	PATTERNS
0	27	– (mates
1	78	1 (only move)
2	246	2
3	81	5
4	198	8
5	471	17
6	592	24
7	683	27
8	1433	52
9	1712	54
10	1985	75
11	2854	101
12	3597	139
13	4194	172
14	2166	82
15	390	12
	TOTAL:	950

Fig. 3(b) – Pattern numbers for Black to move.

EXAMPLE

Internally the squares of the chessboard are numbered consecutively, starting with zero in the bottom left-hand corner.

Black to move; White to mate in seven moves (14-ply), WITCH plays black. (K denotes a black king.)

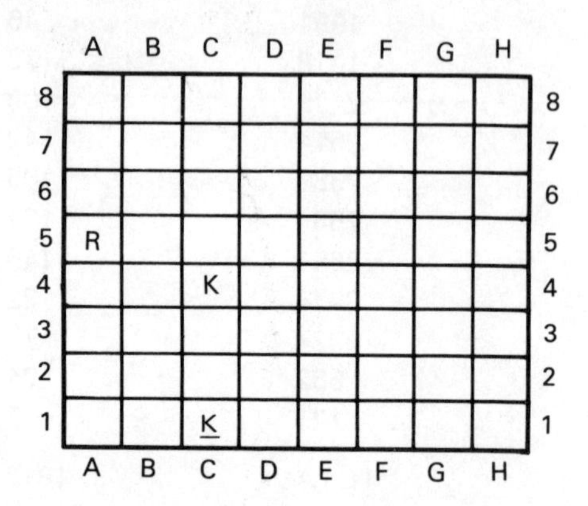

Plausible moves – 2 to 11 and 2 to 9

Search tree –

2 – 11 2 – 9

32 – 34 32 – 36

Time – 7.4 secs.
Move played – 1 . . . Kcl–d2 (2 to 11)
Reply expected – 2. Ra5–e5 (32 to 36)
Reply played – 2.Ra5–e5

Plausible moves – 11 to 3 and 11 to 10

Search tree –

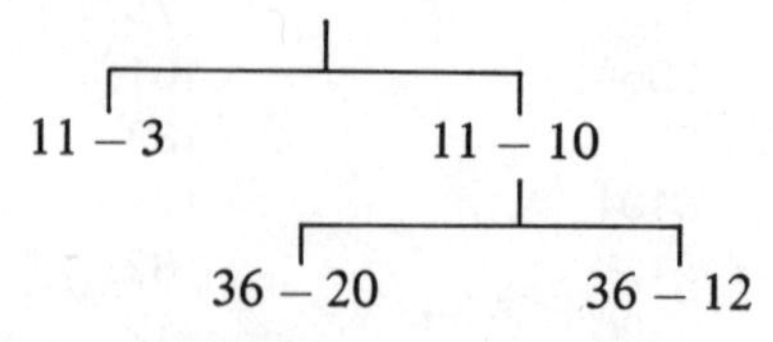

Time – 8.3 secs
Move played – 2. . .Kd2–c2 (11 to 10)
Reply expected – 3.Re5–e2 (36 to 12)

Reply played – 3.Re5–e2

Plausible moves – 10 to 3 and 10 to 2

Search tree –

```
              |
     ---------------------
     |                   |
   10 – 3             10 – 2
     |
   26 – 19
```

Time – 14.0 secs
Move played – 3. . .Kc2–d1 (10 to 3)
Reply expected – 4.Kc4–d3 (26 to 19)
Reply played – 4.Kc4–d3

The rest of this game is not interesting as only single plausible moves were generated. The remainder is given in tabular form for the sake of completeness.

Plausible move	Time	Move played	Reply played
3 to 2	2.5	4. . .Kd1–c1	5.Kd3–c3
2 to 1	2.8	5. . .Kc1–b1	6.Re2–h2
1 to 0	2.2	6. . .Kb1–a1	7.Kc3–b3
0 to 1	2.5	7. . .Ka1–b1	8.Rh2–h1 mate

CONCLUSIONS

This project has shown that it is possible to construct a Shannon type B chess-playing program to play a very basic endgame perfectly. It further shows that with the correct plausible move generation and an efficient tree searching algorithm, the program can do so much more efficiently than a brute-force Shannon type A program.

More important, however, it proves that the knowledge needed for plausible move generation need not be perfect and can be generated automatically. After introspection and consolidation, the quality of the information is reasonable.

REFERENCES

Banerji, R. (1976), Learning to solve games and puzzles, in J. C. Simon (ed.), *Computer Oriented Learning Processes,* Noordhoff.

Berliner, H. J. (1974), Chess as problem solving: The development of a tactics analyzer. Ph.D. Thesis. Carnegie-Mellon University.

Berliner, H. J. (1979), The B* tree search: A best-first proof procedure, *Artificial Intelligence,* **12**, 23–40.

Clarke, M. R. B. (1977), A quantitative study of King and Pawn against King, in M. R. B. Clarke (ed.), *Advances in Computer Chess 1,* Edinburgh: Edinburgh University Press.

Huberman, B. J. (1968), A program to play chess end games, Stanford Technical Memo CS 106. Stanford University.

Messerschmidt, H. J. (1980), Parallel programming for a chess endgame database, *Software – Practice and Experience,* **10**, 475–487.

Nilsson, N. J. (1965), *Learning Machines: Foundations of Trainable Pattern – Classifying Systems,* New York: McGraw-Hill.

Tan, S. T. (1973), A knowledge based program to play chess endgames, in A. G. Bell (ed.), *Computer Chess,* Atlas Computer Laboratory.

5

Knowledge-based problem-solving in AL3†

Ivan Bratko
Institut 'Jozef Stefan', 61001 Ljubljana, Jamova 39, Yugoslavia

---

ABSTRACT

The AL3 System is described in the paper, and its behaviour illustrated by its application to a chess endgame. AL3 is a rule-based problem-solving system in which the problem is stated as a 'target' to be proved or disproved. Each executional cycle, triggered by a pattern-match, produces new facts about the problem. The facts are used as new axioms for proving or disproving the target. Executional modules, called methods, which implement the domain-specific knowledge, generate and manipulate objects such as hypotheses about the problem, plans for solving problems and 'pieces-of-advice'.

INTRODUCTION

AL3 (Advice Language 3) is a problem-solving system whose structure facilitates the implementation of knowledge for a chosen problem domain in terms of plans for solving problems, 'pieces-of-advice', patterns, motifs, etc. AL3 is a successor of AL1 and AL1.5 (Bratko and Michie, 1980a and b; Mozetic, 1979). Experiments in which AL1 was applied to chess endgames established that it is a powerful tool for representing search heuristics and problem-solving strategies. The power of AL1 lies mainly in the use of a fundamental concept: piece-of-advice. A piece-of-advice suggests what goal should be achieved next while preserving some other condition. If this goal can be achieved in a given problem situation (e.g. a given chess position) then we say that the piece-of-advice is 'satisfiable' in that position. In this way AL1 makes it possible to break the whole problem of achieving an ultimate goal into a sequence of subproblems, each of them consisting of the achievement of a subgoal prescribed by some piece-of-advice. The control structure which chooses what piece-of-advice to

†This article is an abbreviated version of one which appeared in *Machine Intelligence 10*, eds. J. E. Hayes, D. Michie and Y-H. Pao (Ellis Horwood, 1982).

apply next consists of a set of 'advice tables', each of them being specialised in a certain problem subdomain. Each advice table is a set of rules of the form

if precondition *then* advice-list

If more than one rule-precondition is satisfied then simply the first rule is chosen. Advice-list is an ordered list of pieces-of-advice. Advice-list is interpreted so that the first satisfiable piece-of-advice in the list is executed. The satisfiability is checked by simple depth-first search.

This comparatively simple control structure has several advantages: simplicity, neatness of solutions, susceptibility to formal proofs of correctness of strategies. However, its disadvantage is that it is difficult to implement problem-solving strategies which make extensive use of higher-order concepts, such as plans, and which also do 'meta-level' reasoning about plans and pieces-of-advice themselves. It is sometimes desirable that the system be able to create a new piece-of-advice, or in a case of its failure, modify it according to the cause of the failure.

AL1.5 removed some minor defects of AL1. One improvement was to allow recursive calls of pieces-of-advice within a piece-of-advice. But the basic control structure of AL1 was preserved.

AL3 is an attempt at facilitating the use of higher-order concepts by providing a more flexible control structure over the basic mechanisms of AL1. Experiments with AL3, described in this paper, were implemented in Prolog (Pereira, Pereira and Warren, 1978). The problem domain used in these experiments is a chess ending king and pawn vs. king and pawn with passed pawns. Examples of using AL3 in another chess ending are described by Bratko and Niblett (1979). Although these experiments demonstrate how AL3 can be used for knowledge-based problem-solving using higher-order concepts, they should not be considered as completed at this stage. Many questions need further investigation, such as: in what ways, in general, can different plans be merged for achieving a desired combined effect? Examples of related research, also using plans for chess problem-solving, are given by Tan (1977), Pitrat (1977) and Wilkins (1979).

EXAMPLE: SOLVING A CHESS STUDY

Consider a chess endgame study in Fig. 1 to illustrate the way AL3 uses problem-domain knowledge. The pawn on h5 is threatening to run down to h1 and promote to a queen. White can try to stop this threat with his king, but the king on h8 is too far away to catch the Black pawn. Another idea for White is to queen his own pawn. But if the White pawn moves ahead, the Black king can easily move closer to stop the pawn and capture it if necessary. The position looks lost for White. However, there is a surprising plan for White which preserves the draw.

The following is a simplified trace of AL3's behaviour when solving the problem of Fig. 1. The problem is stated by an initial query, 'Can White draw?', and the following hypothesis, H0, is investigated:

H0: White can draw?

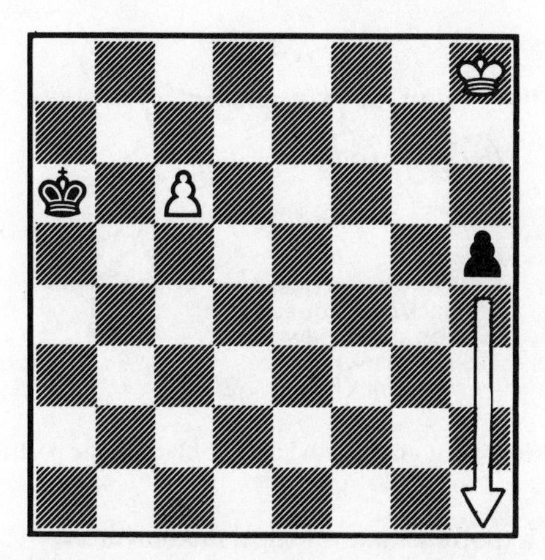

Fig. 1 – A study by Reti. White to move; can White draw? Black pawn is threatening to run to square h1 and promote to a queen as indicated by the arrow.

This causes another hypothesis to be generated

H1: Black can win?

and a logical relation between both hypotheses is provided:

$H0 \Leftrightarrow \text{not } (H1)$

That is: H0 is logically equivalent to not H1. This logical relation is called a 'fact' about our problem.

Now the system may consider the hypothesis H1, and one method for solving problems in the system's knowledge-base suggests a plan for Black: push Black pawn towards h1 while preserving a *holding goal* 'Black pawn alive and not White pawn successfully promoted' until a better goal is achieved: 'Black pawn promoted'. Call this plan BPQ (Black pawn queens). This and subsequent plans are illustrated in Fig. 2. A hypothesis about plan BPQ is now generated

H2: Plan BPQ succeeds?

together with the fact

$H2 \Rightarrow H1.$

A method which 'knows' how to refute plans now proposes: try to refute plan BPQ by either destroying its holding goal or its better goal. Thus two refutation plans are proposed for White.

1. Plan SBP (Stop Black pawn): move White king toward the Black pawn path.
2. Plan WPQ (White pawn queens): promote White pawn by pushing it toward square c8.

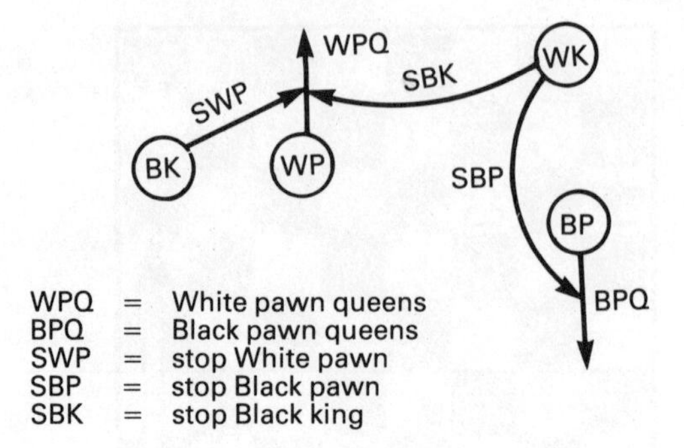

Fig. 2 – Illustration of plans for White and Black in the position of Fig. 1.

Two corresponding hypotheses and a logical relation are:

H3: SBP refutes BPQ?

H4: WPQ refutes BPQ?

H3 v H4 ⇒ not (H2)

There is a lemma in the knowledge-base which recognises on the basis of distance among pieces that H3 is false. But another lemma, about pawn races, establishes that H4 is true. This gives, using logical relations among hypotheses: H2 is false. Thus the simple Black plan BPQ (push Black pawn and queen) does not succeed.

One method in the knowledge-base, considering this failure and the cause of the failure, proposes a refinement of plan BPQ, obtaining plan BPQ1. The skeleton of BPQ1 is BPQ, but in the meantime the Black king has, if necessary, to stop the White pawn by moving toward the White pawn path. Now neither of White's counter plans WPQ and SBP refutes the plan BPQ1.

The repertoire of simple ideas for White is not exhausted, but more complicated ideas can still be tried. First, plan WPQ is refined obtaining plan WPQ1. The skeleton of WPQ1 is WPQ refined by the idea of bringing the White king toward the White pawn path in order to prevent Black's plan SWP (stop White pawn). It turns out that WPQ1 also does not refute BPQ1. However, there is one more idea for White: a disjunctive combination of plans WPQ1 and SBP. The plan, based on this idea, WPQ1 *or* SBP does refute Black's plan BPQ1. The solution that saves the White position is finally: White king moves diagonally from h8 to f6 or e5 all the time pursuing the idea of the 'or' combination of plans WPQ1 and SBP. The diagonal White king moves serve both plans. Then, depending on Black's reactions, one of the component plans refutes Black's BPQ1, ensuring the draw.

OVERVIEW OF AL3

The overall structure of the AL3 system is shown in Fig. 3.

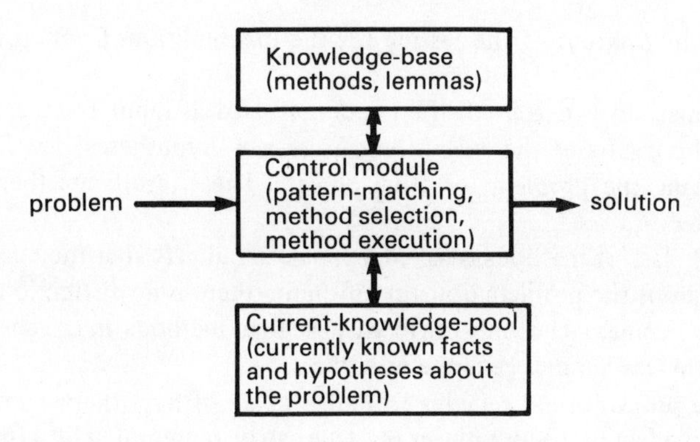

Fig. 3 – The AL3 system.

The main modules of the system are:

- a knowledge-base which contains *methods* that 'know' how to solve particular problems, and *lemmas* (or theorems) about the problem domain that can be applied during the problem-solving process;
- a current-knowledge-pool (CKP containing the already known *facts* and *hypotheses* about the problem being solved, and other objects that are relevant to the problem;
- the *control module* which decides what method, or lemma, to activate next.

(1) The knowledge-base

Methods in the knowledge-base are, in the terminology of Waterman and Hayes-Roth (1978), pattern-directed executional modules. They can be thought of as specialised subroutines for solving particular kinds of subproblem, or for providing a suggestion about how to solve a (sub)problem.

For example, one method for the problem domain of the king and pawn vs. king and pawn chess ending says: If one side (say White) is planning to promote his pawn, then a counter-plan for Black is to stop the advancing White pawn by bringing the Black king in front of the pawn. Together with this, a hypothesis is generated that this Black plan refutes White's plan and the following fact is provided: If this hypothesis is true then White's plan fails. The necessary precondition for this method to be executed is the existence of a hypothesis that White can promote his pawn.

Each method is defined by (a) its precondition, (b) a procedure for its execution, and (c) its characteristics. The characteristics include, for example, an estimate of how difficult the method is to execute; i.e. what computational resources will be spent on the execution of the method.

Preconditions are predicates on the current-knowledge-pool (CKP). They are implemented so that they do not only return the truth value. If the precondition is satisfied, the 'context' which satisfies the precondition is also returned as a by-product of the testing for the precondition. Context is simply a part of CKP.

When a method is executed, the context is used as input for the method's procedure. The results of the execution can be new hypotheses, new facts, new plans for solving the problem, or other objects. These results are then used to update the CKP.

A special class of methods is called *lemmas* to indicate that they correspond to theorems about the problem domain. Formally there is no distinction between methods and lemmas. The only difference is that methods may generate new hypotheses whereas lemmas generate only facts.

Facts are propositional calculus formulae made of hypothesis names. Thus, for example, the fact that a hypothesis H is true can be represented by a formula:

$$H$$

The fact that if hypothesis $H1$ is true then $H2$ is false can be represented by

$$H1 \Rightarrow (\text{not}\ (H2))$$

(2) The current-knowledge-pool

CKP contains:

- hypotheses about the problem, including the user's definition of the problem which is to be solved,
- a user's query, called a 'target', which is to be proved or disproved, together with the current known facts about the problem,
- plans, pieces-of-advice and other objects that are in any respect relevant to the problem-solving task and have thus been generated so far during the problem-solving process.

(3) The control module and executional cycle of AL3

The control module supervises the problem-solving process which consists of a sequence of executional cycles. To carry out each executional cycle the control module does the following: it analyses the current target and checks if enough facts about the problem are already known to imply an answer. If not, the control module matches the preconditions of the methods and lemmas against the CKP to find an applicable set of methods and lemmas. This set is called the *conflict set.* A method or a lemma in the conflict set is then selected on the basis of a cost-benefit criterion. The selected method should produce new facts, so as most economically to further the problem-solving process.

Prolog code for the top level of operation of AL3, including the main executional cycle, is given in Fig. 4. Notational conventions are those of the Edinburgh implementation of Prolog (Pereira, Pereira and Warren, 1978). For solving a problem, the target is initialised by the user's query, and an upper limit on computational resources that may be spent on solving this problem is specified.

```
problem:–
    initialise (Target, Resources),
    solve (Target, Resources, Answer, Explanation),
    display (Target, Answer, Explanation).

solve (Target,_,yes, nil):–
    proved (Target).

solve (Target,_,no, nil):–
    disproved (Target).

solve (Target, Resources, unknown, nil):–
    exceeded (Resources, Target).

solve (Target, Resources, Answer, [Note | Esp1] ):–
    applyknbase (Target, Resources, Target1, Resources1, Note),
    solve (Target1, Resources1, Answer, Exp1).

applyknbase (T, Res, T1, Res1, Note):–
    selectmethod (T, Mname, Context),
    execute (Mname, Context, Facts, Note, Spent),
    update (T, Facts, T1),
    subtract (Res, Spent, Res1).
```

Fig. 4 – Prolog code for the top level operation of AL3.

The Prolog procedure

solve (Target, Resources, Answer, Explanation)

produces an answer: 'yes', 'no', or 'unknown' if it was not found before the resources were exhausted. It also produces an explanation of the answer. The explanation is a list of notes supplied by the methods when activated during the problem-solving process. The main executional cycle is performed by the procedure

applyknbase(Target, Resources, Target1, Resources1, Note)

It updates the variable Target with new facts (producing Target1) and the variable Resources, obtaining Resources1, i.e. the resources left for the rest of the task.

REPRESENTATION OF TARGET AND FACTS

Both target and facts are represented by propositional calculus formulae. A target, T, can be thought of as a formula that the system is trying to prove or disprove. If T is a theorem then T has been proved; if not (T) is a theorem then

T has been disproved; if T is neither of these, then new facts, F, when found, are used as new axioms. The target T is updated by F giving a new target, $T1$:

$$T1 \equiv (F \Rightarrow T)$$

Now the goal becomes to prove or disprove $T1$.

To enable efficient manipulation, target and facts are represented in the system as sets of clauses (also called 'lines') of the form

$$a_1, a_2, \ldots, a_m \Rightarrow b_1, b_2, \ldots, b_n$$

meaning

$$a_1 \wedge a_2 \wedge \ldots \wedge a_m \Rightarrow b_1 \vee b_2 \vee \ldots \vee b_n$$

All a_i and b_j are hypothesis names. The logical connective between clauses is conjunction. Any propositional formula can be converted into this form by Wang's algorithm (e.g. Raphael, 1976). This form will be referred to as the c-form.

Sometimes set notation will be used in the following way. Capital letters $A, B, \ldots$ will denote sets of hypothesis names. If $A = \{a_1, \ldots, a_m\}$ and $B = \{b_1, \ldots, b_n\}$ then

$$A \Rightarrow B$$

represents the line

$$a_1, \ldots, a_m \Rightarrow b_1, \ldots, b_n$$

In this notation, a target in the c-form will be written as

$$\begin{bmatrix} A_1 \Rightarrow B_1 \\ A_2 \Rightarrow B_2 \\ \ldots\ldots\ldots \\ \ldots\ldots\ldots \end{bmatrix}$$

$A_i = 0$ represents the truth value 'true'
$B_i = 0$ represents the truth value 'false'.

A line $A \Rightarrow B$ is a tautology if
(1) A is false, or
(2) B is true, or
(3) $A \cap B \neq \emptyset$

A target is *proved* if all its lines are tautologies (i.e. the target is a theorem).

A target can be decomposed into a product of its 'subtargets', where the subtargets themselves have the form of a target, e.g.

$$T = T1 \times T2$$

The multiplication rule is:

if $T1 = \begin{bmatrix} A_1 \Rightarrow B_1 \\ \ldots\ldots \\ A_m \Rightarrow B_m \end{bmatrix}$ and $T_2 = \begin{bmatrix} C_1 \Rightarrow D_1 \\ \ldots\ldots \\ C_n \Rightarrow D_n \end{bmatrix}$

then $$T = T1 \times T2 = \begin{bmatrix} A_1 \cup C_1 \Rightarrow B_1 \cup D_1 \\ A_1 \cup C_2 \Rightarrow B_1 \cup D_2 \\ \ldots\ldots\ldots\ldots \\ A_1 \cup C_n \Rightarrow B_1 \cup D_n \\ A_2 \cup C_1 \Rightarrow B_2 \cup D_1 \\ \ldots\ldots\ldots\ldots \\ A_m \cup C_n \Rightarrow B_m \cup D_n \end{bmatrix}$$

A target

$$T = T_1 \times T_2 \times \ldots \times T_N$$

is a theorem if at least one of its subtargets T_i is a theorem. The multiplication operation is associative and commutative. These properties provide a basis for different strategies of problem decomposition.

An easy way of updating the target by new facts is through the use of multiplication. The principle is: to update a target T with facts F, represent T and F in the c-form by

$$[\text{true} \Rightarrow T]$$

and

$$[F \Rightarrow \text{false}]$$

The updated target is then

$$[F \Rightarrow \text{false}] \times [\text{true} \Rightarrow T] = [F \Rightarrow T]$$

It may be advantageous to keep the target in the product form, delaying the multiplication, or to carry out the multiplication only on part of the target. For example, complete multiplication on a target

$$F1 \times F2 \times T$$

may result in a new target which is bulky and difficult to manipulate with many lines. Instead, a partial multiplication of $F1 \times F2 = F$ may reduce the number of lines, giving a handy new target represented by the product $F \times T$.

Another reason for keeping the target in the product form is that if the subtargets consist of basically disjoint sets of hypotheses then the product of the subtargets corresponds to a natural decomposition of the problem. Each subtarget then corresponds to a comparatively independent subproblem. This enables the system to focus its attention on subproblems themselves.

Facts of the form 'Hypothesis a is true' or 'a is false' can be added simply by substituting the value of a into the lines of the target and applying simplification rules for logical expressions. Facts of more complex forms are transformed into the c-form and then added as a new multiplication factor. Thus, for example, a fact

$$a \Rightarrow b$$

is properly transformed into the c-form by the following operations. The factor to be added is

$$(a \Rightarrow b) \Rightarrow \text{false}$$

Its c-form is obtained by the following transformation (using Wang's algorithm):

$$(\text{not}(a) \vee b) \Rightarrow \text{false}$$

This is equivalent to

$$\text{not}(a) \Rightarrow \text{false} \qquad \text{and}$$
$$b \Rightarrow \text{false}$$

giving finally

$$\begin{bmatrix} \text{true} \Rightarrow a \\ b \Rightarrow \text{false} \end{bmatrix}$$

Table 1 presents some useful transformations of typical forms of facts into the corresponding c-form representations.

The goal of the problem-solving process is either to prove the target or to disprove it, i.e. to demonstrate that the target is a theorem or that its negation is a theorem. Both alternatives can be dealt with by keeping two targets during the problem-solving process: a *positive* and a *negative* target. If the positive target becomes a theorem then the initial target has been proved; if the negative target becomes a theorem then the initial target has been disproved. For example, assume that the initial goal was to answer the question: Is hypothesis h true or false? Then the corresponding positive and negative targets in the c-form are [true $\Rightarrow h$] and [$h \Rightarrow$ false] respectively. New facts, when generated, are added multiplicatively to both positive and negative targets.

After inserting a truth value for a hypothesis name or after carrying out a multiplication operation, targets may become messy and redundant. They can be tidied up by applying the following simplification rules:

(1) Delete tautological lines.
A line $A \Rightarrow B$ is a tautology if $A \cap B \neq \emptyset$.
A line false $\Rightarrow B$ is a tautology.
A line $A \Rightarrow$ true is a tautology.

Table 1
Some useful transformations of facts into the c-form. For a given fact F, the right-hand side constructs in the table are logically equivalent to $F \Rightarrow$ false.

Fact	Fact in the c-form
$a \vee b \vee c \vee \ldots.$	$\left[\begin{array}{l} a \Rightarrow \text{false} \\ b \Rightarrow \text{false} \\ c \Rightarrow \text{false} \\ \ldots\ldots \end{array}\right]$
$a \wedge b \wedge c \wedge \ldots.$	$[a, b, c, \ldots \Rightarrow \text{false}]$
$a \vee b \vee c \vee \ldots. \Rightarrow h$	$\left[\begin{array}{l} h \Rightarrow \text{false} \\ \text{true} \Rightarrow a, b, c, \ldots. \end{array}\right]$
$a \wedge b \wedge c \wedge \ldots. \Rightarrow h$	$\left[\begin{array}{l} h \Rightarrow \text{false} \\ \text{true} \Rightarrow a \\ \text{true} \Rightarrow b \\ \text{true} \Rightarrow c \\ \ldots\ldots \end{array}\right]$
$a \vee b \vee c \vee \ldots. \Leftrightarrow h$	$\left[\begin{array}{l} \text{true} \Rightarrow h, a, b, c, \ldots. \\ a, h \Rightarrow \text{false} \\ b, h \Rightarrow \text{false} \\ c, h \Rightarrow \text{false} \\ \ldots\ldots\ldots \end{array}\right]$
$a \wedge b \wedge c \wedge \ldots. \Leftrightarrow h$	$\left[\begin{array}{l} h, a, b, c, \ldots. \Rightarrow \text{false} \\ \text{true} \Rightarrow a, h \\ \text{true} \Rightarrow b, h \\ \text{true} \Rightarrow c, h \\ \ldots\ldots\ldots \end{array}\right]$

(2) Delete lines that are implied by other lines.
A line $A \Rightarrow B$ *implies* another line $A1 \Rightarrow B1$ within the same subtarget if $A \subseteq A1$ and $B \subseteq B1$.

(3) Insert truth values for hypothesis names whose truth values are implied by the targets. The truth value of a hypothesis h is implied if h appears on the same side of all the lines of a positive (sub)target and on this same side of all the lines of a negative (sub)target. The value is:
(a) if h appears on the left then h is true;
(b) if h appears on the right then h is false.

This decision is based on the fact that the positive and negative targets cannot both be theorems.

EXAMPLE: SEARCHING AND/OR GRAPHS IN AL3

This section presents a detailed example to illustrate the whole basic AL3 machinery at work. In the example a miniature knowledge-base is used for searching AND/OR graphs. The knowledge-base does not contain any heuristics to guide the search. It consists of one lemma, GOALTEST, and one method, EXPAND, whose detailed Prolog definition is given in Fig. 5.

```
        /*** Lemma GOALTEST ***/

precond(goaltest, [H,X] ) :-
        hyp(H,goal (X)).
exec(goaltest,[H,X] ,[[H] ⇒ false] ) :- goalnode(X),!.
exec(goaltest,_,[true ⇒ false] ).

        /*** Method EXPAND ***/

precond(expand,[H,X] ) :-
        hyp(H,goal(X)).

exec(expand,[H,X] ,Fact) :-
        findall(Y,succ(X,Y),Ylist),
        (Ylist = [] ,!,Fact = [true ⇒ [H] ] ;
        findall(Hname,newhyp(Hname,Ylist),Hlist),
        getfact(H,Hlist,X,Fact)).

newhyp(Hname,Ylist) :-
        member(Y,Ylist),
        genhyp(Hname,goal(Y)).

getfact(H,Hlist,X,[([H|Hlist] ⇒ false)|Lines] ) :-
        andnode(X),!,
        findall(true ⇒ [H,H1] ,member(H1,Hlist),Lines).

getfact(H,Hlist,X,[(true ⇒ [H|Hlist] )|Lines] ) :-
        ornode(X),!,
        findall([H,H1] ⇒ false,member(H1,Hlist),Lines).
```

Fig. 5 – Prolog code of a knowledge-base for searching AND/OR graphs. The base assumes that the control module prefers lemmas to methods.

The precondition for both is the existence of a hypothesis H:

goal (X)?

where X is a node in the AND/OR graph being searched, and goal(X) means that there exists a solution subgraph for X. If X is a terminal node which 'trivially' satisfies the goal-condition then the lemma returns the fact that H is true.

Let $Y_1, \ldots, Y_n$ be the successor nodes of a node X. The method EXPAND, when executed on the context $[H, X]$, generates hypotheses $H_1, H_2, \ldots, H_n$ of the form

goal(Y_i)?

In addition, new facts are generated, namely: If X has AND successors then the facts are:

$$H \Leftrightarrow H_1 \wedge \ldots \wedge H_n$$

If X has OR successors then the facts are

$$H \Leftrightarrow H_1 \vee \ldots \vee H_n$$

The Prolog code in Fig. 5 generates these facts already transformed into a proper form according to the transformation rules in Table 1. Figure 6 shows part of the trace produced by AL3 when solving the problem

goal(a)?

for the AND/OR graph in the top part of the figure.

CONCEPTS MANIPULATED BY AL3

In principle, the AL3 system as described in the previous sections is not limited to any special formalism for representing methods for problem-solving, or to any special class of concepts to be used for solving problems. In this section we present a formalism and a number of concepts that are useful for solving combinatorial problems in general and chess problems in particular. These concepts were used in the experiments with AL3 on chess endgames.

(1) Piece-of-advice

A fundamental concept of AL1, piece-of-advice, proved to be extremely valuable not only for representing knowledge but also because it provides a good formal basis for precise definition of other concepts. A piece-of-advice is a five-tuple

$$(X, BG, HG, MCX, MCY)$$

where X is the side (White or Black) to which A belongs, BG and HG are predicates on positions, called *better-goal* and *holding-goal* respectively, MCX and MCY are predicates on moves, called *move-constraints,* for side X and side Y respectively.

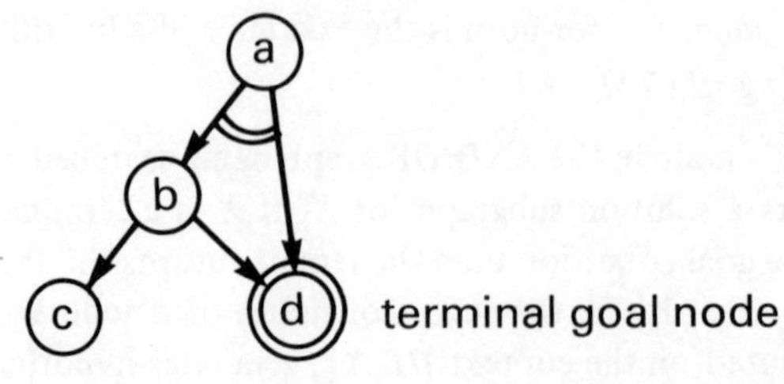

Current-knowledge-pool	Next execution cycle
Positive Target	Conflict set (method names: contexts)
true ⇒ [h:0]	1 expand: [h:0,a]
Negative Target	Which? 1.
[h:0] ⇒ false	Executed expand on context [h:0,a]
Hypotheses	New facts
1 hyp (h:0,goal (a))	[h:0,h:1,h:2] ⇒ false
	true ⇒ [h:0,h:1]
	true ⇒ [h:0,h:2]

Current-knowledge-pool	Next execution cycle
Positive Target	Conflict set (method names: contexts)
true ⇒ [h:0,h:1]	1 goaltest: [h:1,b]
true ⇒ [h:0,h:2]	2 goaltest: [h:2,d]
	3 expand: [h:1,b]
Negative Target	4 expand: [h:2,d]
[h:0,h:1,h:2] ⇒ false	Which? 1.
Hypotheses	Executed goaltest on context [h:1,b]
1 hyp(h:0,goal(a))	
2 hyp(h:1,goal(b))	New facts
3 hyp(h:2,goal(d))	true ⇒ false

Fig. 6 – Part of trace, produced by AL3, when searching the AND/OR graph in the top part of the figure.

Throughout the paper X and Y are used to represent both sides. Thus X can be either White or Black, and Y is always the opponent of X. Besides merely selecting a subset of legal moves, move constraints can impose an ordering on the moves that are selected. This becomes important for practical reasons when searching a game tree.

A tree T is called a forcing tree for a piece-of-advice

$$A = (X, BG, HG, MCX, MCY)$$

in a position Pos, iff T is a subtree of the game tree rooted in Pos, such that:

(1) for every node p in T: $HG(p)$;
(2) for every nonterminal node p in T: not $BG(p)$;
(3) for every terminal node p in T: $BG(p)$ or p is a Y-to-move position from which there is no legal move that satisfies MCY;
(4) there is exactly one move in T from every X-to-move nonterminal node in T; that move must satisfy MCX;
(5) all legal moves from any nonterminal Y-to-move position in T that satisfy MCY are in T.

A piece-of-advice A is *satisfiable* in a position Pos iff there exists a forcing-tree for A in Pos. This is denoted by:

$$\text{sat}(A, Pos)$$

In fact, a piece-of-advice defines a subgame with two possible outcomes: win or loss. Legal moves of this subgame are defined by the move constraints and terminal positions of the subgame are defined by predicates better-goal and holding-goal. A position Pos is won for side X with respect to the subgame corresponding to a piece-of-advice A if sat(A, Pos); otherwise it is lost for X with respect to A.

Note an important detail in the above definition of forcing tree: if (1) $HG(Pos)$ and not ($BG(Pos)$), and (2) Y-to-move in Pos, and (3) no Y-move in Pos satisfies MCY then Pos is a terminal node of a forcing tree. This interpretation of the 'no-move' condition ensures the following relation for any piece-of-advice and any position:

$$\text{sat}(\,(X, BGX, HGX, MCX, MCY), Pos) \Leftrightarrow$$
$$\text{not sat}(\,(Y, \text{not}\,(HGX), \text{not}\,(BGX \text{ and } HGX), MCY, MCX), Pos)$$

This relationship will be referred to as 'inverse advice relationship'. However, this definition sometimes necessitates the test for stalemate in chess being explicitly stated in the goals of a piece-of-advice to avoid anomalous behaviour.

Some other useful relations concerning the satisfiability of related pieces-of-advice are given in Bratko and Niblett (1979).

(2) Plans

A *plan* is a quadruple

$$(X, BG, HG, MCX)$$

where X is the side to which P belongs, BG and HG are predicates on positions called better-goal and holding-goal, and *MCX* (move constraints for side *X*) is any schema for selecting and/or ordering *X* moves. An example of such move constraints is a White king 'macromove' between two specified squares not exceeding a specified length, e.g.:

macromove(white-king, c2, e1, length $\leqslant$ 3)

This macromove denotes the set of all possible king paths between squares c2 and e1 of length at most 3 moves (see Fig. 7). A plan with such move constraints allows any legal White king move along this macromove.

Fig. 7 – White king macromove from c2 to e1 in at most 3 moves.

Move constraints can also prescribe an ordering of moves. For example the above king macromove can be ordered with respect to increasing length of the king paths.

A plan $P = (X, BG, HG, MCX)$ is said to *succeed* in a position *Pos* iff

sat(A, *Pos*)

where A is a piece-of-advice

$A = (X, BG, HG, MCX,$ anymove)

This is denoted by

suc (P, *Pos*) $\Leftrightarrow$ sat (A, *Pos*)

Let *Px* and *Py* be two plans

$Px = (X, BGX, HGX, MCX)$
$Py = (Y, BGY, HGY, MCY)$

Then plan Py refutes plan Px in a position Pos iff

$$\text{not sat}(A, Pos)$$

where A is a piece-of-advice

$$A = (X, BGX \text{ or not } (HGY), HGX, MCX, MCY)$$

This is represented by

$$\text{ref}(Py, Px, Pos) \Leftrightarrow \text{not sat}(A, Pos)$$

An equivalent definition is

$$\text{ref}(Py, Px, Pos) \Leftrightarrow \text{sat}(A1, Pos)$$

where $A1 = (Y, \text{not } (HGX), \text{not } (HGX) \text{ or not } (BGX) \text{ and } HGY, MCY, MCX)$. The equivalence of these two definitions can be proved by using the inverse advice relationship.

Note that it is possible that a plan Py does not succeed (i.e. its better goal is not attainable) but Py may still refute a plan Px.

(3) 'Or' combination of plans

Let $P1$ and $P2$ be plans

$$P1 = (X, BG1, HG1, MCX1)$$
$$P2 = (X, BG2, HG2, MCX2)$$

A plan

$$P = P1 \text{ or } P2$$

is called an or-combination of $P1$ and $P2$. The better goal of P is $BG1$ *or* $BG2$. Precise combinations of the goals and move constraints of $P1$ and $P2$ can be defined by the following AL3 method for investigating the success of or-plans.

Method OREXPAND

Precondition

hypothesis(H, suc($P1$ or $P2$, Pos)),
$P1 = (X, BG1, HG1, MCX1)$
$P2 = (X, BG2, HG2, MCX2)$

Action

1. Generate hypotheses: hypothesis (Ha, suc ($P1, Pos$)),
   hypothesis (Hb, suc ($P2, Pos$))
2. If Y-to-move in Pos then generate all legal successor positions $Pos_1, \ldots, Pos_n$ of Pos, else generate legal successor positions $Pos_1, \ldots, Pos_n$ such that the moves $Pos \rightarrow Pos_i$ satisfy either $MCX1$ or $MCX2$ or both. The ordering of

$Pos_1, \ldots, Pos_n$ is a rough ordering by the criterion 'first satisfy both move constraints', and a fine ordering as prescribed by $MCX1$ and $MCX2$.

3. Generate:

   hypothesis($H1$, suc($P1$ or $P2, Pos_1$))

   ....

   hypothesis(H_n, suc($P1$ or $P2, Pos_n$))

4. Return facts

   (a) if X-to-move in Pos then

   $$Ha \vee Hb \Rightarrow H1 \vee H2 \vee \ldots \vee Hn$$
   $$Ha \vee Hb \vee H1 \vee \ldots \vee Hn \Leftrightarrow H$$

   (b) if Y-to-move in Pos then

   $$Ha \vee Hb \Rightarrow H1 \wedge H2 \wedge \ldots \wedge Hn$$
   $$Ha \vee Hb \vee (H1 \wedge \ldots \wedge Hn) \Leftrightarrow H$$

(4) Modification of plan by plan

Let $P1$ and $P2$ be two plans for side X. The modification of $P1$ by $P2$ is a plan $P = P1\ mod\ P2$, such that the goal of P is the same as the goal of $P1$, but the sequence of steps of $P1$ may be interrupted by inserting steps of $P2$. An AL3 method for investigating the success of a modified plan is:

Method MODEXPAND

Precondition

hypothesis(H, suc ($P1$ mod $P2, Pos$)),
$P1 = (X, BG1, HG1, MCX1)$,
$P2 = (X, BG2, HG2, MCX2)$

Action

1. Generate: Hypothesis (Ha, suc ($P1, Pos$)).
2. If Y-to-move in Pos then generate all legal successors $Pos_1, \ldots, Pos_n$ of Pos else generate legal successors $Pos_1, \ldots, Pos_n$ satisfying $MCX1$ or $MCX2$ or both. The ordering of $Pos_1, \ldots, Pos_n$ is a rough ordering by 'first satisfy both move constraints', then 'satisfy $MCX1$', then 'satisfy $MCX2$', and a fine ordering as prescribed by $MCX1$ and $MCX2$.
3. Generate:

   hypothesis($H1$, suc ($P1$ mod $P2, Pos_1$))

   ....

   hypothesis(Hn, suc ($P1$ mod $P2, Pos_n$))

4. Return facts:
   (a) if X-to-move in Pos then

$$Ha \Rightarrow H1 \vee \ldots \vee Hn$$
$$Ha \vee H1 \vee \ldots \vee Hn \Leftrightarrow H$$

   (b) if Y-to-move in Pos then

$$Ha \Rightarrow H1 \wedge \ldots \wedge Hn$$
$$Ha \vee (H1 \wedge \ldots \wedge Hn) \Leftrightarrow H$$

A KPKP KNOWLEDGE-BASE

A small AL3 knowledge-base is now outlined for the king and pawn vs. king and pawn chess ending with both pawns passed (pawns not on the same file or on adjacent files). Correct play in this ending can be very difficult, as indicated by many chess studies from this domain (e.g. Averbach and Maizelis, 1974). An example was given in Fig. 1.

The KPKP knowledge-base contains two lemmas. One, CATCHPAWN, decides whether a king can stop a running opponent's pawn. The other, PAWN-RACE, decides which pawn wins a pawn race.

The methods in the base implement basic motifs of the KPKP ending with passed pawns and some more general 'meta-level' ideas about plans. The following is an informal description of the most important methods. Appropriate facts generated by the methods are obvious. At present the KPKP knowledge-base is not complete in the sense that it produces correct play in any position from this domain.

Method WIN
To win it is necessary to queen the pawn and not allow the opponent's pawn to queen successfully.

Method DRAW
To investigate the question 'Can one side draw?', consider the question 'Can the other side win?'.

Method PUSH
One plan for queening is to push the pawn.

Method STOPPAWN
One way of preventing an opponent's plan to queen the pawn is to stop it with the king. It is assumed that the capture of that pawn implies that the pawn has been stopped.

Method RACE
One counter-plan against a queening plan is to queen one's own pawn.

Method STOPKING

If an opponent's plan consists of a king macromove, then it may be refuted by a king's intervention: own king macromove intersecting the opponent's king macromove.

Method MODIFYPLAN

If a plan $P1$ fails against an opponent's plan R then $P1$ may be successfully improved in the following way: find a plan, $P2$, which it is hoped will refute the plan R, and propose a new plan: $P1$ modified by $P2$, i.e. $P = P1$ *mod* $P2$. To find $P2$, AL3 solves a local subproblem with its own local target of refuting R. To solve the local subproblem AL3 may use all the knowledge in the knowledge-base.

Method ORPLAN

If two plans, $R1$, and $R2$, are known not to refute an opponent's plan P, then the or-combination of $R1$ and $R2$, i.e. $R = R1$ *or* $R2$, may refute P.

Method SEARCH

This method converts a hypothesis of the form suc(*Plan*, *Pos*) or ref(*Plan*1, *Plan*2, *Pos*) into sat(A, *Pos*) where A is a corresponding piece-of-advice, and checks the satisfiability of A by searching the game tree. The method can be very expensive and is therefore used only occasionally.

Method EXPAND

Expands a hypothesis of the form suc(*Plan*,*Pos*) by generating successor positions of *Pos*, subject to move constraints in *Plan*, and hypotheses that *Plan* succeeds in the successor positions. New facts are generated according to who is to move in *Pos* and according to the form of *Plan* (see expansion rules for $P1$ *mod* $P2$ and $P1$ *or* $P2$ above).

Fig. 8 – White to move, can White win? Correct is Ke4–f3 stopping the Black pawn. After that, the White pawn cannot be stopped.

To illustrate how this knowledge-base works, consider the position in Fig. 8. AL3 is asked the question 'Can White win in this position?'. Fig. 9 shows the current-knowledge-pool at the moment when AL3 has found a correct plan for White to win. This is: queen the White pawn by pushing it and in the meantime stop the Black pawn with the White king if necessary.

```
Current-knowledge-pool
______________________

Positive Target

[h:4,h:5] ⇒ [h:0,h:1,h:2,h:3,h:8]

Negative Target

[h:0,h:1,h:4,h:5] ⇒ [h:2,h:3]

Facts
1   h:3 is false
2   h:5 is true
3   h:7 is true

Hypotheses
1   hyp(h:0,canwin(w,pos))
2   hyp(h:1,suc(p:1,pos))
3   hyp(h:2,suc(p:2,pos))
4   hyp(h:3,ref(p:3,p:2,pos))
5   hyp(h:4,ref(p:4,p:2,pos))
6   hyp(h:5,ref(p:5,p:2,pos))
7   hyp(h:6,suc(p:5,pos))
8   hyp(h:7,ref(p:6,p:5,pos))
9   hyp(h:8,suc(p:2 mod p:6,pos))

Plans
1   plan(p:1,w,queenwin(w),
    alive(w) & (not queendraw(b)),any)
2   plan(p:2,w,queenwin(w),
    alive(w) & (not queendraw(b)),push(w))
3   plan(p:3,b,stopped(w),nil,macro(b,k,path(w,p)))
4   plan(p:4,b,queendraw(b),alive(b),any)
5   plan(p:5,b,queendraw(b),alive(b),push(b))
6   plan(p:6,w,stopped(b),nil,macro(w,k,path(b,p)))
```

Fig. 9 – AL3's current-knowledge-pool at the moment when a correct plan has been found for the position in Fig. 8. The symbol 'pos' denotes that position. Goals in the plans mean: queenwin(w): White pawn has queened and position is won for White; queendraw(b): Black pawn has queened and position not lost for Black; alive(w): White pawn not captured; etc.

DISCUSSION

There are several ways of looking at the AL3 system. One way is that AL3 is a theorem-prover which accepts a problem in the form of a formula to be proved or disproved. If the formula is neither a theorem nor a contradiction then AL3 tries to find new facts about the problem. The new facts are then used as additional axioms for proving or disproving the initial formula. In this sense each executional cycle aims at producing the most useful new axioms, such that they bring the formula as close as possible towards a theorem or a contradiction.

Another view of AL3 is that AL3 is a problem-solver which uses a special formalism for problem representation. This formalism can be thought of as a generalisation of two known schemas for problem representation: the state-space representation and the AND/OR graph representation (see, for example, Nilsson (1971)). With respect to the logical relationships among the nodes in the problem space, the state-space representation could be called an 'OR-graph' representation, because all the sibling nodes in the state-space are disjunctively related. In this sense, the AND/OR graph representation is a generalisation of the state-space representation. Further, the AL3 representation is a generalisation of AND/OR graph representation, and could be therefore called a 'general graph' representation, 'general' because it allows any logical relationship between the neighbouring nodes in the problem-space. This logical relationship is defined by new facts that can be any propositional calculus formula.

AL3, viewed as above, solves problems by searching a problem space that does not consist only of objects defined by the problem domain itself (e.g. rules of the game), but also of higher-order concepts like plans, macromoves, and pieces-of-advice. There is no formal distinction in the knowledge-base of AL3 between rules of the game and knowledge about how to solve problems.

Very little has been said about the control module of AL3 which implements the overall problem-solving strategy. One such strategic decision is whether to keep the current target in the form of a product or to carry out the multiplication immediately, or to do the multiplication only partially, on some of the subtargets. In the experiments with AL3, described in this paper, the control module used the following simple strategy:

1. Do every multiplication in the target immediately.
2. Find 'interesting' hypotheses by simply counting the number of hypothesis occurrences in the left- and right-hand sides of the lines in the target. Hypotheses with high frequencies are interesting. Include in the conflict set only lemmas and methods that are applicable to interesting hypotheses, and that produce 'complementary' facts (that is, if an interesting hypothesis tends to occur on the left-hand side in the target then a complementary fact contains this hypothesis on the right-hand side).

3. Choose a lemma or a method from the conflict set in the following order of preference: first lemmas, then easy methods, then difficult methods (methods in the knowledge-base are characterised by 'easy' or 'difficult').

Design of more sophisticated control strategies seems to be necessary for solving larger-scale problems. One way of improving the above simple strategy is to (partially) delay the multiplication operation when updating the target and thus control the growth of the target. Another improvement, aiming at the reduction of the possibly very time-consuming matching of method-preconditions against the complete CKP, is to limit this matching to a 'window' in CKP only. The window consists of the hypotheses dealt with in the previous executional cycle and their neighbouring hypotheses. Thus the window provides a mechanism for focusing AL3's attention on a part of CKP.

Another interesting problem for further experiments is concerned with the inclusion of more 'meta-knowledge' into the knowledge-base to facilitate more sophisticated reasoning about plans and pieces-of-advice. Such knowledge could provide rules for deciding whether a given plan, *P*1 say, is more specific than another plan, *P*2; if it is and if *P*2 is known to fail then *P*1 also fails. Even very simple 'meta-methods' in the KPKP knowledge-base are sufficient for discovering concepts like a joint action of a king and a pawn. For example, if White's plan is to queen his pawn by pushing the pawn, and a Black king macromove refutes this plan by stopping the White pawn, then White's plan can be modified by a White king macromove preventing the Black king macromove. This effectively results in the idea: support the advance of the White pawn by the White king.

ACKNOWLEDGEMENTS

The author would like to thank Professor Donald Michie for encouragement and support, Tim Niblett for collaboration at the previous stages of this research, and the Edinburgh Prolog development group (Lawrence Byrd, Fernando Pereira and David Warren) for their continuous advice on the Prolog implementation of AL3. The following institutions made this work possible by providing financial and other support: British Science Research Council, Machine Intelligence Research Unit, University of Edinburgh, Scotland, Faculty of Electrical Engineering and J. Stefan Institute, Ljubljana, Yugoslavia.

REFERENCES

Averbach, Y. and Maizelis, I. (1974), *Pawn Endings,* London: Batsford.

Bratko, I. and Michie, D. (1980a), A representation for pattern-knowledge in chess end-games, in Clarke, M. R. B. (ed.), *Advances in Computer Chess 2,* Edinburgh: Edinburgh University Press.

Bratko, I. and Michie, D. (1980b), An advice program for a complex chess programming task, *Computer Journal,* 23(4), 353–359.

Bratko, I. and Niblett, T. (1979), Conjectures and refutations in a framework for chess end-game knowledge, in Michie, D. (ed.), *Expert Systems in the Microelectronic Age,* Edinburgh: Edinburgh University Press.

Mozetic, I, (1979), *Advice language and the AL 1.5 program system. Work report and manual.* Ljubljana: J. Stefan Institute.

Nilsson, N. J. (1971), *Problem Solving Methods in Artificial Intelligence,* New York: McGraw-Hill.

Pereira, L. M., Pereira, F. C. N. and Warren, D. H. D. (1978), *User's guide to DECsystem-10 Prolog,* University of Edinburgh: Dept. of Artificial Intelligence.

Pitrat, J. (1977), A chess combinations program which uses plans, *Artificial Intelligence* 8, 275–321.

Raphael, B. (1976), *The Thinking Computer: Mind inside Matter,* San Francisco: W. H. Freeman.

Tan, S. (1977), Describing pawn structures, in Clarke, M. R. B. (ed.), *Advances in Computer Chess 1,* Edinburgh: Edinburgh University Press.

Waterman, D. A., Hayes-Roth, F. (1978), *Pattern-Directed Inference Systems,* New York: Academic Press.

Wilkins, D. (1979), Using patterns to solve problems and control search, Ph.D. Thesis, Stanford University: Computer Science Department.

6

Strategy in chess endgames

H. J. van den Herik
Delft University of Technology, Department of Mathematics,
Julianalaan 132, 2628 BL DELFT, The Netherlands

ABSTRACT

The formulation of rules of strategy in chess endgames has proved to be difficult if such a formulation is required to lead to correct play and to be equally relevant to human players and to computer programs. This paper first discusses chess thinking in connection with strategy in chess endgames. The strategies of some chess grandmasters for a given position of the endgame King, Knight and Pawn vs. King (KNPK) are compared. From this, tentative conclusions are drawn about the relation between pattern-based representations of knowledge in human minds and the associated strategies.

In elementary endgames, it is not playing strength which determines strategy; rather, strategy depends on the concepts the player has in mind. Starting from one set of these concepts and strategies, a computer-implemented model is presented in which pattern knowledge is combined with conventional depth-first searching. One of the aims of the construction of the model has been to gauge to what extent the use of pattern knowledge may be incorporated in computer programs in a manner similar to that in which it is obviously present in grandmaster thinking.

Heuristic considerations determine the choice of trade-off point between directly using implemented knowledge and relying on systematic searching. Moreover, the program's user is in control of the depth of search to be applied. The knowledge implemented is derived from chess practice and from strategy as recommended in textbooks.

The model is instantiated by an algorithm for the KNPK endgame. Examples of its playing strategy are given and a comparison between its play and the play of some chess grandmasters is made; the program's and the human being's 'information processing capabilities' are tentatively contrasted. Two potential generalisations of the model are presented: one to other subgoal-directed endgames, another to analogous endgames complicated by additional Pawns. Finally, the prospect of similarly treating other endgames for which there exists a body of theoretical knowledge is briefly touched upon.

INTRODUCTION

In chess endgame books, the strategy of elementary as well as complex endgames is outlined. These strategies are based on the analysis of practical games, the authors' own experience and indications from theory. The latter may range from hints derived after a cursory examination to systems of proven facts, arrived at after thorough investigation.

The ideas of endgame publicists such as Averbakh (1977, 1979), Chéron (1970–1973), Euwe (1940–1941), Fine (1941) and others have proved difficult for the chess programmer to implement, although they are rather easy for a player to understand (Berliner, 1975; Bratko, Kopec and Michie, 1978).

One of the problems in endgames is that the issue is not computing as such, but handling plans and trying to reach favourable positions. This means that a chess player (and equally a chess program) must know

(i) which plans are feasible, i.e. capable of being realised according to the rules of the game;
(ii) which plans are available in any given position;
(iii) which plans, both feasible and available, are applicable to the given position in the sense that they lead to a potentially more favourable position.

In order to choose among such plans the player as well as the program must know *what kind* of positions are favourable. Here the question of which positions are favourable is the most important one; the complementary question *why* just these positions are favourable is of subordinate importance to the program, as it is to a human player, if he has learnt the endgame variations by heart. Of course, to the human player *understanding the plan* eliminates much rote learning. Grandmasters can be presumed always to understand the plan.

Understanding is defined here as real knowledge of the relation between cause and effect, where 'cause' is built up from chess rules and board data. So, *understanding a chess plan* implies the ability to predict the consequences of taking some decision. In order to understand an applicable plan the program needs knowledge.

Adding knowledge of chess endgames to a program may seem very easy, since there are many chess books containing techniques, endgame tricks and examples, general rules and, especially, exceptions to them. The problem is that it turns out to be surprisingly difficult to implement this knowledge in a direct or obvious way. Even apart from this difficulty, the amount of knowledge to be added obviously depends on the desired quality of the program's play.

In this paper a method of implementing endgames is described which uses the representation of knowledge approach as suggested by Bramer (1975, 1977), but combines this with conventional depth-first searching, with the aim of producing play which is *correct* in the sense of always winning where possible, but not necessarily *optimal*, i.e. always winning in the smallest possible number of moves.

GRANDMASTER STRATEGIES

The general problem as posed by Von Neumann (1928) – 'The players S_1, S_2, . . . , S_n play a given game Γ. How must one of the participants S_m play in order to obtain the best possible result?' – does not yield a practical solution for the game of chess.

In spite of its being a game with perfect information (von Neumann and Morgenstern, 1944), the nature of chess is such that S_m's strategy cannot in general be explicitly exhibited for arbitrary positions. However, it is explicit strategies which chess programs must follow. This leads naturally to an interest in the knowledge of chess players, especially of superior chess players.

The research of de Groot (1946, 1965) and Jongman (1968) is important for explaining the differences in playing strength between a grandmaster and an average player, but their findings are not directly transferable to programs. The main point of de Groot's work is that the grandmaster knows how to handle a particular position and that this is why he immediately sees the right move. 'The very fact that he (i.e. the master) has managed to build up such an extensive and finely differentiated system of fecund experience, that he has become so extraordinarily skilled, is the pristine proof for his 'masterly' disposition' (de Groot, 1965, p. 321).

Hence, computer chess programmers are interested in the lines of strategy followed by grandmasters. Unfortunately, most of the time there does not seem to be a single correct or optimal strategy, not even for the elementary endgames. In addition it turns out that each grandmaster may have preferred ways of his own to apply to a particular position.

The highest goal in chess is of course to give checkmate. However, before reaching that goal, many intermediate goals (subgoals) normally have to be attained. It will be shown that the playing strategy used to reach a subgoal differs from one grandmaster to another. Thus the question arises: which grandmaster should the program mimic?

In January 1981, during the Hoogoven tournament (Wijk aan Zee), the position diagrammed in Fig. 1 was submitted to four grandmasters, the American 1980 co-champion Walter Browne, the English grandmaster Anthony Miles, the Dutch grandmaster Genna Sosonko and the Russian grandmaster German Svesnikov.

The diagrammed position was one of a set of KNPK endgames presented to them. The purpose of these King, Knight and Pawn vs. King endings being

Fig. 1 – White to move.

presented was to gain hints from practice as to how to represent knowledge to best advantage in endgame programs.

The agreed procedure with these grandmasters was that they were to express their first thoughts, after which they would play a white move. All necessary black moves were played by the author, the grandmasters then continuing and so on.

To all four grandmasters it was immediately clear that the position was won for White. All four suggested that the first subgoal to be reached was manoeuvring the King nearer to the Pawn in order to support the Pawn when advancing to the promotion square, since promotion is one of the major subgoals towards mate.

Sosonko played the move 1.Kf8 and after 1 . . . . Kf6 he continued (playing the Black as well as the White men): 2.Nh1 Kg5 3.Kg7 Kh4 4.Nf2 Kg5. Sosonko then broke off, commenting: 'and so on . . .'. It will be seen later why this is interesting.

Svesnikov showed a different way to reach the subgoal stated: 1. Kf8 Kf6 2. Ke8 Ke6 3. Kd8 Kd6 4. Kc8 Kc6 5. Kb8 Kd6 6. Kb7 . . . (the author supplying the black moves).

Exactly the same line was followed by the English grandmaster Miles. After having shown their strategies, the experimental subjects were confronted with the alternative, starting with 1.Ng4 or 1.Nh1. Svesnikov reacted: 'My line is better because Black has no chance'. Miles stated even more strongly: 'Of course not! In this case correct play is simple' [meaning that only elementary means should suffice for this elementary ending].

The American grandmaster Browne suggested, after a first glance: 1. Ng4 Kg5 2. Kg7 . . . . Having been told the other strategy, which is combinatorially shallower, Browne repudiated it violently. When he heard that some other grandmasters had shown a clear preference for 1. Kf8, he reacted: 'These people have the slowest brain activity'.

What conclusions can be drawn from the strategic concepts of the grandmasters? Firstly, even when they agree on the subgoal to be reached, the execution of the ways in which they try to reach it may vary greatly. Secondly, even among grandmasters there may be controversy about strategies. It follows, thirdly, that there is no unique strategic approach for the positions given and others like it, not even at grandmaster level.

To be sure, psychological elements do enter here. Yet the third statement above stands. The grandmasters do not act out of stubbornness; in many other KNPK endgames, the grandmasters proved quite prepared to withdraw their statements.

Looking at this experiment from the point of view of a computer chess programmer, three tentative conclusions may be drawn. In endgames it is important for the program:

(i) to understand the plan applicable to the configuration and to know which (sub)goals to strive for, i.e. the program needs a classification of (sub)goals and plans and furthermore, it needs a procedure for choosing among them;
(ii) to look for a path or at least the start of a path which will lead to the (sub)goal as chosen in the first stage;
(iii) to generate clearly plausible moves in accordance with the plan and path chosen.

We have to remark that, in elementary endgames, it is not playing strength which determines strategy; rather strategy depends on the flexibility of the concepts the player has in mind. A model for one subdomain of the KNPK endgame will be described below. The strategy associated with this model is that of Miles and Svesnikov, i.e. the strategy in which a stable configuration such as [Nf2, h3] will not be broken up, even temporarily, in order to gain a tempo.

The model is a combination of pattern recognition (the knowledge of a grandmaster) and goal-directed search (the way of thinking of a grandmaster). Before describing the model in detail, some attention will be paid to the representation of knowledge, more especially, following Bramer (1975, 1977) to that of pattern knowledge.

THE REPRESENTATION OF KNOWLEDGE

Chess programmers had the hope, in the 1960s and early 1970s, that a few simple but powerful techniques, such as fast tree searching and α-β pruning, could be identified. These, it was expected, would suffice to create an intelligent chess program. However, it turned out that the fundamental problem of understanding the chess position was not a matter of inventing a few powerful techniques but rather the question of how to represent large amounts of knowledge in a fashion that permits effective searching by programs (Goldstein 1976).

Bramer (1975), introducing the concept of *equivalence classes*, by contrast did not admit any searching at all beyond a depth of one ply. In his view, the program should know explicitly how to use its knowledge in an elementary endgame, such as King and Rook vs. King (KRK) or King and Pawn vs. King (KPK). Bramer has described his concepts in several publications (1975, 1977, 1979, 1980a, 1980b). The following is a summary of his ideas, from which the work described in this paper is developed.

Throughout the following, White is taken to be the stronger side, as is usual, and it is assumed that White is first to move; unless otherwise stated. Bramer's basic move-finding algorithm is then as follows:

a. generate the set Q of all immediate successor positions of a position p;
b. find the highest ranked element of Q, say q;
c. play the move corresponding to q.

In step (b), the word *find* means find without any search. The only difficulty is, of course, how to achieve the ranking, i.e. the ordering of the elements of Q. In order to induce such a ranking on Q, an overall ranking is defined on the set Q^* of all legal BTM (Black to move) positions for the endgame in question. The idea is to assign each position in Q to exactly one of a number of disjoint and exhaustive subsets partitioning the set Q^*. The aim is that each subset of the partition, termed a *class*, should correspond to some significant static feature of the endgame as perceived by chess-players, e.g. 'Black is in check'.

The connection between 'partition', 'feature' and 'class' is given by regarding features as equivalence relations, on which a fundamental theorem reads: 'Let F be an equivalence relation in Q^*. Then the quotient set Q^*/F is a partition of Q^*'. This allows the programmer to list static board features $F_1, F_2, F_3, \ldots$ etc. which then induce a partition in the above sense. Then the positions belonging to one subset are equivalent in the sense that they have one definite, possibly composite, feature in common, e.g. 'Black is in check and cannot capture the Rook'. In general, the feature is a composite predicate function, as it is in the example. If position q shows feature F_i then F_i is defined to be *true* for q.

Because it is essential that a position should belong to one and only one class, it may appear that the predicate functions will be very complicated (e.g. Black is in check *and* Black is not checkmated *and* White's Rook cannot be captured). This would mean that for all q:

$$F_i \supset \neg F_j \text{ for all } j \neq i.$$

To avoid this complication, Bramer has placed the emphasis on the order of execution of the tests. For any position q this is expressed by

$$F_i \supset \neg F_j \text{ for all } j < i.$$

In order to effect the closure of the equivalence relation Q^*, it is necessary to introduce a residual class with the empty feature F_n such that

$$F_n \equiv (\neg F_j \text{ for all } j < n)$$

i.e. F_n is true if and only if all preceding features F_j are false.

The basic procedure for finding the class to which q belongs is then to compare each feature F_i in turn with the current board configuration, q, until the first *true* feature is found. Further comparison is neither necessary nor permitted. Each class has its own class value, uniformly assigned to all positions belonging to the class.

Note that the ordering of *features* is totally unrelated to the ordering of the *playing value* of positions. For example, class 1 might be: 'Black is checkmated', with class 2: 'Black is stalemated'. In general, it is preferable to choose an ordering of features which simplifies the specification of subsequent ones. To quote an example (following Bramer (1975)): Let the classes be

1. Black is checkmated;
2. Black is stalemated;
3. Black can immediately capture White's Rook;
4. The Kings are in vertical opposition, with Black in check along the rank.

Then the position: White: Ke5, Rd7; Black: Ke7 belongs to class 3, not to class 4, although condition 4 holds. Yet, due to the ordering, condition 4 will not be applied: the predicate function F_4 is to be interpreted as 'the Kings are in vertical opposition, with Black in check along the rank *and* Black is *not* checkmated *and* Black is *not* stalemated *and* Black can *not* immediately capture White's Rook'.

From this, it will be clear that several different partitions of Q^* are possible, depending on the choice of the features in a given endgame and their ordering. But even grandmasters will sometimes have different or differently ordered lists of features in mind. The grandmasters' lists depend on their subjective evaluations of the positions and on the way of reaching the (sub)goal they have in mind. This means that it is often impossible to decide which ordered list of features is the better.

The highest ranked element of Q, as per step (b) of Bramer's algorithm, is the position with the highest class value. In order to break ties, Bramer introduces *associated functions*, the number of which may vary among classes. This means that while positions in the same equivalence class have the same final evaluation *functions*, the values assumed may vary among these positions.

The basic procedure described above is sufficient to produce algorithms matching expert play for the elementary endgames KRK and KPK (Bramer (1980c)).

As the complexity of the endgame increases, however, it is likely that a point will be reached where the number of equivalence classes needed will increase beyond reason. Thus, Bramer's KRK program needs 11 equivalence classes for a nearly optimal strategy, while his KPK program needs 20 classes for a correct strategy and 38 for an optimal strategy. To reduce the amount of knowledge required for more complex endgames, the use of deeper search is appropriate.

Bramer and Clarke (1979) propose an extended version of the equivalence class model where much deeper searching is permitted in a controlled fashion, to reduce the quantity of knowledge which has to be stored, but this has not yet been put to practical use. The model described in the remainder of this paper represents an alternative approach to extending Bramer's work.

Note that the opposite approach has been usual in conventional chess-playing programs: these proceed, in principle, from a searching approach, while their use of knowledge is applied only towards reducing the amount of search required.

A MODEL FOR STRATEGIES IN ENDGAMES

From the foregoing it would appear that the question: 'How to model a correct strategy in a given endgame?' is rather difficult to answer. Even if there were a complete data base available for the endgame in question, the solution would not be simple. The reason for this lack of simplicity derives from the fact that in any conceivable data base, the millions of positions can only be roughly divided into won, drawn or lost, at most specifying for each the number of moves separating each position from the result achievable by the optimal path.

Yet, human beings can be taught to play specific endgames. They are taught to do so by statements of *rules*. Paradoxically, one may have encyclopaedic knowledge about every position's value (won, drawn or lost) and even about its deviation from the optimal path without being able to derive rules from this body of knowledge.

Fortunately, the strategy to be followed in most endings is codified in textbooks. One of the main tasks in computer chess today is to transfer the rules so codified to appropriate strategies for programs, along with the representation of such textbook knowledge.

The model presented here combines the representation of chess knowledge as equivalence classes with depth-first tree searching. Taking this representation, a *structural* approach has been adopted. The advantage of this approach is that it permits modifications of the underlying algorithm in a simple and natural way and that, equally, the way in which knowledge is represented is clear and reasonable to the human player. The alternative is the procedural approach. For the same type of endgame a procedural algorithm may, in general, be easier to construct and almost certainly will be computationally more efficient.

As against this, the algorithm is considerably more difficult for the programmer to modify and for the chess-player to probe.

In practice, the distinction between the two approaches is not clear and most of the time the algorithm in question will combine elements of both. Bratko and Michie (1980) have described a rather procedurally based approach to representing pattern knowledge in chess endgames. Their approach uses pattern recognition to invoke a goal-directed search, whereas the model presented here starts searching for a pattern only when there is no match of the current position with the list of (sub)goals.

This combination of pattern knowledge and goal-directed search represents, in the author's view, a major stride forwards towards the simulation of a grand-master's thinking. Attention will be paid to 'knowledge' rather than to computing *per se*, because it is believed that knowledge is the determining factor in a grand-master's play.

As mentioned before, the model differs from conventional tree-searching in that the search is subject to *a priori* controls. These controls come under the following headings, to be discussed in turn:

- what triggers the major decisions?
- the depth of the tree;
- the width of the tree;
- the form of the evaluation functions;
- the evaluation of the terminal positions in the tree;
- the method of backing up.

As stated before, the KNPK endgame will be taken as the domain for the model, concentrating on positions with a rook pawn, because these positions induce the largest number of exceptions within the KNPK domain. The aim of the construction will be *correct* play, in the sense of always winning when possible, but not necessarily in the smallest possible number of moves.

WHAT TRIGGERS THE MAJOR DECISIONS?

As pointed out above, it is practically impossible to list a complete set of general rules for finding immediately the best successor of a given position. Still, an attempt may be made to apply *some* well-defined set of rules. If, in a succeeding position, no rule of this set is applicable, *all* the *Black* moves from this position will be generated. (These are, once again, positions with White to move.) Next, for these positions an attempt will be made to apply yet another, though analogous set of rules.

This implies two distinct sets of evaluation functions, one to apply after a White move and one after a Black move. The advantage of this approach is that some further searches are inhibited, regardless of who is to move (for examples, see van den Herik (1980).

The introduction of two sets of evaluation functions leads naturally to a tree structure of the following general shape:

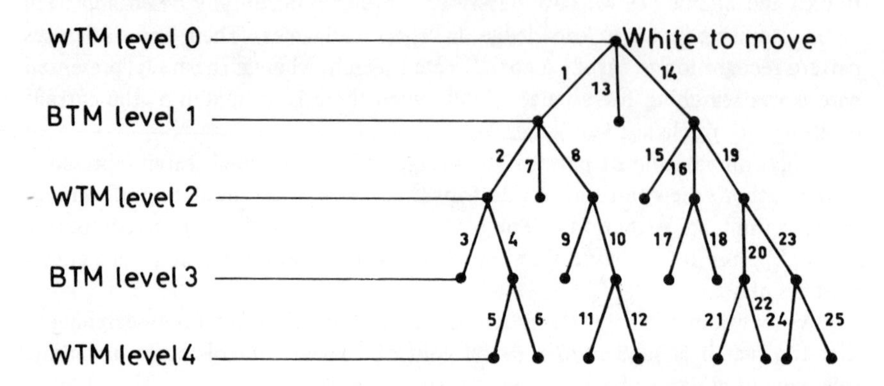

[The numbering of the branches corresponds to the sequence of traversal of this tree.]

After each white move in this tree, i.e. at the odd levels, the position (node) is evaluated by *stop*, a function which yields a predicate value; it can be seen as the element controlling in a node whether searching should go on (*stop* ≡ false) or not (*stop* ≡ true). An analogous process will be pursued at the even levels by the function *halt*, which is of course distinct from *stop*. The form of these functions will be discussed in more detail below.

Having reached the maximum depth of searching, values are assigned to each position so reached (regardless of the truth or otherwise of *stop* or *halt*). At these terminal nodes, WTM level 4 in the figure above, either the function *whiteval* or the function *blackeval* is defined depending on the side to move at that level. Only *whiteval* would be defined at level 4 in the example.

In summary, the model constructs a tree with a variable but limited depth and a fan-out which will vary with the level (ply). Both depend on the given position.

THE DEPTH OF THE TREE

The practical bounds on tree-searching algorithms are the time consumed and the storage available. In order to delay attaining these bounds, control over the depth and/or the width of the search is desirable. This control is possible in this construction, because it encourages limiting both the depth and the width of the (sub)trees to be traversed.

An ideal to strive for might be that even when the program is permitted an n-ply search, it should refrain from searching further whenever a search through fewer plies had yielded sufficient information for a move to be decided upon. It will be shown below that this ideal can be approached by proper matching of *stop* and *halt* with the generation of plausible moves for White *only*. The limit of this ideal is a one (or even zero) ply search. This means that, in theory, in the limit, goal-directed search amounts to direct pattern recognition. This is justly so, because chess is, in terms of game theory, a finite game with perfect information (von Neumann and Morgenstern, 1944). The obstacle is that to all practical intents and purposes it has to be treated as an infinite game.

Confronted with this pseudo-infinite nature, the depth of search appropriate to playing the KNPK ending well has to be determined. In practice, it has turned out that, with good evaluation functions, a 3-ply search is sufficient to make a program play a correct KNPK endgame, where 'correct' denotes win-preserving, avoiding repetitions in a winning position and observing the fifty-move rule.

In the present implementation of the program, the depth of search is variable and may be set by the user. The moves found using different settings of search depth may differ, even though all are winning.

THE WIDTH OF THE TREE

The balance between implemented knowledge and possible searching is highly determined by the possibilities of a particular position. Consider Fig. 2. It is obvious to any chess player that the White King has to move to the King-side. The human player will not waste time on configurations subsequent to 1. Kc5, 1. Kc4 or 1. Kc3; additional expertise allows him to skip 1. Kd5 and 1. Kd3 too. Similarly, the patterns after 1. Na1, 1. Na3, 1. Nb4 exclude themselves from consideration.

Fig. 2 – White to move.

The trade-off between knowledge and search in our program is primarily based on the evaluation functions *stop* and *halt*. They are the controlling elements in the nodes of our tree. However, they do not eliminate positions such as those after 1. Kc5 from being generated. In order to prevent the generation of inappropriate moves, a heuristic function, called *reject*, has been introduced which transforms the generator of all legal moves into a generator of all plausible moves for this endgame.

Since the author believes that generating only plausible moves is the most obvious means of reducing the width of the tree, even for elementary endgames, the when and how of this width reduction is seen to be essential to the problem, as it appears to be to grandmasters as well. The function *reject* has been designed with precisely this idea in mind, viz. in order to curtail, although heuristically, the set of legal White moves to its subset, that of the plausible White moves.

In contrast to a strategy for White, where generating plausible moves is sufficient, the strategy of generating just the plausible, but not all legal moves for Black is a serious source of error. It is found that *all* legal Black moves have to be considered if White's continuation is to be certified as correct. After the generation of the totality of Black's moves, those found to be implausible are discarded by the function *stop*. (For an example supporting this statement, see van den Herik (1980)).

Of course, caution is needed when introducing such curtailing, especially if the plausible move generator is to be applicable to less simple positions. For instance, Fig. 1 imposes the need to generate a move leading to some benefit at some succeeding stage. It would be regrettable if the program prematurely excluded a move, such as 1. Kf8, because it had been rejected as implausible at the first stage. Missing the winning continuation once is worse than occasionally computing an additional move and its branches. Part of the function *reject* has been previously published as an example in van den Herik (1980).

THE FORM OF THE EVALUATION FUNCTIONS

The structural knowledge representation to be used for special endgame configurations has been outlined above. Four distinct evaluation functions are needed to act on this representation. The functions *stop* and *halt* operate at alternating plies. Not surprisingly, these functions present considerable similarities.

The main representational technique is the partitioning of positions into equivalence classes. This technique is applied to all four of the functions. Note in passing that *stop* ≡ true also triggers the evaluation of the position reached, by causing *stop* to assign a value to *valuepos*.

One of the differences between *stop* and *whiteval* is that *whiteval* always has to assign a value to a position, whereas *stop* may conclude: since the current position does not match any pattern described in the equivalence classes given, it must belong to the residual class. This implies *stop* ≡ false, in which case there is no assignment to *valuepos*: the search must go on.

When the maximal depth of search is reached, that position must be evaluated, further searching being disallowed. Then, whenever *stop* ≡ false or *halt* ≡ false, the assignment of *valuepos* will be done by the evaluation functions *whiteval* or *blackeval.* These functions have been constructed on principles similar to those of *stop* and *halt*, their classes depending on less detailed conditions. If a position does not belong to one of these classes, then it clearly belongs to a residual class; this too will cause the value of the position to be assigned to *valuepos.* An important feature in the function *blackeval* is the Kings' being in opposition horizontally, vertically or diagonally (cf. Fig. 1).

Some attention will now be paid to the construction of *stop* (and *halt*). The set of equivalence classes can be divided into three subsets. The first subset is that set of classes which leads to a win, irrespective of Black's play. The second subset is the set of classes which implies that at least some move(s) of Black will result in a draw or Black's stalemate. The third subset is the residual class where it is uncertain whether the position is won or drawn.

When a pattern (i.e. a class feature) matches the current board position, a value has to be assigned to that pattern. While each *class* has a value of its own (its class value), this is not sufficient, because the value of that particular *position* is required. The position value is the corresponding class value plus or minus values depending on observed characteristics, e.g. on the distance of the Pawn to the promotion square, the distances WK–WP, WN–WP, BK–WP and so on, W standing for White and B for Black. Any distance is expressed as the fewest number of moves for a King to go from one square to the other. In the value given by the evaluation function, the current level of search also enters. The values assigned to each class have been chosen on heuristic grounds, as has the ordering of the equivalence classes.

It should be observed that the values of the actual positions belonging to different classes may change the order of the values of the moves expected when merely looking at the class value. This is not accidental, but essential, because otherwise:

a. the Pawn would not move ahead;
b. the number of equivalence classes would be approximately five times larger, due to the various cases with the Pawn on h2 or h7 having to be distinguished.

The need for this property is shown by an example in van den Herik (1980).

The number of equivalence classes within the four functions is: 22 for *stop*, 12 for *halt*, 4 for *whiteval* and 7 for *blackeval*. The number of classes in the function *stop* can be safely reduced, but then the searches will be extended, which is contrary to the stated objective of the model, viz. to add as much knowledge as may be needed in order to achieve a maximal curtailment of search effort.

THE EVALUATION OF THE TERMINAL POSITIONS IN THE TREE

In the KNPK endgame there are two possible outcomes: White wins or the game is drawn. In game theory (von Neumann, 1928) this is denoted by 1 (won), and 0 (drawn). In the program this scale has been multiplied by a factor of 1000. Hence, the unique *mated* value is 1000.

The value assigned to a position does not allow the position itself (not even always its position class) to be reconstructed. The most that can be stated is that the three following statements hold:

(i) values in the range 501 to 1000 imply a win;
(ii) values in the range 101 to 500 imply that the program cannot tell whether the position is a win or a draw;
(iii) values in the range 1 to 100 imply a draw with proper play by Black.

A position in which the program cannot decide whether it is winning is discussed below. Experiments such as the one described in connection with Fig. 1 show that skilled human chess-players, too, cannot always decide between won and drawn positions.

THE METHOD OF BACKING UP

Trees constructed by the model described in this paper can be treated in the same way as the trees built up by conventional depth-first search chess-playing programs. Values assigned by the appropriate evaluation functions to positions in the terminal nodes of the tree have to be backed up. Many techniques exist for tree traversal; the α-β minimax technique has been chosen though with some refinements (Knuth and Moore, 1975; Maurer, 1979). When analysing Black's moves, the chopper technique (Birmingham and Kent, 1977) has been introduced as a further refinement. This refinement is not applicable to White, because in the KNPK endings White always has a choice of moves, even with the plausible move generator.

An overall strategy is imposed on the tree traversal by investigating the white moves in a fixed order: pawn move(s) first, followed by king moves, with knight moves last. The reason for this order is that the aim of the program is to bring the pawn to the back rank. Because the King often has to co-operate with the advancing Pawn, the king moves are examined after the pawn moves.

The knight moves can be considered as a finishing touch, serving to expel the black king from the corner or to protect the Pawn by trying to reach a stable position.

Other techniques, such as the killer heuristic for the Black moves (Frey, 1977; Slate and Atkin, 1977; Birmingham and Kent, 1977) are currently disregarded. A 3-ply search is apparently sufficient for KNPK endgames and generating the black countermoves in a special order does not save much time.

IMPLEMENTATION

The program has been written in the C programming language, observing the principles of structured programming, and has been constructed modularly; it uses C functions (Kernighan and Richie, 1978). It is currently implemented on a PDP 11/70, running under the UNIX operating system in the Department of Computer Science of the Delft University of Technology.

In its present form it is interactive and is used for demonstrations. The program is not a learning program, the partition into equivalence classes is fixed just as the theory published in endgame books is fixed. The structural representation facilitates the readjustment of the equivalence relations, should this be desirable.

PERFORMANCE OF STRATEGY

Chess is not a game of moves, but a game of plans and concepts; this is especially true for the endgame. Recalling Fig. 1, two possible strategies can be distinguished: the positional strategy (1. Kf8 . . .) and the tactical strategy (1. Ng4/Nh1 . . .). In the model preference has been given to the positional strategy. In a 3-ply search and with a competent human opponent the play runs 1. Kf8 Kf6 2. Ke8 Ke6 3. Kd8 Kd6 4. Kc8 Kc6 5. Kb8 Kd6 6. Kb7 Kd7 7. Kb6 Kd6 8. Kb5 Kd5 9. Kb4 Kd4 10. Kb3 Ke3 11. Kc3 . . . . Of course, it would have been possible to incorporate the other strategy into the program by distinguishing further subgoals within the designed subgoals, leading to additional equivalence classes. At this point, Sosonko's moves become of particular relevance. Having chosen the positional strategy first (1. Kf8), he realised that this would lead to a protracted game, for which reason he switched to the tactical strategy (2. Nh1). This change of mind gives a revealing glimpse into the thinking model of a grandmaster. However, it is hardly conceivable to program a computer so as to have second thoughts.

It was mentioned previously that even skilled players are sometimes unable to decide at first glance whether a position is won or drawn. The position shown in Fig. 3 is offered as a case in point. Seven grandmasters (Browne, Euwe, Larsen, Miles, Sosonko, Svesnikov and Timman) were confronted with this position. They were invited to voice their opinions about it. Six grandmasters suggested 1.Ng6 and one 1.Nf7. Only two grandmasters were certain that their moves, 1. Ng6 and 1. Nf7 respectively, were the first move to victory. One grandmaster was completely certain of his move but could not immediately

Fig. 3 – White to move.

decide whether it was a won or a drawn position. Four grandmasters stated that they certainly would start with 1. Ng6, but that the position was drawn. One grandmaster persisted in this opinion, even after long thinking.

The moves produced by the program will now be considered. At three plies deep, with Black's moves also played by the program, the following sequence is produced: 1.Ng6 Kf3 2.Kb2 Kg4 3.Ne5+ Kf4 4.Nd3† Kf3 5.h3 Ke4 6.Nf2+. Now a stable position has been reached which is similar to that of Fig. 1.

At six plies deep the program plays 1. Nf7, with almost the same continuation. The difference is due to the sensitivity of *whiteval* and *blackeval* to depth of search and/or to the difference in invocation pattern of these evaluation functions.

It is evident that straightforwardly advancing the Pawn, 1. h4 will lead to a draw. When voicing their opinions, most grandmasters convinced themselves of this fact by pursuing one or two branches resulting from this line of potential play. No grandmaster seriously considered a king move. Apparently, a king move was not plausible to the 'information processing capability' of these grandmasters. Therefore, it is of interest that, at eight plies deep, the program 'sees' that it can manoeuvre the King nearer to the Pawn (an important subgoal). Accordingly the program starts with 1. Kb2!, which in fact is a good start for a win. So it turns out that both knight and king moves preserve the won character of the position. The fact that it was only a pawn move which failed to win was unexpected to the grandmasters in the sample.

GENERALISATION

The significance of these investigations in the field of knowledge representation is the attempt to understand the conceptual background of why a particular move has to be played in a given position and what the consequences of this move represent conceptually. In the model, five functions have been introduced (*stop, halt, whiteval, blackeval* and *reject*) to cover the subdomain of the KNPK ending including a rook Pawn. The structural representation allows the strategy the program follows when dealing with a particular position to be understood. Two generalizations seem possible:

(i) The model described may prove applicable to more difficult endings, particularly those that require subdivision into phases (i.e. trying to reach specified subgoals in a stated order). Examples of such difficult endings are KNNKP (e.g. Bisguier–Matanović, Bled, 1961, cited by Bijl (1980)) and KRPKBP (e.g. Timman–Velimirović, Rio de Janeiro, 1979, cited by Timman (1979)).

(ii) The model may prove applicable to types of endgame requiring similar manoeuvres but containing additional Pawns. A generalized program might recognise these positions and would conclude that they must lead to a KNPK ending. Such a position arose in Salov–Maiorov, Soviet Union, 1979 (cited by Orbaan (1980)) where Black's actual play was in error. In short, the position was White: Kd3, f5; Black: Kf7, Nd2, a7; Black to move. Black's play was 1. . . . Nb3? 2. Kc4 Na5† 3. Kb5 Nb7 4. Ka6 Drawn; Black would have won if he had played 1. . . . Nf3, in the spirit of the KNPK program (cf. the analysis of Fig. 3). Black would then finally have reached the stable configuration [Nc6, a7].

In an attempt to gather further evidence of the usefulness of the model, sets of equivalence classes for other endgame configurations, such as KBNK are now being constructed. Even if this approach should prove successful, it would take a vast amount of time to implement, say, Fine's *Basic Chess Endings* (1941) in a similar manner. However, once the strategic lines had been implemented, it is probable that they would prove to be better teaching aids than today's textbooks.

To be sure, programs as well as textbooks will continue to contain erroneous evaluations, but imperfect knowledge has not prevented human beings from achieving ELO ratings of 2650. This implies that a computer program need not always play perfectly in order to be rated a grandmaster. For passing the expert test, an occasional non-optimal strategy or even the missing of a winning continuation now and then is not necessarily disqualifying.

ACKNOWLEDGEMENTS

The author wishes to thank I. S. Herschberg and H. J. M. Lombaers for many valuable suggestions on the substance of this paper and for their careful scrutiny of the English version. The competent technical assistance of B. Broere and of Ms. J. W. Pesch, who did the typing and corrections on the text editor of the

PDP 11/70, is also gladly acknowledged as having been essential to the production of this paper.

REFERENCES

Averbakh, Y. and Chekhover, V. (1977), *Knight Endings,* London: Batsford.

Averbakh, J. (1979), *Lehrbuch der Schachendspiele* Band 1 und Band 2, Autorisierte Übersetzung aus dem Russischen: Hermann Mohaupt, Berlin: Sportverlag.

Berliner, H. J. (1975), Chess as problem solving: the development of a tactics analyser. Ph.D Thesis, Computer Science Department, Carnegie-Mellon University.

Bijl, C. M. (1980), *Het Eindspel, Koning + 2 Paarden tegen Koning + Pion,* Leidschendam: Theorie en Praktijk.

Birmingham, J. A. and Kent, P. (1977), Tree-searching and Tree-Pruning Techniques, in Clarke M. R. B. (ed.), *Advances in Computer Chess 1,* Edinburgh: Edinburgh University Press, 89–97.

Bramer, M. A. (1975), Representation of knowledge for chess endgames. Technical Report, The Open University: Faculty of Mathematics, Milton Keynes, England.

Bramer, M. A. (1977), Representation of knowledge for chess endgames: towards a self-improving system. Ph.D. Thesis, The Open University: Faculty of Mathematics, Milton Keynes, England.

Bramer, M. A. and Clarke, M. R. B. (1979), A model for the representation of pattern–knowledge for the endgame in chess, *Int. J. Man–Machine Studies,* **11**, 635–649.

Bramer, M. A. (1980a), An optimal algorithm for King and Pawn against King using pattern knowledge, in Clarke, M. R. B. (ed.), *Advances in Computer Chess 2,* Edinburgh: Edinburgh University Press, 82–96.

Bramer, M. A. (1980b), Pattern-based representations of knowledge in the game of chess, *Proceedings of the Conference on Artificial Intelligence,* Amsterdam.

Bramer, M. A. (1980c), Correct and optimal strategies in game playing programs, *Computer Journal,* **24**(4), 347–352.

Bratko, I., Kopec, D. and Michie, D. (1978), Pattern-based representation of chess endgame knowledge, *Computer Journal,* **21**(2), 149–153.

Bratko, I. and Michie, D. (1980), A representation for pattern-knowledge in chess endgames, in Clarke, M. R. B. (ed.), *Advances in Computer Chess 2,* Edinburgh: Edinburgh University Press, 31–56.

Chéron, A. (1970–1973), *Lehr- und Handbuch der Endspiele,* Band I, II, III und IV, Berlin-Frohnau: Siegfried Engelhardt Verlag.

de Groot, A. D. (1946), Het Denken van den Schaker, een Experimenteel-psychologische Studie. Proefschrift, Universiteit van Amsterdam. N. V. Noord-Hollandse Uitgevers Maatschappij, Amsterdam.

de Groot, A. D. (1965), *Thought and Choice in Chess* (second edition, 1979), The Hague-Paris-New York: Mouton Publishers.

Euwe, M. (1940–1941), *Het Eindspel,* Deel 1 t/m 12, 's-Gravenhage-Batavia: G. B. van Goor Zonen's Uiteversmaatschappij.

Fine, R. (1941), *Basic Chess Endings,* Bell and Hyman (London) in association with David McKay Company, Inc. (New York).

Frey, P. W. (1977), An introduction to computer chess, in Frey, P. W. (ed.), *Chess Skill in Man and Machine,* New York-Heidelberg-Berlin: Springer-Verlag, 54–81.

Goldstein, I. (1976), The role of representation in artificial intelligence, *ACM 76 Proceedings of the Annual Conference, Houston, Texas,* 69–71.

Jongman, R. W. (1968), Het Oog van de Meester. Proefschrift, Universiteit van Amsterdam, Assen: Van Gorcum and Company N. V.

Kernighan, B. W. and Richie, D. M. (1978), *The C Programming Language* (Bell Laboratories, Murray Hill, New Jersey), Englewood Cliffs: Prentice-Hall.

Knuth, D. E. and Moore, R. E. (1975), An analysis of alpha-beta pruning, *Artificial Intelligence,* **6**, 293–326.

Maurer, W. D. (1979), Alpha-beta pruning, *Byte,* **11**, 84–96.

Orbaan, C. (1980), Kombineren, *Schaakbulletin,* **154**, 597–598.

Slate, D. J. and Atkin, L. R. (1977), Chess 4.5: the Northwestern University chess program, in Frey, P. W. (ed.), *Chess Skill in Man and Machine,* New York-Heidelberg-Berlin: Springer-Verlag, 82–118.

Timman, J. H. (1979) Rond het Bord in 50 zetten, *Schaakbulletin,* **144**, 17–25.

van den Herik, H. J. (1980), Goal-directed search in chess end games, *Delft Progress Report,* **5**(4), 253–279.

von Neumann, J. (1928), Zur Theorie der Gesellschaftsspiele, *Math. Ann.,* **100**, 295–320. Reprinted (1963) in Taub, A. H. (ed.), *John von Neumann Collected Works,* Vol.VI, 1–26. Oxford: Pergamon Press [Quoted in translation].

von Neumann, J. and Morgenstern, O. (1944), *Theory of Games and Economic Behaviour,* Princeton: Princeton University Press.

7

Refinement of correct strategies for the endgame in chess

M. A. Bramer
Mathematics Faculty, The Open University, Milton Keynes, MK7 6AA England

ABSTRACT

The relative merits of playing strategies which are either 'optimal' or 'correct' (i.e. which do or do not invariably select shortest–path winning moves) are discussed, and a method is described for testing whether a given playing algorithm is correct.

An extension of this method gives two procedures (one fully automatic, one semi-automatic) for producing fully correct algorithms by a process of iterative refinement, based on an analysis of 'win-trees'.

As an example, a correct algorithm produced in this way using a pattern-based representation of expert knowledge is given for the endgame King and Rook against King.

CORRECT AND OPTIMAL STRATEGIES

The research described in this paper arises as part of a project aimed at developing algorithms modelling as closely as possible the chess-player's knowledge of the endgame, as a means of investigating the problems of representing (and incrementally refining) human knowledge in a well-defined and small scale but nevertheless highly complex domain.

Although knowledge-based algorithms have been produced for a number of endgames in recent years, it is notable that conventional chess-playing programs using deep search with simple evaluation functions generally perform very badly in endgames, where knowledge, rather than calculation, is probably the major factor in human play. It is perhaps significant that the endgame is traditionally regarded as the phase of the game which most accurately discriminates between the stronger and the weaker player.

A fundamental problem which arises in constructing and refining endgame-playing algorithms is the quality of performance at which the programmer should aim. Taking, for ease of argument, the case where White is the 'stronger' side and all legal positions are either wins for White or draws, one possible answer is that White should always aim to win (whenever a win is possible) in the smallest possible number of moves against best play by the opponent, i.e. should always select a *shortest path* winning move. Another possibility is that White should merely aim to win whenever possible, against any defence by Black, but not necessarily in the fewest possible moves. Such strategies are classified as *optimal* and *correct,* respectively, by Bramer (1980).

It should be noted that the property of optimality relates to the move selected by the program in every specific position for a particular endgame, whereas the property of correctness relates to the performance of the program as a whole. It is possible that a correct program may play many non-optimal moves, but all moves must be correct in the sense that in every position in which the player to move can win, he eventually does so.

There would seem to be two principal reasons for aiming at developing optimal algorithms rather than correct ones. Firstly, they can readily be verified automatically given a data base of the best move (or moves) in every position, with only one wrong move being needed to refute optimality. Methods of generating such data bases are given by Ströhlein (1970), Clarke (1977) and others. Data bases now exist for *inter alia* the endgames King and Rook against King (KRK), King and Queen against King (KQK), King and Rook against King and Knight (KRKN), King and Pawn against King (KPK) and King and Queen against King and Rook (KQKR). Even when a data base does not exist, one clearly 'time-wasting' move in human examination of the program is enough to refute optimality. The second reason is simply that optimal algorithms are intrinsically stronger than correct ones. It would hardly be impressive to develop a correct algorithm for KRK, say, where in some positions White took 250 moves to win instead of the theoretical maximum requirement of 16 (regardless of the 50-move drawing rule for chess). Thus the depth of the longest winning sequence for a correct algorithm is a significant factor.

There are, however, a number of objections to developing optimal algorithms as a research aim. As previously mentioned, one important aim of constructing endgame playing programs is as a means of investigating the problems of representing human knowledge in a well-defined and small scale but nevertheless highly complex domain. It is virtually impossible to believe that even the strongest players in the world could perform optimally in complex endgames such as King, Rook, Knight and five Pawns against King, Rook, Bishop and four Pawns. Nor is it feasible to imagine that optimal algorithms (or the data bases against which to verify them) could be created in the remotely foreseeable future for such endgames.

Thus there is both a theoretical objection and a practical bar to producing optimal algorithms beyond a certain level of complexity, whereas it may well be that strong players have the knowledge (and analytical ability) to perform correctly or nearly so in a very wide variety of endgames, that is they are able to win in most, if not all, winnable positions.

An example of an endgame where it is widely believed that a human expert would perform optimally is KPK. Knowledge of this endgame by skilled human players would appear to be sufficient for extremely accurate play in all situations which occur in practice and would appear to be based on a very limited amount of pattern knowledge derived initially from examples and guidance given in standard textbooks and supplemented gradually by practical experience. However, studies by Bramer (1980) suggest that, even for KPK, strong players do not always perform optimally. There are numerous difficult and counter-intuitive cases which arise, mostly of a kind which the human chess-player would dismiss as irrelevant for practical play. It is not necessarily that a master player could not play perfectly in the numerous difficult positions which can occur, given sufficient motivation, but that to do so would require either knowledge of a number of 'special cases' of no real practical value or a willingness to analyse much more deeply than would otherwise be the case in a large number of overwhelmingly won positions. It would be highly inefficient and unreasonable for a human expert to devote either additional memory or deep analysis to positions which for practical purposes are trivial wins.

There is a principle of sufficiency involved here. The game–theoretic maximum number of moves needed for the stronger side to win any winnable KPK position is only 19. The rules allow for 50 moves (without any piece taken or any Pawn moved) before a draw can be claimed. It is simply not worthwhile to overload the memory with numerous special cases (or spend time performing a deep analysis) to achieve optimal play, even assuming this is feasible, if there is a simple algorithm which suffices for correctness, still well within the constraints of the 50-move rule.

On the other hand, the endgame King, Bishop and Knight versus King is thought to require up to 34 moves to win and an error in certain critical positions can easily lead to exceeding the 50-move limit. In these cases it is worthwhile memorizing much more detail of difficult cases, although not necessarily all of them.

So far, the balance of the argument might seem to suggest that the development of a correct algorithm is the more desirable objective. Provided that the number of moves required to win is not excessively greater than the game-theoretic maximum, the likely reduction in detailed knowledge or analysis required to play correctly rather than optimally would appear to more than compensate for the slight loss of quality of play, for computer programs as well as people. There are, however, two important questions to answer:

(a) how can the correctness of an algorithm be tested, either automatically or otherwise?

(b) how can a 'nearly correct' algorithm be refined to perform progressively better, based on an examination of its non-winning play?

In practice, most researchers have so far not attempted to provide reliable performance data for their programs† (even in cases where a data base is available) and instead have seemed content to leave the testing of their algorithms to human experts, either in person or through the medium of test examples published in textbooks. Any such testing is open to the serious objection that, unless exhaustive, it can logically only refute but never prove. Even leaving this consideration aside, this method is intrinsically unreliable. Over a long series of trials, small errors of judgement in assessing the optimal move in every position are inevitably likely to occur. For supposedly correct strategies, the situation might seem to be better but is in fact worse, as a result of the fact that *a move can be both optimal and non-correct.* The explanation of this apparent paradox is that correctness refers essentially to sequences of moves, whereas optimality refers to individual moves independently of one another.

As an extreme example, suppose that for a certain endgame there is only one legal position in which White (the stronger side) can give checkmate in one move, but that in that position he blunders and gives stalemate (a draw) instead. Even if White's play is optimal in every other position, it is clear that White fails to win in all positions for that endgame. Any expert testing which did not include the one critical position would be certain to lead to the wrong conclusion. In general, the contaminating effect of a small number of poor (although possibly win-preserving) moves can result in – in fact, is likely to result in – non-correct moves in many thousands of positions, the great majority of which will pass unnoticed even in extensive expert testing.

Viewed in this light, it is clear that the common practice when testing an endgame-playing program of using human experts or textbook positions to provide effectively a 'certificate of correctness' is of little value when assessing its likely performance in practical play.

Conversely, the knowledge that a program fails to win from, say, 23,000 positions gives no indication of the number or identity of the possibly small number of positions which are really at fault.

An automatic method of testing whether or not a given algorithm is correct is described in the next section, using a modification of the method of generating data bases of optimal moves referred to previously.

TESTING THE CORRECTNESS OF AN ALGORITHM

The basic method of generating data bases of shortest-path winning moves for every position in a given endgame (see, for example, Clarke (1977) or Bramer (1978)) effectively produces a partial minimax game tree for the endgame by backtracking from *terminal positions,* which are all wins for one chosen side.

† Apart from the algorithms reported here, only one other correct algorithm (for KRK, with maximum depth 77 ply – reported by Bratko (1978)) and one optimal algorithm (for KPK – reported by Bramer (1980)) are known.

Modifying this algorithm gives an automatic method of testing the correctness of a playing algorithm for a chosen side (say White). The revised method generates an implicit *win-tree* containing all the positions from which the playing program invariably wins for White, although not necessarily in the smallest possible number of moves. The tree is generated by backtracking from *terminal* positions which are all wins for White, assuming that Black always plays to defer a loss for as long as possible.

The generation method can be summarised as follows (using WTM and BTM to denote White and Black to move, respectively). For simplicity, it is assumed that all terminal positions are Black to move.

1. Mark all positions as either a terminal win for White, illegal or 'unevaluated'.
2. For all unevaluated BTM positions, compute and store the number of legal moves available. (If zero, Black must be stalemated, so mark as a draw.)
3. Backtrack one ply, by generating all legal antecedents (WTM) of the terminal positions. Mark those previously unevaluated (with WTM) as wins in one ply, provided that the program would have selected the move which was reversed.
4. Backtrack from those patterns evaluated at the previous level by generating all their legal antecedents (BTM). For those previously unevaluated (with BTM), decrease the counter of legal moves available by one. Mark any position for which the counter is reduced to zero as a win for White at depth two ply.
5. Continue backing up, from the positions evaluated at the previous level only, to White wins in 3, 4, 5, . . . ply in this way, distinguishing between backtracking to WTM and to BTM positions as in 3 and 4 above. This procedure ensures that every winnable position is included in the tree and gives the smallest number of ply needed for White to win against any play by Black.
6. Terminate when a level is reached at which no new evaluation takes place. The remaining unevaluated positions are not wins for White with the given playing algorithm. If all theoretically won positions are in the tree at this stage then the algorithm is correct.

It will be noted that the win tree contains not *moves* for each side but the *depth* of each position (i.e. the smallest number of ply needed by the playing algorithm to win in each case). These can be used to reconstruct Black's best move or moves in any position, since these will reduce the depth by exactly one ply. (White's moves are given by the playing algorithm and also reduce the depth by one ply.)

EXAMINING THE WIN TREE

The number of theoretically won positions is known for certain endgames.

However, an examination of the win tree can be used to determine whether a playing algorithm is correct, without this knowledge, by the following procedure.

1. Examine the BTM positions in the tree at each of the ply depths 0, 2, 4, . . . in turn.
2. At each level generate all the legal WTM antecedents of the BTM positions examined. If all these antecedents are in the tree (at any level) go on to the next level, otherwise note any WTM positions not in the tree and stop (i.e. do not go on to higher levels). These positions comprise the *error set* for the playing algorithm.
3. The playing algorithm is correct if and only if the highest BTM level is eventually reached (with no legal antecedents found that are not in the tree).

If the algorithm is not correct, then the WTM positions in the error set found at stage 2 are those at the lowest level of the tree which are incorrect, i.e. where White had the opportunity to play a winning move but did not take it *or play any other move which led to a win.* If White's algorithm were changed so that the necessary move was played in each such position to ensure inclusion in the tree, then in general many other positions (both WTM and BTM) would also be included in the tree by virtue of the normal backtracking process of tree generation.

This leads to the following iterative method of refinement of the playing algorithm.

(a) Generate the win tree and examine as described previously.
(b) If the playing algorithm is correct then stop.
(c) If not, then modify the playing algorithm such that the required White move is made in each of the positions in the error set (but no other changes are made) and continue with step (a)†.

It should be noted that the refinement process has no effect on the positions in the tree at the BTM level from which the previous error set was generated by backtracking, or at any lower levels. Thus the next time the tree examination algorithm is applied, it is only necessary to begin with positions at the next highest BTM level.

The refinement process terminates after a finite number of steps, and in general the number of positions for which White's move is modified will be substantially less than the total number of incorrect positions which occurred with the original version of the playing algorithm. Using the error set in this way (and in general working from low to high ply depth at step 1 of the tree

†Step (c) can be implemented in a simple fashion by incrementally building up a *rote* dictionary of the positions concerned, which is examined as the first stage of the playing algorithm.

examination process) has the heuristic value that changing White's moves to include positions at a relatively low level of the tree is likely to introduce the greatest number of new positions during the subsequent backtracking and thus to lead to a relatively short sequence of iterations.

To return to the example given previously where a blunder in the only possible 'checkmate in one move' position, despite optimal play in all others, led to no WTM positions at all in the win tree, the tree examination algorithm will give an error set comprising the 'checkmate in one move' position only and the first iteration of the refinement process will then generate the full win tree.

It is clear that modifying White's moves in some other set of positions, far removed from the checkmate, would most probably lead to a much longer sequence of iterations before a correct strategy was reached.

The previous discussion gives a fully automatic refinement process which is guaranteed to produce a correct strategy, although only experimentation can determine whether the total number of modifications needed at step (c) is acceptably small in any particular case. A possible theoretical objection to this method is that since it is equivalent to inserting a number of 'special cases' in the original playing algorithm, the final correct algorithm will almost inevitably not be in full accord with the spirit of the original, for example as a reasonable representation of the expert's pattern knowledge of the chess domain.

A semi-automatic approach which takes account of this requirement is to refine the original algorithm, not by changing the moves made in individual positions but, for example, by modifying the component patterns of the algorithm within its original framework, and recomputing the complete win tree at each stage until a correct strategy is reached. Here too the method of examining the win tree is of value, since it is reasonable to suppose that most or all of the positions in the error set will have some feature in common to serve as the basis for a change to the algorithm. In particular, since each BTM position examined has many antecedents as potential candidates for the error set, it is probable that a factor linking many positions in the error set will be that the required White move will lead to the same BTM successor. Thus an algorithm which uses patterns of BTM positions to find moves for White, such as that described in the next section , is likely to be particularly amenable to this semi-automated form of refinement. When well-chosen, changes to the program's pattern knowledge are likely to have greater beneficial effect and lead to more rapid convergence than those to individual positions. Naturally, however, if the changes are badly chosen there is no longer any guarantee that the process will terminate.

As a variant, two or more iterations of the automatic refinement algorithm can be used to find a larger set of positions (the union of the error sets) on which to base a change to the underlying patterns comprising the algorithm. An advantage of the semi-automated approach, if successful, is that the final algorithm is likely to be a natural extension of the original, with the same underlying design philosophy.

In passing, it is worth pointing out that a similar semi-automated approach is possible to refinement of an *optimal* algorithm (the equivalent automatic method is the trivial one of modifying White's move in every non-optimal instance independently, as a 'special case'). Examining the data base to find the set of WTM positions at the lowest level (ply 1, 3, 5, . . .) where a non-optimal move is made may help to suggest useful additional or modified patterns, in the same way as the above.

A REPRESENTATION FOR PATTERN-KNOWLEDGE FOR THE ENDGAME

Both the automatic and the semi-automatic refinement methods described above have been used in a series of experiments aimed at producing fully correct strategies for the stronger side (White) in the three fundamental endgames KPK, KRK and KQK.

Although the refinement methods described previously are independent of any particular form of playing strategy, it is necessary to be able to generate White's moves in every winnable position in a reasonable amount of time. For the majority of endgame-playing programs, especially those of a 'procedural' nature, where move-finding frequently requires considerable amounts of search, it is unlikely that this condition can be met. A model for representing endgame knowledge based on the use of patterns of pieces and only a one-ply search is given in Bramer (1977) and Bramer and Clarke (1979). Algorithms constructed using this model are certainly amenable to automatic analysis and automatic (or semi-automatic) refinement within reasonable time constraints, at least for the endgames in question.

In this model it is assumed that the problem is to construct an algorithm to find a move for a chosen side (say White) in any position p, for a given endgame. The basic move finding algorithm is then as follows:

(a) generate the set Q of immediate successors (Black to move) of p;
(b) find the highest ranked member of Q, say q;
(c) play the move corresponding to q.

To achieve step (b) an implicit ranking is defined on the set Q^* of all legal BTM positions for the endgame in question. Each such position is assigned to exactly one of a number of disjoint and exhaustive classes which *partition* the set Q^*.

The ranking of each BTM position is then determined by its *class value* (which is constant for all the positions in any class) and the values of a number of associated functions. These vary from one class to another, in general. For positions in the same class, the functions used are always the same although their values will vary from one position to another. To compare the values of two positions, their class values are compared, with the larger value indicating the higher-ranked position. If there is a tie, the first associated function is used for comparison. If there remains a tie, the second associated function is used, and so on. (Any ties remaining after all the associated functions have been used are resolved arbitrarily.) When comparing the values of associated functions, in some cases the larger value is preferred, in some cases the smaller is, depending on the particular function. The intention is that each class should correspond to some significant static feature of the endgame as perceived by chess-players, e.g. 'Black is in check'. The associated functions correspond to relevant numerical values, such as the distance between the two Kings.

Assigning a position q to a class is achieved by working through a series of predicates (called *rules*) in turn until one is satisfied. (Subsequent rules are not evaluated.) A position q is defined to belong to a particular class N if and only if rule N is satisfied by q and none of the preceding rules are satisfied.

This procedure ensures that each position belongs to only one class and helps to simplify the definition of the rules. To ensure that each position belongs to some class, the final rule is defined to be always *true* for any position q.

With this model, a playing strategy for a particular endgame is specified by

(a) an ordered series of rules which define the membership of each class in turn;
(b) a table giving the class value and the index numbers of the associated functions for each class; and
(c) the definition of each associated function, with an indication of whether the largest [max] or smallest [min] value of each function is preferred.

For each of the three endgames, a fully correct algorithm within the framework of the above model has been produced from an initial version by means of a combination of the automatic and semi-automatic refinement processes described previously.

The refinement of the correct KRK algorithm is chosen as illustrative of the use of the method in practice and is described in detail in the next section. The final correct form of the algorithm for KRK is specified in detail in the Appendix where detailed information about the endgame is also given. Algorithms for the KPK and KQK endgames are given in Bramer (1981), from which this paper is adapted.

REFINEMENT OF A CORRECT ALGORITHM FOR KING AND ROOK AGAINST KING (KRK)

Both the automatic and the semi-automatic refinement processes were applied to an existing algorithm (for White only) for KRK, which was thought to be correct, although non-optimal, as a result of extensive testing against human opponents. The algorithm comprised only fourteen simple classes and is described in Bramer and Clarke (1979).

Surprisingly, the initial version of the win tree contained only 14,978 WTM and 7,654 BTM positions out of totals of 27,352 and 34,968 legal positions respectively (considering only positions in a standard orientation, to which all others are equivalent by symmetry). Since it is known that all WTM positions and all but 3,495 (drawn) BTM positions are theoretical wins for White, it follows that there were as many as 12,374 WTM and 23,819 BTM positions from which the algorithm failed to win when it could (45% and 68% of all legal positions, respectively).

It is clear that these figures give no indication of the true quality of the algorithm, which in practice had won all of a substantial series of test games played against it.

The first attempt at refining the algorithm was by means of the fully automatic process described previously. The first analysis of the win tree produced an error set of only one WTM position, which was at depth 9 ply. The position in question is shown in Fig. 1.

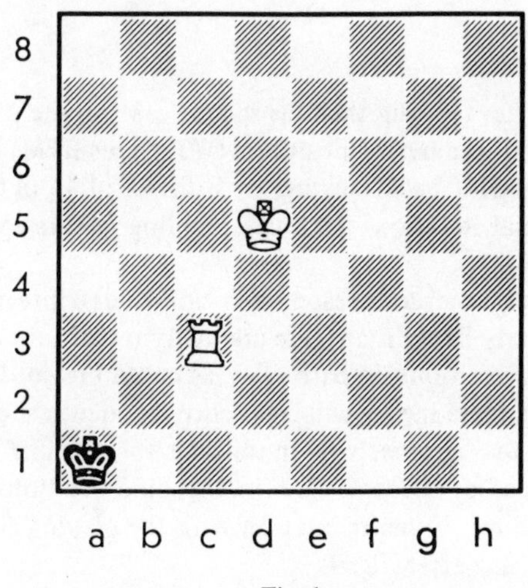

Fig. 1

In this position the program played Rc2 instead of the required Rb3. The playing algorithm was accordingly modified and the win tree regenerated (from depth 10 upwards). This single change resulted in the inclusion of a further 2,339 WTM positions and 3,398 BTM positions in the win tree, leaving 10,035 WTM and 20,421 BTM incorrect positions remaining. The next examination of the win tree revealed an error set of only eight positions, at depth 13 ply. Figure 2 summarises the first six iterations.

Although the iterations were not followed through to a final correct algorithm, Fig. 2 gives a good indication of the contaminating effect of a relatively small number of wrongly played positions. Changing White's move in a relatively small

Iteration	WTM moves adjusted		Total added to win tree		No. of incorrect positions remaining	
	No.	Depth (ply)	WTM	BTM	WTM	BTM
1	1	9	2,339	3,398	10,035	20,421
2	8	13	1,956	2,466	8,079	17,955
3	89	15	3,000	5,184	5,079	12,771
4	176	17	1,188	2,124	3,891	10,647
5	269	19	2,542	6,138	1,349	4,509
6	190	21	621	1,882	728	2,627
Total	733	–	11,646	21,192	–	–

Fig. 2

number of positions (i.e. treating them as special cases in the playing algorithm) causes a far larger total number of positions (WTM plus BTM) to be included in the win tree on subsequent backtracking, by a factor of 45 in the overall totals. For the first and second iterations the corresponding factors are 5,737 and 553, respectively.

This fully automated method treates each 'adjusted' White move as a separate case, whereas it is clearly likely that there are many repetitions of essentially the same moves in similar positions, in particular, as noted previously, that the BTM successors arising after these moves will frequently be identical positions.

The semi-automated approach to modifying the original algorithm began by examining the cause of incorrectness in the nine positions in the first two error sets described above. Experimentation with the playing algorithm revealed the following cycle arising after Fig. 1.

1. Rc2 Kb1
2. Rc3 Ka1 with repetition of position.

Note that it is not important that the move 1. Rb3 required by the backtracking would have won in 9 ply, but that the move originally played by the program (Rc2) did not win. In a position so close to a possible checkmate it is to be expected that White's play will lead to a cycle against some play by Black in a small number of moves. In the above variation, it is not immediately obvious whether it is White's first or second move which is the cause of the cycle. However, the other eight positions in the combined error set provide the answer.

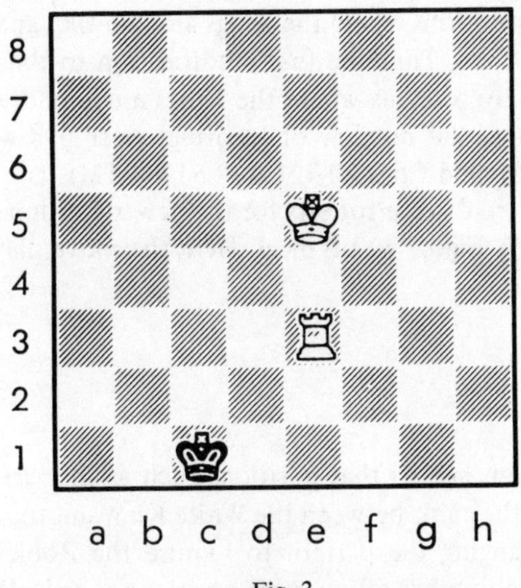

Fig. 3

Thus, for example, in Fig. 3 whether White's Rook is on e3 as shown, or on f3, g3 or h3, the move 1. Rd3 leads to a cycle after

1. ... Kb1
2. Rd2 Kc1
3. Rd3 Kb1, etc.

In this example, it is much easier to see that White's error lies in moving the Rook to d3 and the reason for this is not hard to find. The playing algorithm

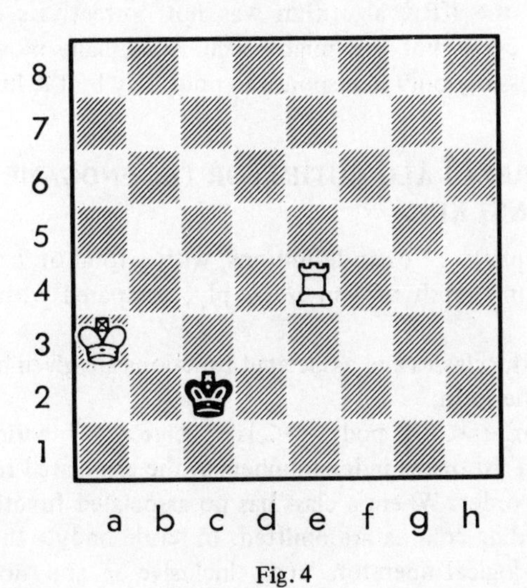

Fig. 4

gives high priority to positions where the Kings are two files apart with the Rook on the file between them. Thus the first modification to the algorithm was to restrict this pattern only to cases where the Kings are no more than three ranks apart. With this change the number of incorrect positions was reduced from 10,035 to 3,291 (WTM) and from 20,421 to 9,513 (BTM). The second modification was based on the first two error sets for the new algorithm. These comprised 18 positions, of which Fig. 4 was typical. Here the move played by White led rapidly to a cycle after

1. Re1 Kd2
2. Re4 Kc2, etc.

The underlying problem here is that positions such as that after 1. Re1, where the Black King is on the rank between the White King and the Rook, are valued extremely highly. Changing the pattern to require the Rook to be above the third rank reduced the number of incorrect positions to only 196 WTM and 906 BTM.

The remaining changes to the algorithm constituted further slight modifications to the same pattern. In each case using error sets appeared to indicate significant positions where the program could be made to cycle and thus greatly assisted the refinement process.

The final algorithm plays correctly in all positions, with a maximum depth of 60 ply (i.e. 30 moves for each side), the total changes made being slight modifications to the definitions of only two patterns out of 14 (classes 9 and 13 in the terminology of Bramer and Clarke (1979)).

Note that testing even by expert human players might never reveal that the original version of the KRK algorithm was not correct. Its errors would in general result in a cycle, but this might occur after many moves of otherwise expert play, and possibly only in response to poor play by the human opponent.

APPENDIX: A CORRECT ALGORITHM FOR THE ENDGAME KING AND ROOK AGAINST KING

The algorithm comprises 14 class definitions, with a total of 7 associated functions. The maximum depth of win is 60 ply, compared with 32 ply for an optimal algorithm.

Definitions of the classes and associated functions are given below.

Rules are given in the form:

Class<class number>: <rule body>⇒<class value>, <function list> where <function list> is a list of the index numbers of the associated functions for the particular class, in order. Where a class has no associated functions, <function list> and the preceding comma are omitted. In <rule body> the symbols &, V and ∿ denote the logical operators 'and', 'inclusive or' and 'not', respectively.

When more than one rule is given with the same <class number>, the entire class definition is the 'inclusive or' of those rules. (Note that class numbers are not placed in strictly ascending numerical order, for compatibility with previous versions of the algorithm given elsewhere.)

Variables wkf, wkr, bkf, bkr, wrf, wrr denote the file and rank co-ordinates of the White King, Black King and White Rook, respectively.

All co-ordinates are measured with respect to White's 'bottom left-hand corner' of the board, i.e. square a1. Thus bkf = 3 and bkr = 7 denotes Black King on square c7. Other variables and functions used in the rule definitions are explained in the glossary which follows the class definitions.

The notation [max] or [min] after each associated function definition indicates that the largest or smallest value, respectively, is preferred.

Specifying class membership for KRK is more complex than for many other endgames such as KPK, since each position can have up to seven others which are equivalent to it by symmetry. These are obtained by reflecting the position about the axes of symmetry shown in Fig. 5.

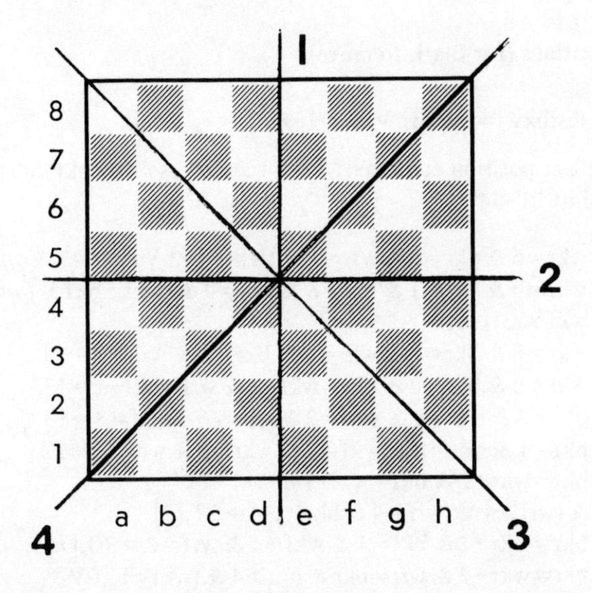

Fig. 5

In the class definitions below no assumptions are made about the orientation of position q. However, it is clearly desirable for each class to be specified with a particular convenient orientation of the board (e.g. 'White King below Black King') in mind, rather than by a separate component for each symmetrically equivalent alternative. This can be achieved in the following way.

(1) Classes 2 down to 9 all require as a necessary condition that $bkr = wkr + 2$. If this condition does not hold but a symmetrically equivalent condition ($bkr = wkr - 2$, $bkf = wkf - 2$ or $bkf = wkf + 2$) does, the position is reflected (about axis 2, 3 or 4 respectively) so that $bkr = wkr + 2$ is satisfied. In all other cases the position cannot fall within any of the classes from 2 down to 9.

(2) A further reflection of the position, in this case about axis 1, is used if necessary, before testing for membership of class 2 (assuming that (1) above is satisfied) to ensure that the Black King is to the left of the White King or on the same file in the left-hand half of the board. This orientation continues for subsequent classes down to 8. Class 9 has a different orientation (which again may require a reflection about axis 1). Finally class 10 assumes an orientation which may require reflections about axis 1 or axis 2, or both. In all three of the above cases (and unlike (1)) the required orientation can always be achieved without loss of generality.

Class Definitions (for Black to move)

Class 1: distbkwr=1 & distwkwr>1 ⇒ 2

Note. Reflect position about axis 1, if necessary, so that $bkf < wkf$ or $bkf = wkf \leqslant 4$.

Class 2: wkr=6 & bkr=8 & wrr=8 & (wkf=bkf V (bkf=1 & wkf=2)) ⇒ 14
Class 3: wkr=6 & bkf=1 & bkr=8 & wrf=2 & (wkf=bkf V (wrr=7 & wkf ≤ 3)) ⇒ 1
Class 4: wkr=6 & bkr=8 & wkf=2 & bkf=1 & wrf>3 ⇒ 13
Class 4: wkr=6 & bkr=8 & bkf=wkf−1 & wrf=bkf−1 ⇒ 13
Class 4: bkf=2 & bkr=8 & wkf=2 & wkr=6 & wrf=3 ⇒ 13
Class 12: bkf=1 & bkr=8 & wkf=2 & wkr=6 & wrf=2 ⇒ 12
Class 13: bkr=wkr+2 & bkf=wrf+1 & wkf=bkf+1 & (wrf>4 V (wrf=4 & bkr>3)) ⇒ 11,[7]
Class 14: bkr=wkr+2 & bkf=1 & wkf=1 & wrf=2 ⇒ 10,[7]
Class 5: bkr=wkr+2 & wrr=bkr & bkr>4 & (wkf=bkf V (bkf= 1 & wkf=2)) ⇒ 9
Class 6: wkf=bkf & bkr=wkr+2 & wrf=wkf+1 & wrr=wkr+1 & bkr>4 ⇒ 8
Class 7: bkr=wkr+2 & bkf ≤ 4 & wkf=bkf+1 & wrr=wkr+1 & bkr>4 & abs(wkf−wrf)≠1 ⇒ 7,[2]
Class 8: wkf=bkf & bkr=wkr+2 & wrf=wkf+1 & bkr>4 ⇒ 6

Note. Reflect position about axis 1, if necessary, so that $bkf \leqslant wrf$.

Class 9: $bkr=wkr+2 \;\&\; distbkwr \geqslant distwkwr \;\&$
$bkf<wrf \;\&\; bkr>4 \;\&\; wrf<6 \;\&\; wrr=wkr+1$
$\&\; abs(wkf-bkf) \leqslant 3 \Rightarrow 5,[2,3]$

Class 9: $bkr=wkr+2 \;\&\; bkf=wkf-2 \;\&\; wrf=wkf-1 \;\&$
$wrr \geqslant 4 \;\&\; bkf<5 \;\&\; bkr>wrr \Rightarrow 5,[2,3]$

Note. Reflect position about axis 1 and/or 2, if necessary, so that $bkf \leqslant wrf$ and $bkr \geqslant wrr$.

Class 10: $wrf>bkf \;\&\; wrr<bkr \;\&\; \sim (wkr=wrr$ and $bkr=wrr+1$
$\&\; bkf<wkf \;\&\; wkf<wrf) \;\&\; \sim (wkf=wrf$
$\&\; bkf=wrf-1 \;\&\; bkr>wkr \;\&\; wkr>wrr) \Rightarrow$
$4,[1,4,5,6]$

Class 11: true $\Rightarrow 3$

Associated Function Definitions

Function 1: min((wrf–1),(8–wrr)) [min]
Function 2: quad [min]
Function 3: abs(wkf–bkf) [min]
Function 4: distwkbk [min]
Function 5: min(abs(wkf–bkf),abs(wkr–bkr)) [min]
Function 6: distbkwr [max]
Function 7: wrr [min]

Glossary

abs(x), min(x,y) – the usual 'absolute value' and 'smaller value' functions.

distwkwr: block distance between White King and White Rook
distbkwr: block distance between Black King and White Rook
distwkbk: block distance between White King and Black King
quad: the number of squares in the quadrant to which the Black King is confined by the White Rook (used in conjunction with Classes 7 and 9 only), i.e. $(8-wrf) \times (8-wrr)$ if $wrf<bkf$, otherwise $(wrf-1) \times (8-wrr)$.

Class Membership Table – for Positions with Black to Move

For this and the following tables, only positions in a standard orientation (to which all others are equivalent by symmetry) are included. The orientation adopted is that the Black King is restricted to the triangle of squares a1-d1-d4 (10 squares), with the other two pieces anywhere on the board. This gives a total of $64 \times 64 \times 10 = 40{,}960$ configurations with each side to move, of which 27,352 are legal WTM (all wins), and 34,968 are legal BTM (31,473 losses, 3,495 draws).

Table 1

Class	Number of positions (BTM)
1	3,478
2	39
3	17
4	113
5	96
6	14
7	93
8	72
9	114
10	24,730
11	6,067
12	10
13	95
14	30
Total	34,968

Number of Positions at each Depth of Win (Table 2)

The depth is the maximum number of moves needed to win against any play by the opponent for White to move (WTM), and the maximum number of moves for which loss can be avoided for Black to move (BTM). The figures for the correct algorithm are given in the main body of Table 2, with the theoretical values for an optimal algorithm given in parentheses. Depth zero losses, BTM, are positions where Black is checkmated.

Optimality levels for Correct KRK Algorithm

Although Table 2 gives the number of positions at each depth for both the correct algorithm and the theoretical 'optimal' case, a more useful estimate, in some respects, of the degree of non-optimality of the correct algorithm is given by comparing the game theoretic depth (obtained from a data base) of each legal WTM position with that of the BTM position to which the final algorithm would play from it.

Table 2

Depth	WTM		BTM	
0	–	(–)	39	(39)
1	273	(273)	113	(113)
2	718	(718)	327	(327)
3	128	(555)	82	(116)
4	211	(346)	90	(282)
5	325	(842)	115	(652)
6	635	(1,391)	287	(793)
7	950	(1,771)	296	(897)
8	855	(2,614)	347	(1,721)
9	821	(2,851)	153	(2,091)
10	663	(2,950)	278	(2,482)
11	816	(2,996)	368	(3,394)
12	932	(3,135)	471	(4,225)
13	970	(3,004)	572	(5,148)
14	1,047	(2,714)	498	(5,728)
15	1,285	(1,005)	1,020	(2,931)
16	1,979	(187)	1,544	(534)
17	1,927	(–)	1,914	(–)
18	1,608	(–)	2,165	(–)
19	1,645	(–)	1,976	(–)
20	1,631	(–)	2,343	(–)
21	1,665	(–)	2,138	(–)
22	1,148	(–)	2,249	(–)
23	1,580	(–)	2,834	(–)
24	1,434	(–)	3,199	(–)
25	975	(–)	2,233	(–)
26	649	(–)	1,861	(–)
27	342	(–)	1,267	(–)
28	115	(–)	552	(–)
29	23	(–)	122	(–)
30	2	(–)	20	(–)
Total wins	27,352		31,473	
Draws	0		3,495	
Total legal	27,352		34,968	

Maximum depth 30 moves, i.e. 60 ply – correct algorithm
16 moves, i.e. 32 ply – optimal algorithm

If the difference (BTM depth-WTM depth) has the value of −1 ply, for some WTM position, then White's move is optimal. If not, then in all cases the difference will be an odd integer with value at least +1. (This case arises where, for example, the BTM depth is 10 ply for a WTM depth of 9 ply, i.e. after Black's best move, the WTM depth is the same as it was originally.)
The table below summarizes the ply difference for White's move in every position for the correct algorithm.

Table 3

Move played is optimal	18,386	(67.2%)
Move played increases depth by 1	4,694	(17.2%)
Move played increases depth by 3	2,434	(8.9%)
Move played increases depth by 5	1,199	(4.4%)
Move played increases depth by 7	422	(1.5%)
Move played increases depth by 9	138	
Move played increases depth by 11	59	
Move played increases depth by 13	20	
Total	27,352	

REFERENCES

Bramer, M. A. (1977), Representation of knowledge for chess endgames: towards a self-improving system, Ph.D. thesis, The Open University.

Bramer, M. A. (1978), Computer-generated databases for the endgame in chess, *Mathematics Faculty Technical Report,* The Open University.

Bramer, M. A. (1980), An optimal algorithm for King and Pawn against King using pattern knowledge. In Clarke, M. R. B. (ed.), *Advances in Computer Chess 2,* Edinburgh University Press, pp. 82–96.

Bramer, M. A. (1981), Machine-aided refinement of correct strategies for the endgame in chess. *Mathematics Faculty Technical Report,* The Open University.

Bramer, M. A. and Clarke, M. R. B. (1979), A model for the representation of pattern-knowledge for the endgame in chess, *Int. J. Man-Machine Studies,* **11**(5), pp. 635–649.

Bratko, I. (1978), Proving correctness of strategies in the AL1 assertional language, *Information Processing Letters,* 7(5), pp. 223–230.

Clarke, M. R. B. (1977), A quantitative study of King and Pawn against King. In Clarke, M. R. B. (ed.), *Advances in Computer Chess 1,* Edinburgh University Press, pp. 108–118.

Ströhlein, T. (1970), Untersuchungen über kombinatorische Spiele. Ph.D. thesis. Munich: Technische Hochschule.

8

Construction of planned move trees for chess pawn endings

Helmut Horacek
Strohgasse 5/8, A1030 Wien, Austria

INTRODUCTION

The model described in this paper is applicable for all legal chess positions containing the kings and up to eight pawns for each side. It does not perform particularly well in solving 'technical' problems like the KPK ending; nor does it work perfectly in special positions which require, for example, treatment by the 'coordinate square' method. Good results can be expected for relatively quiet positions with reasonably straightforward pawn relationships all over the board.

In dealing with a given position, the first step is to recognise feasible goals out of a set of well-defined ones (such as king invasion in the enemy's territory, passed-pawn handling and creation of pawn weaknesses). The model makes use of various patterns corresponding to characteristic parts of positions. Each goal has a certain combination of patterns associated with it. Their presence in the actual board position is the necessary condition for the selection of a specific goal. Patterns specify piece locations which can be either fixed, restricted or variable. Symmetries by colour and side and possible shifts of positions along files or ranks or both are considered.

Chess-specific notions such as passed pawn, candidate pawn and breakthrough point can be described in this manner. Some patterns have pointers to prepared move trees which represent tactical manoeuvers such as a simple pawn breakthrough or a typical king invasion by a pawn sacrifice.

Once a goal is selected, one or more related plans become important. Two ways of producing structurally different plans are considered. Adaptation of a prepared move tree to the actual board position is one method of plan realisation. The other is determination of a path to a certain destination square. Knowledge about location and classification of pieces and squares is taken from the corresponding patterns. Series of moves representing 'pawn to promotion square', 'king to critical passed pawn square' or similar paths can be created like this.

The results can be used to sort moves for a Shannon type-A program or as a plausible move generator for a type-B program. Because of limited memory and time resources this approach only seems reasonable with a small selection of data. Knowledge about possible events at deeper tree levels also seems useful for search control and evaluation.

KNOWLEDGE REPRESENTATION: PATTERN RECOGNITION

A big problem in planning intelligent systems is the choice of knowledge representation especially with regard to further manipulation. For the model described in this paper, a rather complex data structure is specified, which is mainly used for pattern recognition. A basic component of these patterns is the so-called bit board. Four bit boards, representing the locations of the kings and the pawns for both sides, form a complete 'board' for pawn endings. Pattern recognition in a given position is achieved by means of three such boards: a 'fixed-board', a 'not-board' and a 'variable-board'. For a pattern described in this way to be considered present in an actual game position:

(i) The position must include all the pieces contained in the 'fixed-board' (on the same squares).
(ii) None of the pieces on the 'not-board' may appear on the same square on the actual one.
(iii) If a king is specified on the 'variable-board' it must stand on one of the indicated squares on the actual board, and similarly for pawns (treating each file separately).

Knowledge about the chess-specific meaning of a pattern is supported by classification of some important types of pawn and some key squares, such as passed pawn, guarded pawn, critical square and breakthrough square. This knowledge is not necessary for the recognition of a pattern but is used as essential reference by the move-generation routines.

On some occasions, a pattern has a connection to another one which represents (part of) a position arising after a certain series of moves. Piece location differences between the two patterns can then serve as start and end squares for king and pawn paths.

Tactical variations containing captures, attacks and counterattacks cannot be represented in the data structure described above. However, some typical variations can be prepared as move trees and included in the data base. If a characteristic part of a position is recognised which suggests consideration of a certain tactical variation, the corresponding move tree is added to the results.

A special problem of pattern recognition is the case of nearly identical positions which should be treated as the same. The concept of the 'variable-board' deals with a large proportion of such similarities. Furthermore, some routines for making geometric changes to positions are available (reflection along the middle line and interchanging of sides, including colour change). Finally, a further bit board, called 'start-board' serves to indicate all feasible shifts of a pattern. All bit boards and the corresponding pattern classifications are (logically) placed on the 'start-board'. The whole pattern is then shifted until its lower left corner square (a1) covers any of the squares pointed out by the 'start-board'. Any parts of the pattern which are then located off the edge of the 'start-board' are pruned. Uncovered areas of the 'start-board' are added as empty squares to the pattern. Additionally no 'essential' part of the pattern must be over the edge of the 'start-board'.

MOVE GENERATION

The central position in the model is occupied by the so-called 'goals'. Their structure is a very simple one. Each goal represents the connection between a set of patterns and a set of move-generating plans. Recognition of all the connected patterns is the necessary condition for consideration of a selected class of plans.

The model distinguishes two structurally different methods of move generation. For tactical sequences, move generation is performed simply by using the referenced move tree, with necessary changes and shifts according to the related pattern. For positional goals, construction of piece paths is realised. A path is defined by specifying a moving piece and a set of classified 'end squares'. The moving piece must be selected by one or more classifications recognised by the corresponding patterns. All specified classifications must belong to the same square. End squares are identified in the same way, except that a set of squares is required, not a single square. Piece paths are then constructed as follows, depending on the type of piece.

(i) For a pawn path, only squares which are located on the same file as the pawn itself are valid end squares. All pawn moves are subsequently generated until the most distant end square is reached. For example, consider a white pawn on e4 and the end squares d6, d7, e6 and e7. The valid end squares are e6 and e7 (both on the e-file). The path consists of e4-e5-e6-e7, e7 being the 'last' end square on the file, e6 being reached earlier on the path. No checking is provided if all pawn moves are legal ones in the actual game. It is, of course, possible that an advancing pawn can be blocked by a king after a few moves. Furthermore, the moving pawn can be '*en prise*' somewhere on its path. However, since a complete static analysis is not the aim of a plan, these problems should be discovered elsewhere (probably during an associated search). The only purpose of the plan is to mark the pawn moves as worthy of further consideration.

(ii) King path construction is slightly more complicated. All squares blocked by a player's pawn or attacked by an enemy pawn are treated as not accessible to the player's king. The location of the enemy king and possible changes in the pawn structure are not taken into account. With these restrictions, an optimal king path is constructed, and depending on the number and location of the end squares this may consist of one or more branches. Several different branches can lead to the same end square because of the particular geometry of king moves. Each end square the king can reach by a series of legal moves appears in at least one branch. In this paper a simplified representation of the resulting branches is used. Squares of equal distance from the start square form a *level*, irrespective of which branches they belong to. A square cannot appear in two different branches at different distances from the starting square because the king path is an optimal one. Thus, a series of levels, starting with squares of distance one from the starting square, and finishing with the most distant end squares represents the whole path. Consider a king path from d4 to the squares b7, b8, e7, e8 in the figure below.

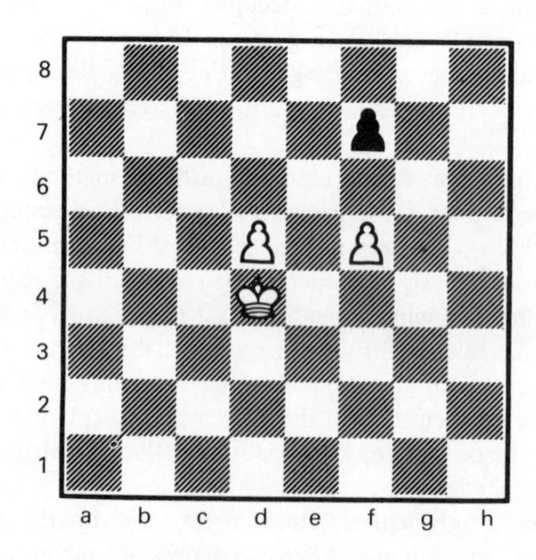

White pawns on d5 and f5 and a black pawn on f7 determine the restricted squares d5, f5, e6 and g6. The whole path consists of four levels, as follows:

Starting square	1st level	2nd level	3rd level	4th level
			a7	
		b6	b7	
	c5	c6	c7	b8
d4	e5	d6	d7	e8
		f6	e7	
			f7	

The above method shows one possible way to gain knowledge about the distance of the king from an end square and the moves required to get there. Additionally, a move to a square of a higher level can be considered as a 'progress' move; moves to squares of the same level as tempo moves. Sometimes tempo moves at level zero and moves which lengthen the whole path by one or two levels seem useful.

EXAMPLES

The following examples describe some goals together with their connected patterns and plans. Figures are given for the non-trivial patterns. Piece symbols are printed differently depending on the type of board they belong to. Pawns and kings on the 'fixed-board' are printed normally. Pieces on the 'variable-board' are printed diagonally and those on the 'not-board' are printed upside-down. This form of presentation in one single board is believed to be much clearer than three parallel boards would be. It is possible that a square may be occupied on more than one of the three boards. In such cases, the most important piece is printed on the board and the other ones are mentioned below the diagram.

Plans are described by chess-specific notions, especially concerning a moving piece and end squares. Positions taken from grandmaster games for which the treated goal has a decisive meaning are also discussed.

Example 1: Passed-pawn handling

Goal: Deal with passed pawn

Pattern 1

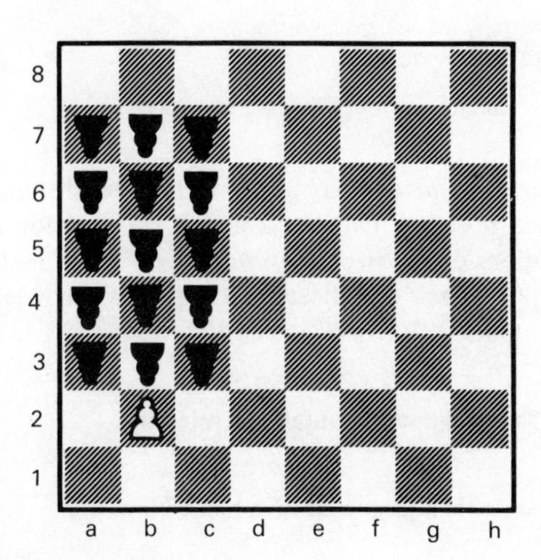

b2: white passed pawn

b3-b8: black blockade squares

a3-a8, c3-c8: white advance squares

(All shifts are permissible, except eighth rank passed-pawn locations.)

Plans

(with white king on c1 and black king on c5)

1st plan

White passed pawn moves to white promotion squares:
b2-(b3-)b4-b5-b6-b7-b8

2nd plan

White king moves to white advance squares and white critical squares:

```
          a4 a5 a6 a7
       b3 b4 b5 b6 b7 a8
Kc1- c2-c3-c4-c5-c6-c7-c8
     d2 d3 d4 d5 d6 d7
        e3 e4 e5 e6
           f4 f5
```

3rd plan

Black king moves to black blockade squares:

```
     b4
     c4  b3
     b5  b7
Kc5-    -   -b8
     b6  c7
     c6
     d6
```

4th plan

Black king moves to white passed pawn:

```
      b4
Kc5 -    - b3 - b2
      c4
```

The following four patterns are very general ones, which must be recognised in every legal chess position. Patterns 2 and 3 are used for various plans to determine the locations of the two kings. Patterns 4 and 5 are 'empty' patterns (all boards are empty). Their classification is important knowledge for all plans dealing with passed pawns.

Pattern 2

All squares of the 'variable-board' contain a white king.

Pattern 3

All squares of the 'variable-board' contain a black king.

Pattern 4

7th and 8th ranks are classified as critical white squares.

Pattern 5

All 8th rank squares are classified as white promotion squares.

Example 2: King breakthrough by temporary pawn sacrifice

Goal: (Special) king breakthrough

Pattern

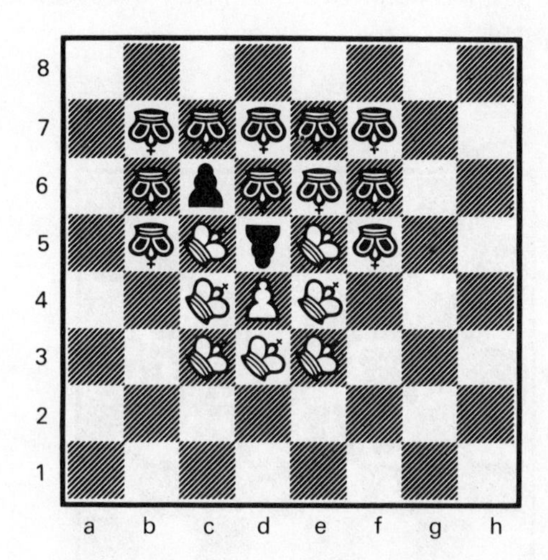

The 'not-board' also contains white pawn on c4, d5, e4, black pawn on e6, e7, c7, black king on c3, c4, d5, e4, e3.
(All shifts are feasible.)

Plan
prepared move tree:

```
                d5
        ________|________
       |        |        |
      cd5:      c5      else
       |             ____|____
      Kd4           |    |    |
       |           dc6:  d6   Kd4
      any
       |
      Kd5:
```

This is a typical sequence in pawn endings. A similar manoeuvre is found in some middle game positions. A pawn which is often weak is removed in order to control the new empty square (d4 in this case) by pieces. A diverted enemy pawn (d5 in this case) protects the square (d4) against frontal attacks by major pieces. For pawn ending this idea is useful in blocked positions (see example below) as well as in open positions (in order to gain space).

The following position occurred in the game Wade–Kadiri at the Siegen Olympiad. White to move.

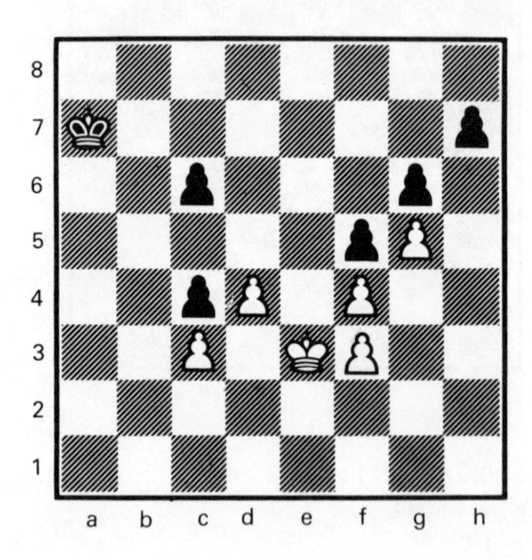

A good plan for White is the king path over the a-file to the breakthrough square b4 (a square beside a blocked or fixed enemy pawn which is not in phalanx and can not be guarded by another pawn). A clever search reveals that this plan is not sufficient because of Black's Ka5-Kb5-Ka5. . .

However, White has the move 1. d5!

If now

(a) 1. . . . Kb6; 2. dXc6, KXc6; 3. Kd4, Kb5; 4. Kd5+-
(b) 1. . . . cXd5; 2. Kd4, Kb6; 3. KXd5, Kb5; 4. Kd4+-

Alternatively, if (c) 1 . . . . c5, then White's chances have been improved. The pawn on d5 is lost, but the Black king loses so much time in winning it that the White king can invade the Black position via the a-file.

Example 3: Mate threat
Goal: Mate drive

Pattern 1

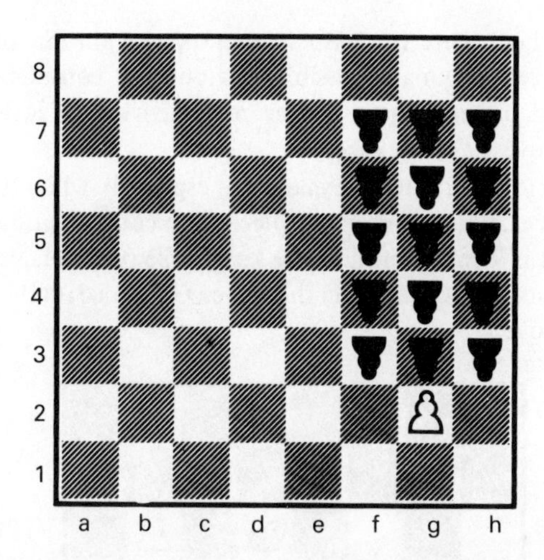

g2: white passed pawn ('special') – only feasible on g2-g6; b2-b6 is gained by symmetry.

1st plan

White passed pawn moves to g6: g2-(g3-)g4-g5-g6

2nd plan

White king moves to f7(assume play begins with white king on f4)

      e5   e6
Kf4 - f5 - f6 - f7
      g5   g6

Pattern 2

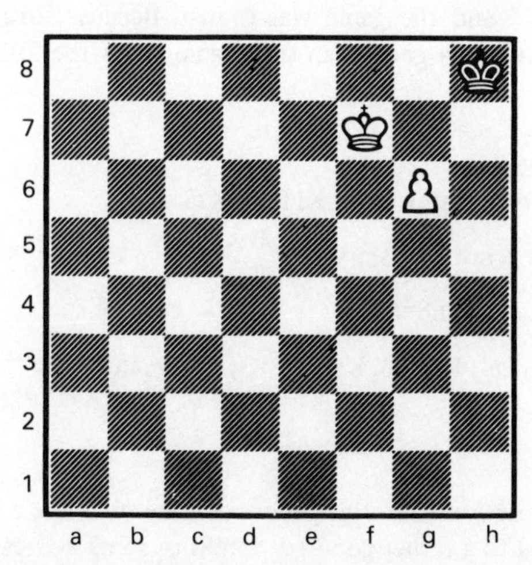

A position to reach. White mates in 3. 1. g7+,Kh7; 2. g8=Q+,Kh6; 3. Qg6 mate. (No shifts are feasible.)

In positions where there is a passed pawn on a knight file, on the sixth rank or below, the above checkmate possibility should be considered. Once having reached the second pattern, mate can be realised without losing a tempo (all moves are check moves).

This fact is very important for evaluation, especially when the opponent has good counter-chances. Even a promoted piece is no compensation for the opponent, except when it is located on the same knight file or its adjacent bishop file.

The next position also occurred in the Siegen Olympiad, in the game Bouaziz–Pomar. White to move.

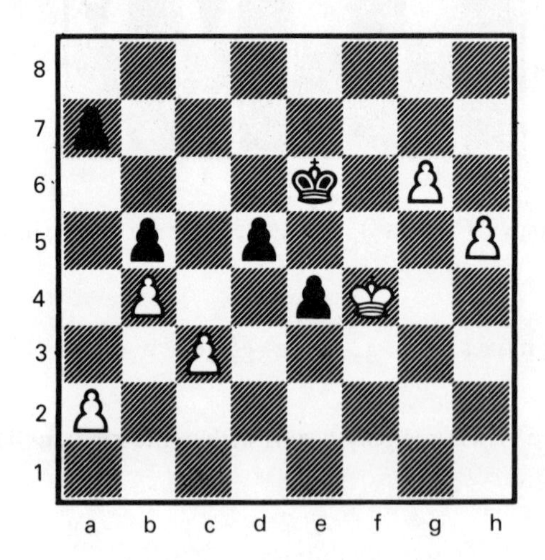

Bouaziz played 1.g7? and the game was drawn. Because advancing the passed pawn on the h-file is also a good plan (see Example 1), the following 'prologue' could arise:

1. h6,Kf6; 2. h7,Kg7;

Published analysis now gives 3. Kg4! Kh8; 4. Kf5 . . . ,

but the tempo move is not necessary:

3. Kf5 !, e3; 4. Ke6, e2; 5. h8=Q+!

('Promotion quiescence') Kh8; 6. Kf7, e1=Q; 7. g7+ and mate in two.

CONCLUSIONS

The data structures described in this paper could be used like a box of children's bricks. They can lead to a rather good treatment of some non-easy pawn endings. Experiments with practical positions are advisable, resulting in an extended and improved data base. A clever search algorithm based on the generated move trees should consider plan moves and tempo moves as well as a simple quiescence including, at least, promotions and captures. Conventional evaluation criteria such as material balance, weak pawn and passed pawn estimation seem rather inadequate, especially for pawn endings. They sometimes can produce rather good moves, but their estimates of how great an advantage is, which side has the advantage, etc. are often faulty. Evaluation of the number of moves necessary to achieve a certain goal and the feasibility and value of that goal (checkmate is worth more than promotion etc.) seems to be a better but rather difficult approach.

The position below is an extremely complicated one, which is given to show the limitations of the model described here. However, even much simpler positions can go beyond the limits of a possible representation.

Analysis by three excellent grandmasters was necessary to discover the correct solution. Perhaps some sophisticated patterns can be found to describe the growth of a distant white passed pawn on the h-file by e5, h4, Kf4, f3, g4.

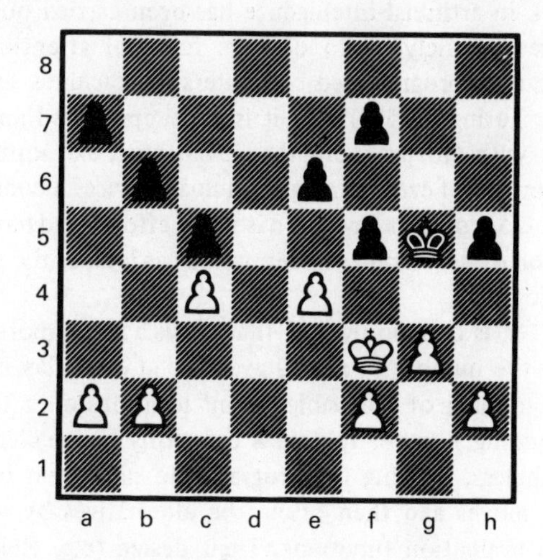

Tal–Korchnoi
Moscow 1968.
White to move.

The effect of the tension created by Black's 1 . . . f6 after 1. e5 can hardly be calculated. The relation between the action on the queen's and the king's side is too complex for the data structures which have been presented. All the significant transformations of the pawn structure (which are very numerous in this position) make it very difficult for any chess-playing program to handle.

PART III – GO

INTRODUCTION

J. A. Campbell
Department of Computer Science, University of Exeter, Exeter EX4 4QL, England

The game of Go has appeared only sporadically in the literature of artificial intelligence by comparison with the concentrated coverage of chess. This may perhaps be understood as a cultural phenomenon; not only is there a near-universal appreciation of the basic ideas of chess in the geographical locations in which most work in artificial intelligence has been carried out, but chess has also been recognised publicly as an obvious focus of attention for work on 'intelligent' behaviour of programmed computers or machines since at least the mid-1940s (e.g. see Turing (1959)). But it is also appreciated among those who have experimented with Go programs that it has been extraordinarily difficult to reproduce the standard of even a struggling human novice. A consequence of this appreciation is that Go programs have been isolated efforts, and have not benefited through an evolution or development over periods as long as the growing periods of the best chess programs.

Why is this so? It is commonly said that Go is a much more complex game than chess because the number of moves available at each play is often between 150 and 361 (the number of accessible vacant locations on a 19 × 19 board), while the corresponding number for chess can easily be smaller by a factor of 5 or more. Nevertheless, existing Go programs do not begin by considering a complete range of moves and then prune the alternatives by use of minimax strategies on static evaluation functions. Their design (e.g. Reitman & Wilcox (1980), Zobrist (1970)) relies instead on features, aspects of pattern-recognition, and low-level heuristics. If these means of simplification are in fact oversimplifications, then the poor performance of Go programs is understandable. Yet the evidence of texts by expert players on elementary play in Go is that the human player's initial heuristics are of equivalent complexity; Ishigure (1973) presents convincing examples. This is not to say that human and programmed heuristics are equivalent, except in somewhat superficial respects such as the recognition that good play in the opening phase of a Go game consists of establishing influence in particular narrow bands of territory parallel to the edges of the board. What seems evident is that the two types of heuristics at present are simply *different.* In other words, there has been insufficient study of the nature of productive low-level heuristics to allow identification or invention of good ones. Therefore the recent revival of interest in Go among some workers in artificial intelligence is welcome. Two of the papers in this section of the book indicate the state of the Go art in the recent past, just at the point where an expansion of Go programming activity on an unprecedented scale is predictable. This prediction follows from the fact that such activity, within computer science and knowledge-based computing, has been rendered both respectable and desirable in Japan, the main stronghold of Go, by the publication (Moto-oka, 1981) of the 'automatic formula-understanding system' subgoal in the Japanese report on fifth generation computing systems. This subgoal includes the production of a program or programs to play what appears to be a non-professional but strong level of Go.

The paper by Green, below, introduces the basics of the game itself, in a form tailored to the interests of readers concerned first with computing and artificial intelligence. This is followed by the discussion by Sander and Davies of a relatively new Go program which deals only with play in the early stages of a game. This program, as described, takes account of the most basic principles of command of territory, and uses strategies referring to patterns of players' tokens (stones) which have analogues in some elementary texts on Go. The authors still do not claim any more than novice-standard play for the program – probably because examples in the elementary texts can often be rephrased to imply that improvement in the standard of play requires the development of implicit (for the human player) or explicit (for the programmer) models of complex interactions between the patterns. However, their paper makes the necessary point that one must first have the right building-blocks for one's models. This question deserves much more study from the viewpoint of artificial intelligence.

The main claim of the paper by Lehner is that look-ahead techniques of the kind used routinely in chess programs are unnecessary in Go because there exist large recognisable families of sequences of Go plays in which the broad effects on a game are the same for all members of each family. His principle of 'representative search' is that one need only examine one representative of a family to discover the approximate value of the tactics (or, if one is fortunate, the strategy) associated with that family. This seems to match the explanations of good players (e.g. those who annotate published games) concerning sequences of plays – but such reasoning is not a part of existing Go programs, no doubt because it is too imprecise for tastes refined on the test cases of computer programming and chess. It is a constructive challenge for researchers in artificial intelligence to express the reasoning in a form which is both precise and programmable in some high-level sense.

The system of rating of Go players is mentioned in the papers which follow, though not in any detail. However, this system carries some promising implications for study of the game in the context of artificial intelligence. In particular, it is a stable and reliable indicator of performance, which can be related both to human learning periods and to types of Go problem which a player can solve. Its original purpose is to establish a handicap in a game with unevenly matched players; the difference in their ratings indicates the number of additional stones which the weaker player is permitted to place in specified positions on the board initially. The lowest rating is a high numerical value of *kyu*, which decreases as the standard improves. A standard of 20-*kyu* play is that of an extremely innocent novice, but it seems that no present Go program deserves a rating higher than this. Beyond 1-*kyu*, which represents a respectable amateur level of play, the next rating is *shodan* or 1-*dan*, the lowest rank of a numerically increasing scale on which the top level is in principle 9-*dan*, in practice less, and on which the best European amateurs are around 6-*dan*. This amateur scale is not easily comparable with the *dan* scale on which Japanese professional players are rated, because a scale itself is normalised in effect by the results of large numbers of games between players a small distance apart on that scale, and games betweeen amateurs and 'comparable' professionals are relatively rare. However, a rough estimate is that n-*dan* amateur performance is comparable to professional $(n-x)$-*dan* standard, where x has a value which is probably closer to 6 than to 5.

Studies reported in the volume edited by Heine (1980) indicate a simple relationship between the rating in *kyu* of a person introduced to Go for the first time and the period spent in acquaintance (continued play without serious study of theoretical material) with the game since that first introduction. This suggests that an important component in novice play is the use of general human procedures for two-dimensional pattern-recognition, and that general considerations not specific to Go should be enough for programs based on adaptive pattern-recognition to achieve eventually a 5-*kyu* (say) standard of Go play by brute-force methods. If such a result is found, the interesting question will then be one of what further improvement in play can be reached by continuing with the same approach. Any positive conclusion in this direction should have significance for general problems in pattern-recognition, as well as for Go itself.

Most published Go problems, unlike chess problems, illustrate situations which are not artificial and which can arise in the course of normal games. Therefore, if problems can be linked to the rating system, it may be possible to arrange a hierarchy of relevant ideas or patterns as a graded programme of challenges for researchers in artificial intelligence. Seen from this point of view, probably the most helpful book in the Go literature is one by Miyamoto (1975), which makes exactly a linking of this kind.

Few Go problems are posed in terms of the entire 19 × 19 board; instead, they refer to local or quasi-local situations. In the last-mentioned reference, the implication is that even quite strong play can be assessed as such, in terms of its response to these situations. It is interesting that the papers of Green and Lehner which follow both say the same thing, in different ways: Lehner in his concept of (non-global) representative search, and Green in his suggestion that the classical technique of solving large problems by reduction to smaller sub-problems (e.g. on a board smaller than 19 × 19) is highly relevant to Go. Given these observations and the present state of computerised Go, it is clear that the reward per unit of research time invested in studies of this game is far higher than for chess, and probably higher than for any other game, as far as general lessons for artificial intelligence are concerned.

The Ishi Press (address: CPO Box 2126, Tokyo) publishes an extensive range of literature on Go in English, most of which is post-introductory and best approached after a reading of good introductory books such as those of Iwamoto (1976) and Fairbairn (1977). Go has also been the subject of study and introductory writing by at least one experienced chess player (Lasker, 1960); the contrast with Japanese texts is instructive, and is due in part to the different cultural background against which Go and the essentially equivalent Chinese game of Wei-chi have flourished. While it is not possible to give a short recipe for the kind of cultural immersion which is needed if one is to see the world in the Japanese or Chinese player's perspective, there are two books which provide easily accessible samples: a novel by Kawabata (1978) and an exercise in comparative politics by Boorman (1969).

References to national Go societies in Europe and North America have information-values which may decrease with time, because of the possibility that addresses may change. However, at the time of writing, the British Go Association can be contacted through its Membership Secretary at 60 Wantage Road, Reading. In addition to membership subscriptions the Association sells publications, and should be able to advise on current addresses of national societies in some other countries. An appendix to the book by Iwamoto (1976) gives a selection of such addresses.

REFERENCES

Boorman, S. A. (1969), *The Protracted Game.* Oxford University Press, New York.

Fairbairn, J. T. (1977), *Invitation to Go.* Oxford University Press, Oxford.

Heine, K. (ed.), (1980) *Proceedings of the 2nd Seminar of Scientific Go-theory.* Institut für Strahlenchemie, Mülheim a.d. Ruhr.

Ishigure, I. (1973), *In the Beginning.* Ishi Press, Tokyo.

Iwamoto, K. (1976), *Go for Beginners.* Penguin Books, Harmondsworth, Middlesex.

Kawabata, Y. (1978), *Le Maître, ou le Tournoi de Go.* Albin Michel, Paris.

Lasker, E. (1960), *Go and Go-Moku.* Dover Publications, New York.

Miyamoto, N. (1975), *What's your rating?* Ishi Press, Tokyo.

Moto-oka, T. (ed.), (1981), *Fifth-Generation Computing Systems,* North-Holland, Amsterdam.

Reitman, W. and Wilcox, B. (1980), The Structure and Performance of the Interim. 2 Go Program. In K. Heine (1980), pp. 105–124.

Turing, S. (1959), *Alan M. Turing.* W. Heffer and Sons Ltd., Cambridge, England.
Zobrist, A. L. (1970), Feature Extraction and Representation for Pattern Recognition and the Game of Go. Ph.D. Thesis, University of Wisconsin: Microfilm no. 71–3, 162.

9

Go and artificial intelligence

H. S. Green
Department of Mathematical Physics, University of Adelaide,
Adelaide, South Australia 5001, Australia

ABSTRACT

A description of the game of Go is given in formal terms suitable for implementation on a computer. An attempt is made to isolate the unsolved problems in the formulation of a program capable of playing the game at a level comparable with human intelligence.

INTRODUCTION

The development of computer programs for playing board games is recognised as one of the more important fields of application of artificial intelligence. Programs are already widely available for playing a game as complex as chess at a level superior to that of the average human player, and the major problems involved in the construction of chess-playing computers may well be regarded as solved in principle. It is therefore surprising to find that, in spite of the commitment of considerable effort and ingenuity, no comparable system has been devised for playing the oriental game of Go. This is certainly not because the game is less important than chess, judged by the number of people playing it or by any obvious objective criterion. In Japan, China, and other oriental countries, Go is even more popular than chess is in the West; and the simplicity and internal logic of the game gives it an appeal, especially to mathematicians and scientists, which should guarantee a rapidly increasing number of devotees in Western countries. There is an enormous literature devoted to the game of Go, most of it in Japanese but also in English following efforts by the Ishi Press in Tokyo and various Go associations to cater for occidental players. The scientific analysis of the game has also begun to acquire a literature in English. Heine (1980) has contributed to and published a recent symposium of papers in this area, in which he cites Go as 'a perfect game for giving new hints for progress in the field of Artificial Intelligence'.

Yet the more advanced Go-playing programs are still very rudimentary. Probably the best known of these has been developed by Reitman and Wilcox (1976, 1980), but their program has not yet reached a playing strength comparable to that of any human player except the most inexperienced novice. The impression remains that there are problems in the area which have not yet been precisely formulated. Sander and Davies, in the following paper, describe an approach to the problems associated with the opening, which has the merit of being based on general principles rather than an attempt to codify the *joseki* and *fuseki* evolved mainly by the Japanese as a result of experience. (*Joseki* are opening sequences in the corners of the Go board, and *fuseki* are opening strategies which take account of the whole board.) It will, however, be necessary eventually to refine the principles to the point where the level of play is at least equal to that prescribed by experience, since it is well established that most games of Go are won or lost in the opening. But the problems associated with the middle game will probably be the most challenging, since even the top-ranking Japanese professional players are apt to make mistakes in this phase of the game.

It is a peculiarity of Go that the value of a move is greatest near the beginning of the game and, with good play, declines steadily throughout the game to a point where it is obvious that no further advantage can be gained by either player. The Japanese rules provide for the termination of the game at this stage and also provide a simple procedure for determining the score of each player. Since it is the difference in the scores of the two players which determines the result of the game, each play throughout the game should be decided in the light of its probable effect on the scores. Thus the essential problem in devising a computer program might be regarded as the determination of a reliable estimate of the difference in the final scores, starting from a given configuration on the board. It is known that advanced players do in fact form estimates of the score throughout the game, but in practice such estimates play only a subsidiary role in deciding the most advantageous play, except near the end of the game. Moreover, the considerations involved in forming an estimate of the effect of each play on the final score are so complex that it is probably not feasible to construct a computer program on such lines at present. Instead, it is important to clarify the reasoning by which advanced players determine priorities in the order of play.

In the following, we shall first describe methods of representation of a game of Go within a computer, and how the final score is calculated. From this basis, we shall try to formulate the problems which remain to be solved before computers can match human intelligence in this area.

REPRESENTATION OF CONFIGURATIONS AND GAMES

The game Go is played on the rectangular (almost square) lattice formed by the intersections of 19 horizontal and 19 vertical lines. The choice of the integer 19 is the only somewhat arbitrary feature of the game, and appears to have resulted from a compromise between two objectives: to allow an interesting range of strategies, and to permit the completion of a game within a reasonable length of time. But beginners are often recommended to practise on a smaller board, and many problems characteristic of the actual game can be formulated on such a board. One approach to constructing Go-playing programs therefore commences with lattices of, say, 25 or 81 points, instead of the 361 points on the standard board. In general, we may consider a modification of the game played on the lattice of N^2 points formed by the intersections of N horizontal and N vertical lines. A configuration, or position reached in the course of a game, is obtained by placing black or white stones on some of the lattice points, in such a way that not more than one stone occupies any point. The position on the board may therefore be represented by a square matrix with N rows and columns, whose elements are 0, 1 or 2: 0 if the corresponding point on the board is unoccupied, 1 if the corresponding point is occupied by a black stone, and 2 if it is occupied by a white stone. In Figs. 1 and 2 we give two examples, corresponding to the choice $N = 5$ and $N = 6$, respectively.

$$\begin{matrix} 2 & 2 & 2 & 1 & 0 \\ 2 & 0 & 1 & 0 & 1 \\ 2 & 2 & 2 & 1 & 1 \\ 2 & 0 & 2 & 0 & 0 \\ 0 & 2 & 2 & 2 & 2 \end{matrix}$$

Fig. 1 – A matrix representation of a position in which the white stones are alive and the black stones are dead.

$$\begin{matrix} 0 & 0 & 0 & 0 & 0 & 0 \\ 1 & 1 & 2 & 0 & 2 & 0 \\ 0 & 1 & 2 & 0 & 0 & 0 \\ 0 & 1 & 2 & 2 & 0 & 0 \\ 0 & 0 & 0 & 0 & 0 & 0 \end{matrix}$$

Fig. 2 – A matrix representation of a position in which the white stones can be killed, but the black stones cannot be killed with good play.

Figure 1 represents a game on a board with 5 rows and columns, which is complete in the sense that the player with the black stones has already lost. Figure 2 represents a game on a board with 6 rows and columns, in which the player with the black stones (represented by 1s) can win if he has the right to make the next move, though this is by no means obvious. We shall use these figures to explain the concepts of 'life' and 'death'. But for the present we note that any configurations on the board can be represented by a matrix $A(I, J)$ with entries which are integers (mod 3). This characteristic of the game would seem to make it ideal for computer analysis.

At the beginning of an even game, the board is empty, so that all entries of the matrix $A(I, J)$ are 0. Black's first move changes one of the 0s to 2. Thereafter, black and white play alternately. Each move by black changes a 0 to 1 and each move by white changes a 0 to 2. A player may pass, thus allowing his opponent to make two or more successive moves, but this may be done only with the permission of his opponent, who may exact a penalty in giving permission, according to some versions of the rules. Since there is no conceivable advantage to be gained by passing near the beginning of the game, it seems simpler to ignore this provision of the rules for the purpose of analysis of Go. More essential, indeed vital, to the game, are the rules of capture.

To recognise when a capture has been made it is important for a program to 'know' when a group of stones is 'connected', and to be able to 'count' the number of 'liberties' at a connected group of stones. In a given configuration, the elements $A(I, J)$ and $A(I+1, J)$, or $A(I, J)$ and $A(I, J+1)$, of the associated matrix are considered to be part of a connected group if $A(I, J) = A(I+1, J)$ or $A(I, J) = A(I, J+1)$, respectively. Thus, in Fig. 2, the 1s form a single connected group, while in Fig. 1, the 1s form three separate connected groups (two of which are isolated 1s). The 0s in Fig. 2 may also be considered to form a single connected group. The number of liberties of a connected group of black or white stones is the number of unoccupied lattice points horizontally or vertically adjacent to it, and is therefore the number of 0s horizontally or vertically adjacent to a connected group of 1s or 2s in the matrix $A(I, J)$. Thus, in Fig. 1, the connected group of 2s has 5 liberties, while the connected group of three 1s has 4 liberties. If, after a play by either player in the course of the game, any connected group of black or white stones is found to have no liberties, it is captured and removed from the board; the corresponding 1s and 2s of the matrix $A(I, J)$ are therefore replaced by 0s. This process is clearly implementable without difficulty in a computer program.

There is one further rule, which limits the otherwise unrestricted range of plays available to a player in certain configurations (e.g. that known as *ko*) which may arise during the game. It applies only to plays which would result in the capture of one or more of his opponent's stones. The rule may be stated quite simply; no play may be made if it results in a configuration on the board which has appeared previously during the same game. (In Japan this rule is at present replaced by a more complicated set of rules, but the effect is almost always the same, and it is generally agreed that it should always be the same.) This rule has the desirable consequence that every game must ultimately terminate and also adds much to the interest of some games. However, it somewhat complicates a general computer formulation since it requires a record to be kept of previous configurations in the same game. This complication is offset by the fact that only configurations immediately before and during a sequence of captures need be recorded. Nevertheless, it raises the question of how the sequence of configurations which arise in a game are to be recorded.

The problem of keeping a game record is in fact very much simpler in Go than in chess. In Japanese newspapers and in Go journals, entire game records are represented in one, or at most a few diagrams. These diagrams can also be replaced by a matrix $B(I, J)$ of the same size as $A(I, J)$, in which the entry $B(I, J) = M$ means that the Mth move in the game was played on the point in the Ith row and the Jth column. Since, as a result of capture, it is possible for more than one move to be played on the same point, it is necessary to keep a separate record of moves played on the same point. This record will enable the legality of captures in situations such as *ko* to be determined. The record of a game played on a small lattice of 4 points is shown in Fig. 3.

```
1   3        (3=5=7=11=20=22;    2=9=13=17;
4   2         1=6=10=14=16=23;   4=8=15=18=21)
```

Fig. 3 – Record of a game on a small board. Moves 12 and 19 were enforced passes.

It is evident from the above description that the playing rules of Go are exceedingly simple and very easily formulated in a computer program. This applies also to the rules for determining the outcome of a game, which are naturally very important because they profoundly influence the tactics and some strategies of the game. The Japanese rules differ from those which govern the Chinese game, called Wei-chi, but the effect of the difference on the score is so small (usually zero) that good play is hardly affected by the variation. Pragmatically, the Japanese rules are easier to apply, but the Chinese rules are better for theoretical purposes, and somewhat simpler from the point of view of computer formulation. The Japanese rules require a consensus towards the end of a game, on the question of which groups of stones cannot avoid capture. When neither player sees an advantage in continuing, such stones are removed and added to the stones of the same colour actually captured during the game. A player's score is then the number of unoccupied points completely surrounded by his stones, plus the number of his opponent's stones which have been captured during the game, or removed at the end of the game. The player with the higher score has won. In practice a draw (*jigo*) rarely occurs, and can be avoided altogether by a handicap of five-and-a-half points (for a standard board) awarded against black to compensate for the advantage of playing first. The Chinese require only the addition of the number of stones of a particular colour remaining on the board at the end of the game to the number of vacant points surrounded by stones of that colour. This gives the players' scores, and again the difference in score determines the result of the game.

The practical effect of these rules is as follows. Each unoccupied point completely surrounded by a player's stones at the end of the game forms part of what is known as his territory, and is worth one point. Each 'prisoner or stone captured is worth two points: the point of territory which it vacates and the point which it contributes independently to the score. There are therefore two ways of securing an advantage in the game; by surrounding territory and by taking prisoners. The tactics and strategies of the players are directed to one or other of these ends. In the next section we shall discuss some of the problems which arise in the formulation of tactics and strategy.

EVALUATION OF TACTICS AND STRATEGIES

We have seen that it is a simple task to construct a program which will enable a computer to play Go in accordance with the rules. The rules are in fact so simple that, especially on a large board, there is a wide choice of moves in almost any configuration, and if it were simply a matter of selecting one of the moves available, a random number generator could be used to determine the choice. The result, however, would have no bearing at all on artificial intelligence.

By consideration of the lattice of configurations which can develop from a given configuration $A(I, J)$, it can be seen that there is an optimum score for each player associated with this configuration, which can be attained by perfect play, irrespective of the moves of his opponent. From this point of view, the problem is to select a next move which does not diminish the optimum score: any other move should be regarded as a mistake. On a small board, such as is represented in Fig. 3, it is not hard to determine the optimum score and select a move which will leave it unchanged. It is a perfectly reasonable approach to begin a study of tactics and strategy on very small boards, and to increase the size of the board progressively. Even from the 4-point board of Fig. 3, it will be learned quickly that it is unprofitable to attempt the capture of an opponent's stones by playing adjacent to them, and that the most obvious tactic is usually self-defeating. This principle remains unchanged on large boards; however, it is easy to discover that the range of tactics and strategy increases dramatically with each addition to the size of the board. Thus, the objective of preserving an optimum score soon has to be abandoned in favour of more pragmatic considerations. The lesson of the small board is translated into a maxim: 'do not play close to your opponent's strong stones!' At the beginning of the game, the players find it advantageous to occupy points near the corners of the board, on the third or fourth line of a standard board. The third line is biased towards defence, i.e. the formation of secure territory, and the fourth line towards offence, i.e. attacking hostile stones which venture into the neighbourhood. It is obviously easier to form secure territory in the corners than near the edge of the board, and easier to form territory near the edge than in the centre. Nevertheless it is a mistrake to try to form such territory early in the game, and it is usually a good strategy to balance offensive and defensive moves. Naturally, a play which has both offensive and defensive merits, when available, is usually better than one which has only offensive or defensive value. Near the beginning of a game, each play on the standard board should be worth a minimum of ten points, either in forming territory or in preventing the opponent from forming territory. There is obviously a corresponding but smaller number for smaller boards, which would have to be determined by analytical or empirical methods.

The principles stated above represent the fruit of experience but are not sufficiently precise to determine an optimal program. The program of Sander and Davies, described in the following article, is clearly based on these principles. To sharpen them, it will be necessary to develop an awareness of what may be characterised as urgent plays, which can be called for after the first few moves and thereafter throughout the game. These urgent moves are often by no means obvious, but their neglect by an inexperienced player allows his opponent the opportunity to gain a great advantage. The sequences of moves in a corner area, called *joseki*, are often composed of urgent moves for both parties, and can be interrupted only for even more urgent moves on other parts of the board. It is therefore a test of the efficacy of any program based on general principles that it should be able to recognise urgent moves and play in accordance with *joseki* (or better). This can only be achieved by a complete analysis of sequences of likely moves in the corner area, by no means an impossible task, and a proper evaluation of the results. Here the experience gained with relatively small boards may have a direct application. However, it should be noted that many different *joseki* and variations can evolve from these same initial plays in the corner, and the choice implicit in this variety must be made with reference to developments in adjacent corners and sides.

In Fig. 2 a configuration is shown which requires urgent attention, though this would not be obvious to a player of strength below, say, 4 *kyu*. The critical point is in the first row and the third column; if black plays here he can kill the white stones, and the whole of the top right corner area will become his territory, instead of white's. There is a large number of Go 'proverbs' which help an intelligent player to recognise this type of situation; in this instance: 'There is death in the *hane*'. These proverbs are by no means universal in this application, and sometimes inconsistent with one another, but they help to identify moves worthy of consideration and to distinguish them from other moves which need not be analysed. It would be reasonable to expect a Go-playing program to make such an appraisal of possibly urgent moves in respect of each connected group or potentially connected group on the board. This would involve distinguishing bad or irrelevant moves, and possibly urgent moves which are recommended or suggested by one or other of the Go proverbs. The number of the latter is not necessarily very large. However, corresponding to each of these moves it would be necessary to search each of a number of sequences of urgent or potentially urgent responses to be sure that no vital place is missed.

The development of a computer program capable of recognising urgent moves could be assisted by the examination of collections of Go problems, such as those published by the Japanese master K. Maeda. These problems differ from the usual type of chess problem, in that the configurations involved are similar to those which arise quite frequently in actual games. Also, nearly all of them can be formulated on boards much smaller than the standard size. Ability to solve these problems is quite closely correlated with a player's strength, and a study of them is perhaps the best way to improve quickly in strength. To the novice they give an appreciation of the high degree of subtlety of a good play, and the importance of the order of moves.

The discovery of urgent moves, or moves urgently requiring an answer, is the essence of good tactics throughout the game. Nevertheless, there are many situations in which an urgent move may and should be neglected. Such situations naturally include those where an even more urgent move exists elsewhere on the board, but also more importantly those in which tactics must be subordinated to strategy. Strategic considerations are certainly the most difficult to submit to exact analysis. At the beginning of the game, they influence the choice of *joseki* in adjacent corners, as well as the balanced choice of offensive and defensive moves which have already been referred to. In the early middle game there is usually a need to recognise areas where large amounts of territory are at stake, and to plan an invasion of an area which, if consolidated, will adversely affect the result of the game. A good plan is necessarily flexible, and will allow invading stones either to form a live group within enemy territory, or to escape and link up with friendly stones outside. Another plan is to force the opponent to defend a reduced territory and thereby to gain an advantage elsewhere on the board. Again, the choice of moves which initiate such plans is often decided by very subtle considerations. There is however, a well-known characteristic of what are often called 'ear-reddening' moves, referring to the effect on the opponent in one famous game; they have an effect on several groups of stones at the same time. It is possible that such moves can be determined by the calculation of the 'influence' which a stone placed on a given point can exert on the nearer groups of stones on the board. Some programs already existing operate in this way, but the method of determining influences will need to be refined considerably to approach the standard of intelligent perception required in even moderately good play.

ENDGAME STRATEGY

The endgame in Go may be defined as that part of the game in which no new living groups of stones can be formed by either player. Since questions of life or death are no longer relevant, the game is simplified to an extent that precise analysis is possible even by players of moderate strength. Since the issue of the game is already decided in principle and, indeed, usually obvious to a player of any experience, the endgame is not regarded as very interesting by most players. Nevertheless mistakes are possible, and are frequently made, which could affect the issue. From the point of view of artificial intelligence, the endgame is of special interest, because the problems are better defined and more easily solved, even on a board of standard size. The development of a program for correct endgame play could be regarded as one of the first step towards the formation of a complete program, but does not seem to have been given much attention so far.

The tactics of endgame play are not essentially different from those of the opening or middle game, but the tactics applicable in a given configuration is much more restricted, so that there is usually little difficulty in finding the best move locally. However, there are strategic considerations to which the choice of local tactics must again be subordinated. The strategy of the endgame is very much concerned with what, in Japan, is called *sente* and *gote*. A move is *sente* if it must be answered locally, to avoid an unacceptable loss; it is *gote* if it can be safely ignored, for the time being. The importance of *sente* and *gote* is by no means restricted to the endgame, and tends to be underestimated by weaker players from the opening onwards. A study of its application to the endgame, where there are no other strategic problems of any consequence, is therefore a useful step towards developing an effective overall strategy.

A simple example which illustrates the principle involved is shown in Fig. 4. Here, points numbered 1, 2, and 3 are supposed to be occupied by black stones, occupied by white stones, and unoccupied, respectively. The board in this instance consists of 64 points.

In this position, black may expect to obtain territory on the left side of the board, and white may expect to obtain territory on the right side, extending into the centre. Territory on the upper and lower sides of the board will be divided between the two players. On the upper side, black may safely place a stone on either of the points 3_a or 3_b, in the expectation of connecting it with the existing black stones. By playing 3_b, he will clearly deprive white of more territory on the upper side, but if a standard sequence of moves is followed, he will play the last move in this area, i.e. will have *gote*, and will lose a similar initiative on the lower side (at 3_d). It is therefore better to play at 3_a than at 3_b, since this move will result in *sente* and the opportunity to make a larger gain in the lower side of the board.

A computer program to make correct evaluations of this type will need to compute not only the number of points to be gained or lost at the various

3	3	3	3	3_a	3_b	3	3
3	1	1	3	3	3	3	3
3	1	2	2	2	2	2	3
3	1	2	3	3	3	2	3
3	1	2	3	3	3	3	3
3	1	2	2	2	2	3	3
3	1	3	3	3	3	3	3
3	3	3	3_c	3_d	3	3	3

Fig. 4 – Endgame position in which black has the choice of playing on the vacant points 3_a or 3_b, or 3_c or 3_d.

incomplete boundaries between opposing stones, but also the relative value of *sente* and *gote*. In more complex situations, it will be necessary to assign an optimum order to plays on different parts of the board. This, however, is easily done when the individual local situation has been analysed.

A corner assessment of the endgame will include recognition of a configuration in which, even with moderately good play, no further advantage can be expected by either side. In such a configuration, the game is virtually complete, though it is usual to continue until all *dame,* i.e. unoccupied points not surrounded by stones of a particular colour, are filled. It is important to distinguish such *dame* from points left unoccupied in a *seki*, which cannot be filled by either player without incurring a disadvantage; these points remain occupied and are not part of the territory of either player. Finally, it is necessary to recognise, even at a much earlier stage in the game, groups of stones which cannot be made to live except with the opponent's unlikely cooperation. These are removed at the end of the game and added to the tally of prisoners of the same colour.

CONCLUSION

It should be clear from the above account that the problem of constructing a Go-playing program capable of matching normal human intelligence is difficult but soluble. It can be approached from various directions, some of which have already been tried. However, one important feature of scientific methodology in problem-solving appears to have been neglected so far; the replacement of the actual problem by a simpler problem of the same type. If possible, the simplification should be made in several different directions. In the game of Go, simplification may be achieved by reduction of the size of the board, by restricting attention to Go-problems which illustrate important tactical considerations, or to endgame situations which illustrate some aspects of strategy. By combining the intelligent response typical of these different simplifications of the actual game, one can hope to obtain a program which will play at the level reached by most amateur players.

REFERENCES

Heine, K. (ed.) (1980), *Proceedings of the 2nd Seminar of Scientific Go-Theory.* Institut für Strahlenchemie, Mülheim a.d. Ruhr.

Reitman, W. and Wilcox, B. (1976) *A Program for Playing Go: Interim Report.* University of Michigan, Ann Arbor, Michigan.

Reitman, W. and Wilcox, B. (1980) The Structure and Performance of the Interim. 2 Go Program. In Heine (1980), pp. 105–124.

10

A strategic approach to the game of Go†

Peter T. Sander
Department of Electrical Engineering, McGill University, Montreal, Quebec, Canada H3A 2A7
and
D. Julian M. Davies
Department of Computer Science, The University of Western Ontario, London, Canada N6A 5B9

ABSTRACT

A program has been constructed to play Go which avoids the combinatorial explosion inherent in using tree search to evaluate and select moves. The program uses strategies, generating possible moves according to a top-down or goal-directed organisation. The system also uses hierarchically structured descriptions of the board positions, which are generated bottom-up incrementally at each move.

The program structures are described, and possible improvements are discussed. The program is also compared briefly with other Go-playing programs. The goal-directed organisation of this program may be suitable for adaptation to other 'expert' systems involving perceptual tasks and responses.

INTRODUCTION

We describe an approach to building a program to play Go, based on progressive refinement of 'strategies' to 'goals', and finally to selection of a move. In essence, the program plays moves on the basis of a kind of spatial awareness of the board, and not by forward tree-searching. In this respect it differs from the majority of game-playing programs, particularly most of those for chess, draughts (checkers), backgammon, and other well-known board games.

At the present state of completion, the program plays only the opening game, typically the first twenty or so moves. At the completion of the particular

†This chapter is based substantially on Peter Sander's M.Sc. Thesis (Sander (1979)). The work described was supported in part by the National Science and Engineering Research Council of Canada, under an Operating Grant.

research project, appropriate strategies and goals had not been developed for the middle- and endgames, which take place on a relatively congested board. However, it seems that the overall approach remains appropriate to later stages of the game, and may well apply in some other 'expert' tasks also.

THE GAME OF GO

Go is played with a 19 × 19 board, which starts clear of stones. The two players alternately place their black and white stones (respectively) on unoccupied positions of the board. After a few moves, the board might appear as shown in Fig. 1. (The play leading to this position is analysed in the Appendix.)

The object of the game is for each player to attempt to control as much territory as possible – where territory means board positions not actually

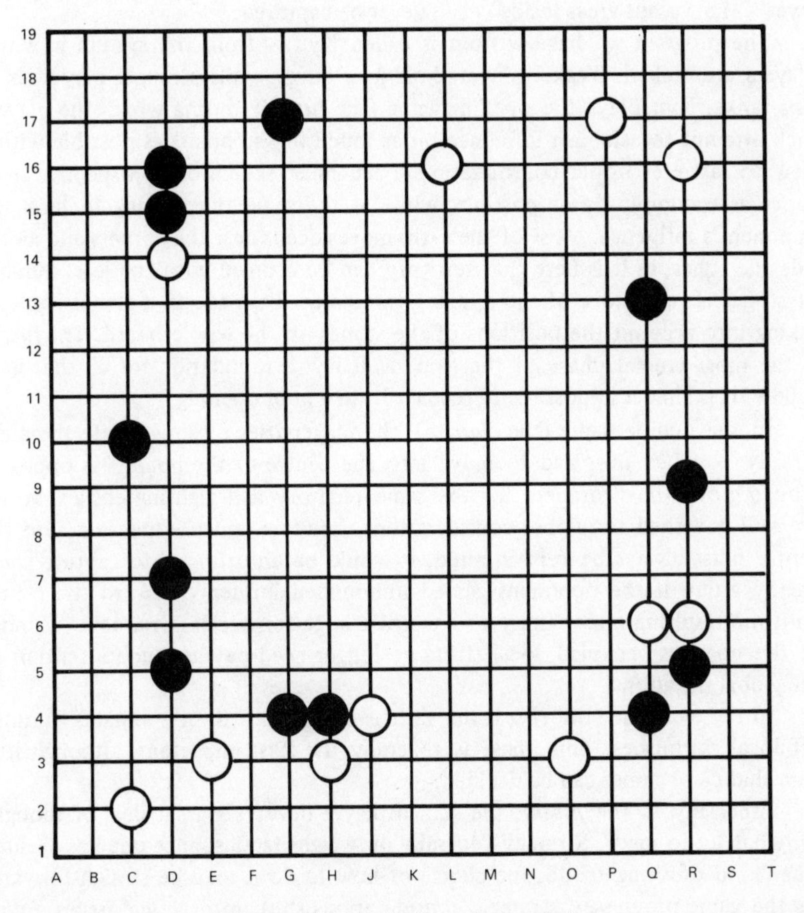

Fig. 1 – *Fuseki* with Kyu playing black.

occupied, but surrounded or fenced off by the player's stones. We note, in passing, that to play Go successfully involves having some 'perception' of the 'spatial' configuration on the entire board, in terms of regions or territories, not just of local arrangements of stones. This facet gives work on playing Go interest for its relationship to visual perception. Spatial awareness also arises to some degree in chess-playing, as in the concepts of developing a good position, or controlling the centre, but is more pervasive in the game of Go.

In practice, the game is not merely a wild race to fence off areas of the board, because of two other considerations. First, it may be desirable to disrupt the opponent's fences or chains of pieces by interposing one's own stones. On the other hand, a set of stones of one colour, if completely and solidly surrounded and filled in by opponent's men is *captured.* So territory might sometimes be gained by permitting the opponent to grab it first, and then capturing it later. Nevertheless, because of the way the rules operate, a group with two (or more) 'eyes' – i.e. vacant areas inside – can never be captured.

The program we have written is called Kyu – from the system in which players are ranked. Weaker players hold *kyu* ranks, while stronger players hold *dan* ranks. Kyu plays the opening game (the *fuseki*), during which the players each attempt to establish influence on as much of the board as possible with a view to later territorial consolidation. Each must sketch out prospective territories as economically as possible, while at the same time trying to limit the opponent's influence. Most of the early moves occur near the corners and alongside the edges, as it is here that territory can be claimed with the least number of stones. Every move of the opening game must be made in a global context, taking into account the positions of the stones on the whole board. The *fuseki* is the most crucial phase of the game as it lays a foundation for all that is to follow. It is almost impossible to recover from a poor opening.

In the middle game (the *chuban*), the player tries to consolidate the areas already sketched out, and to move into the centre of the board. As opposing groups grow, they compete for the same territory and fighting ensues. Moves are still governed by global considerations, however, since expansion into the centre must always be kept in mind. It would be unfortunate to capture some enemy group if the opponent gained unbounded influence toward the centre with the resulting opportunity to construct large territories. Gradually, as more of the board is occupied, local fights no longer need pay as much attention to the global situation.

In the endgame (the *yose*), the shift is complete – it only remains to finish off local skirmishes. This phase is generally the least important, although it is here that close games can be decided.

Especially in the *fuseki*, the skilled player devotes a great deal of thought to 'what to do next'. Strategy generally outweighs tactics; once one has decided what kind of thing to do, the choice of how to do it may be straightforward. As the game progresses, strategic considerations shift into tactical issues, much as the importance of making moves in a global context gives way to using local context.

KYU AND OTHER GAME-PLAYING PROGRAMS

Because the opening game in Go is played almost entirely on the basis of the global situation, and because the number of legal moves at each position is so large (approaching $19^2 = 361$) it is quite out of the question to perform a comprehensive tree-search in order to choose a move. The point of view taken in Kyu is that the best move, or at any rate a good move, will be 'obvious' if the board is interpreted appropriately.

This can be compared with the attempt in chess-playing programs to generate only 'plausible' moves. It seems, however, that the most successful chess programs still owe more to superior speed of tree-searching than to really intelligent generation of 'plausible moves', despite a couple of decades (at least) of awareness that good human players generally consider very few possible moves in any one board position.

Other programs to play Go for which information has been published are those by Zobrist (1970), Ryder (1971) and Reitman and Wilcox (1978). All these programs play complete games, though with only a very low level of skill. Our attention was drawn recently also to the INTERIM.2 program (Reitman and Wilcox, 1979), which (like Kyu) has a distinct strategic element, unlike earlier programs. For comparison, we rate Kyu's opening game at about 30 *Kyu*, weaker than INTERIM.2.

A program to play a game has to be organised to assess ('perceive', 'evaluate') board positions in some appropriate manner. This, in turn, means that board positions and possibilities for action must be appropriately *represented.* Indeed, issues of *representation* and *perception* can be seen as central to a large part of Artificial Intelligence endeavour. The prior Go programs cited (except INTERIM.2) while covering issues of perception and representation, nevertheless rely heavily on local tactical considerations in choosing their moves. In Kyu we chose to concentrate on methods of global perception and representation appropriate to the task, at the cost of not having a complete program.

The approach taken in Kyu, namely to concentrate on global perception issues and to avoid tree-search look-ahead in selecting a move is not always adequate. In the middle- and endgames, there are certain specific situations where a look-ahead analysis is needed. For example, in some cases, to determine the safety or otherwise of a threatened group, it may be necessary to 'count out' a move sequence to determine whether a capture takes place.

However, corresponding problems can arise in the endgame for chess, and the 'brute-force' chess programs are said to be weakest in this domain. This is because they do not have an adequate high-level concept of *strategy* to guide the look-ahead into answering the question of whether a particular sequence of moves can achieve a desired result.

Kyu does play according to high-level strategies, and it was anticipated that a look-ahead mechanism could be incorporated when needed. It would be used in a highly constrained goal-directed manner (very small branching factor) to answer specific questions that arise in consideration of a strategy. Unfortunately, time ran out on the research project. So far as we are aware, there are not yet any successful non-trivial implementations of game-playing programs where the look-ahead mechanism is properly controlled by the high-level strategic components, and invoked only where necessary to supplement 'immediate' perceptual assessment. Berliner (1977) describes progress in this direction in a chess-playing program.

GO PLAYING PROGRAMS

All programs to play Go use some concept of the 'influence' of a stone on neighbouring positions. This is a key concept in appreciating the game.

One of the 'proverbs' of Go can be read as 'Play away from influence, whether the opponent's or your own'. Playing in a region where the opponent has great influence is dangerous because he or she can easily threaten and perhaps even capture one's stones. Playing too close to one's own strong influence is playing inefficiently: a certain amount of territory can be secured, but less than the maximum possible.

Also, all Go-playing programs use a hierarchy of groupings of stones. However, the use made of such a hierarchy varies. The organisation of Kyu is described in the next section. A concept of a 'chain' or 'string' is essential to programming the game, since strings (connected sets of contiguous stones of the same colour) are the groupings which are subject to being captured and which enclose territory.

Zobrist's program (Zobrist (1970)) recognises a higher level of organisation into 'groups'. However, the play is determined primarily on the basis of 'template matching': testing for the presence of specific local configurations on the board, and subsequent selection of a 'nearly canned' response. There is a mechanism for look-ahead which apparently is rarely used.

Ryder's program (Ryder (1971)) uses several levels of groupings: strings, groups, walls, and armies. The play is determined by a static analysis of the board position, with no memory of any strategy in progress, followed by a choice of move according to various Go-specific criteria. Every legal move is considered and evaluated.

Reitman's first program INTERIM.1 (Reitman and Wilcox (1978)) achieves the best performance of the earlier programs, and unlike the others 'keeps track' of what happens at each move, but uses no look-ahead. Nevertheless, the program considers only *local* configurations in deciding what to do, primarily reacting to the opponent's last move as a possible threat in the local environment.

Kyu attempts to use what is successful in Reitman's approach, but to incorporate a strategic planning dimension and to use global information about the board position. Reitman's subsequent work (Reitman and Wilcox (1979)) has followed a parallel path. They attribute the improved performance of the INTERIM.2 program largely to the introduction of their 'PROBE' system, which conducts tactical analysis of the board positions, and also re-evaluates previously considered tactics when relevant board positions change, thus giving a 'strategic' continuity to play.

ORGANISATION OF KYU

Kyu is organised on two principal levels: low-level, perceptual or assessment functions; and high-level, analytical and planning functions. It is written in POP-10 (Davies, 1976) – an implementation of POP-2 (Burstall *et al.*, 1971) for the DECsystem-10.

The low-level perceptual functions are concerned with representing board positions and extracting useful information about the configurations of stones. Stones are perceptually organised into a hierarchy of constructs: *strings, groups,* and *armies.* A *string* is an isolated stone, or a set of four-connected stones of one colour. Strings are the units which actually enclose territory, or which may be captured by the opponent (if not in possession of two 'eyes').

Groups are strings of the same colour in reasonable proximity to each other. This is defined in terms of 'links' between stones – i.e. certain recognised juxtapositions. Since the object of the game is to capture board territory, and since a group dominates its immediate surroundings (even if not technically enclosing them) groups are a key level of perceptual organisation.

Armies are the top level of the hierarchy. They are intuitively sets of groups of the same colour which are too far apart to be one group, but between which no opponent's pieces occur. Two groups form an army if there are unoccupied positions between which come under the influence of both groups simultaneously.

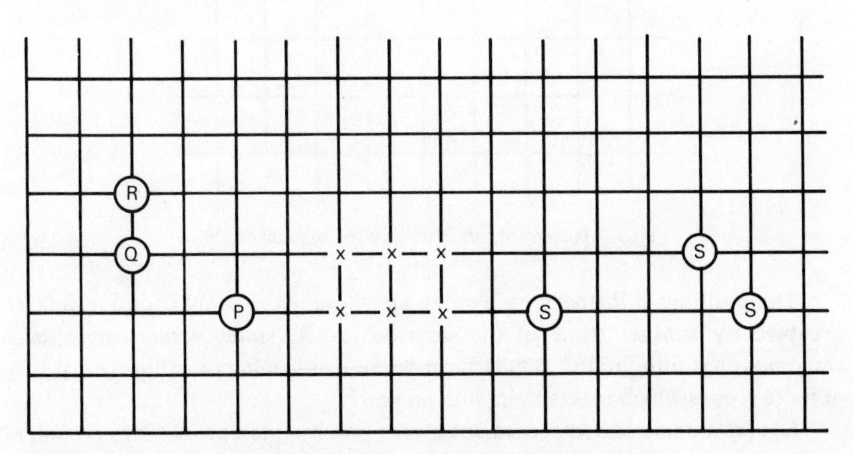

Fig. 2 – Organisation into strings, groups, and armies.

Figure 2 is an example of how the perceptual organisation works. String P is a string consisting of only a single stone, as is each S. Q, R is a two-stone string. There are two groups in the figure: P, Q, R is formed from two strings; the Ss form a three-string group.

All of these strings form one army, which indicates that the player has good control of this portion of the board and stands to gain much territory. He or she will want to play at some of the positions marked 'x' in order to consolidate the army into one group and take firmer hold of the territory. It is easy to see that if the opponent were to establish a group in that central area, then the army would be divided in two, and the territorial gain would be much less.

As mentioned earlier, Kyu considers that each stone exerts influence on the unoccupied board positions near it. The influence of a stone on neighbouring board points is shown in Fig. 3. Black stones spread a positive influence, white stones a negative influence. The total influence of stones on a particular position is just the sum of their individual influences.

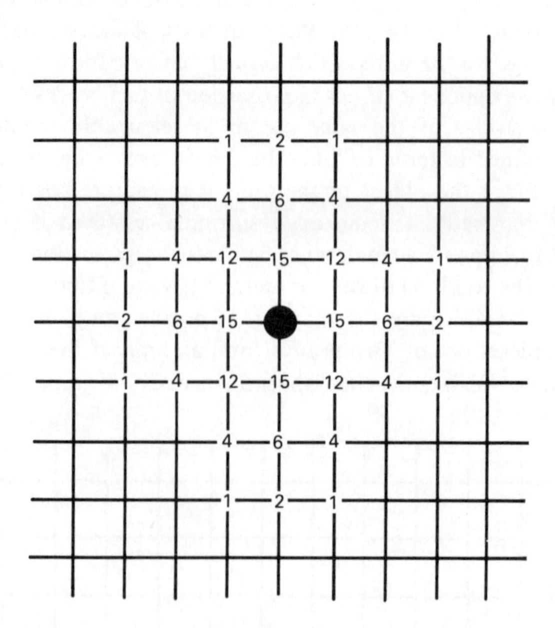

Fig. 3 – Pattern of influence exerted by a black stone.

The positions influenced by a stone are those which would form a 'link' if occupied by another stone of the same colour. As stated earlier, these links conjoin strings into groups. Similarly, it is the overlapping of influences of two or more groups which makes them into an army.

Kyu maintains linked record structures which represent all strings, groups, and armies identified on the board for each player. These structures are related back to, and accessible from, individual board positions. Four 19 X 19 arrays indicate for each position its occupancy, and the strings, groups and armies in which it appears or which have an influence over it.

As each player makes a move, these data-structures are incrementally modified to reflect the changing board positions. This incremental adjustment of the data structures permits fairly complex encoded descriptions of the board to be built at moderate cost, compared to the case when any board position is re-analysed *ab initio* at each move. However, this policy does make it more difficult to program a look-ahead, since changes to the structures made temporarily would have to be undone at the end of the look-ahead. (Alternatively, a complete temporary copy of the structures could be used for the look-ahead, but this also involves a significant overhead cost.) This is a trade-off which appears in any attempt to build a game-playing program, between ease of look-ahead on the one hand, and sophistication of board descriptions on the other.

The updating of descriptive structures at a move takes place in two stages. First the direct effect of the new stone on strings, groups and armies is determined. Then the neighbouring positions are scanned to determine changes in influence on them and changes in group or army membership for those influenced positions.

HOW KYU MAKES A MOVE

The low-level (perceptual) routines maintain a description of the board position in a bottom-up manner as described above. The state-space facing Kyu in choosing what move to make is enormous, so a goal-directed top-down organisation is used. The program is organised in terms of *strategies, goals,* and *tactics* (move generation) in that order. Figure 4 is a diagrammatic overview of the program organisation.

Strategies are modular units of high-level knowledge about how to play Go, and are applicable to every Go game. There are quite a few possible strategies; however, some are specific only to the opening game, others are specific to the middle game, and so on. Possibly, there are strategies specific to certain kinds of configurations. Kyu only possesses strategies for the *fuseki* (opening game).

Goals are instantiations of strategies on the specific game position. For instance, [SIDE_EXTEND_ARMIES] is a strategy that is widely applicable in the opening game; a typical *goal* derived from this would be [SIDE_EXTEND_ARMY 2] which identifies a particular army for consideration.

The *tactical* mechanisms are where the set of *goals* formed for the position are further analysed in order to select a move. The various goals can be regarded as plausible move generators, where each resulting plausible move is identified as to its overall purpose or goal. Kyu does not have an elaborate tactical component; it is in this component that we conceive a look-ahead might be performed to determine low-level consequences of a choice.

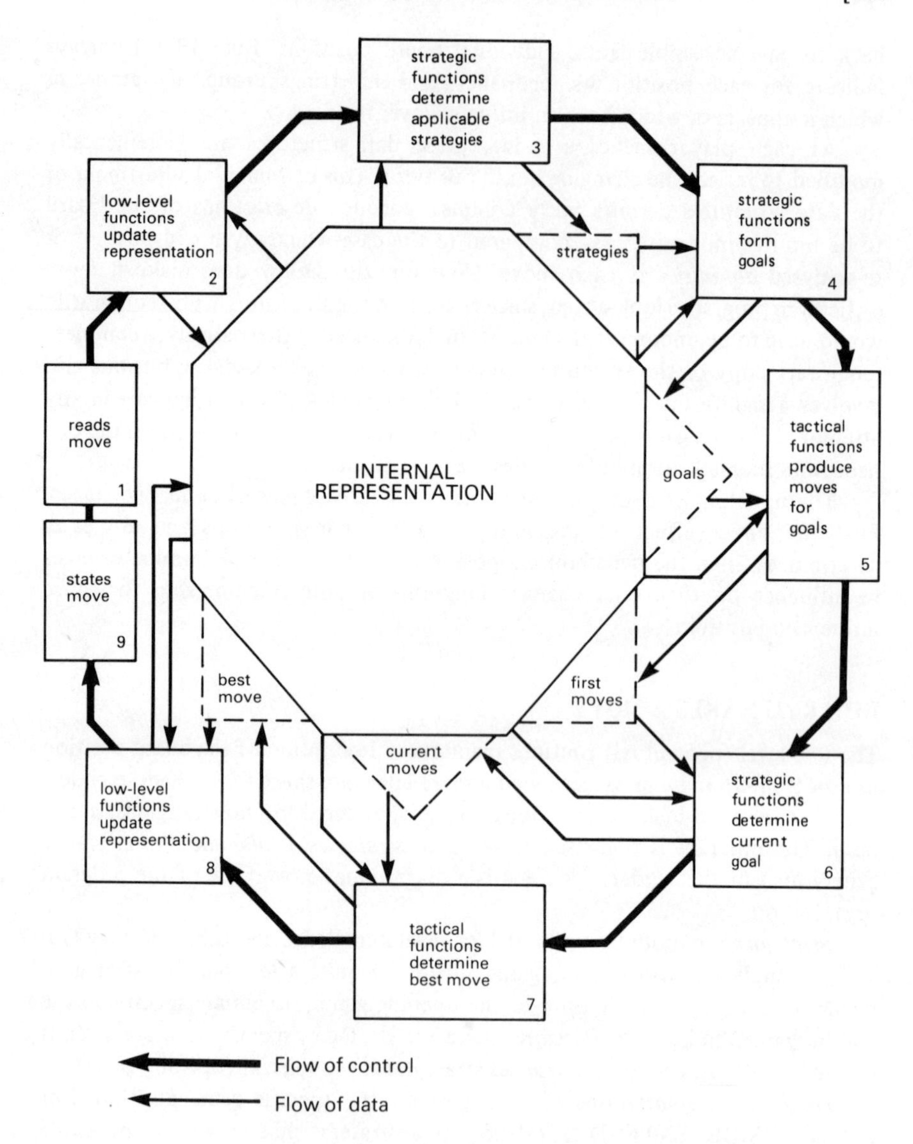

Fig. 4 – How Kyu makes a move.

Kyu's tactical component takes each *goal,* which refers in general to an individual army, group, or string, and computes the specific moves which would achieve or work towards that goal. Once this has been done for all goals, Kyu selects a goal to work on, and then chooses a move, with a preference for a move satisfying several different goals (multi-function moves). Moves fitting several offensive strategies are considered especially valuable.

Kyu revises its set of strategies after each move by the opponent, possibly adding or deleting a strategy from analysis of the updated board description. The strategies are classified (heuristically) into two levels of priority, and these priority levels also attach to the resulting goals. Kyu then selects one of its goals (a high priority one if there are any) as the 'current goal', and this selection is influenced by the notion of 'focus of attention'. Areas of the board that both players have played in recently are preferred for the next move. If several goals seem equally valuable, Kyu chooses one of them randomly. (A better system would be to analyse both at the tactical level, and then choose an optimum move.) Then the possible moves generated for that goal are examined, mainly to see if any is a multi-function move. If there is no obvious preference, a random choice is made again.

The random choices appear to be quite acceptable in the opening game for this program, since the options have already been preselected on the basis of fitting appropriate strategies. A more intelligent program would use limited look-ahead on the moves presented in order to discriminate between them. As the game moves into the middle phase, with more strategies being applicable, and with more goals being generated (because of the larger number of groups on the board) one would expect to find increasingly that individual plausible moves can fulfil multiple functions, and the incidence of equally plausible moves might thereby diminish. This remains speculation at present, since the program arbitrarily stops after 25 moves.

The strategies that the program possesses (for the opening game) are listed below.

Initial strategies

KAKARI	play near corner occupied by opponent
SHIMARI	play near corner occupied by oneself
SIDE_EXTEND_ARMIES	grow from one's own corner base
SIDE_LIMIT_ARMIES	play to limit opponent's growth

(The program does not know any 'canned' standard opening sequences.)

Consolidating strategies

STRENGTHEN_GROUPS	the highest priority, if needed
CONSOLIDATE_ARMIES	turn armies into stronger groups
WEAKEN_GROUPS	attack the opponent
SIDE_EXTEND_ARMIES	as before
SIDE_LIMIT_ARMIES	as before

For example, at a particular point in a game, the consolidating strategies listed above might be selected. They may or may not all be instantiated in the particular position, and could give rise to a set of goals such as

SIDE_EXTEND_ARMY 3
SIDE_LIMIT_ARMY 35
SIDE_LIMIT_ARMY 34
SIDE_LIMIT_ARMY 33
SIDE_EXTEND_ARMY 2
WEAKEN_GROUP 36
WEAKEN_GROUP 35
WEAKEN_GROUP 33

These goals are then analysed to produce lists of moves which would help satisfy them, one list for each goal. This involves only local analysis of the board. Kyu discards goals for which no relevant moves can be generated. The remaining goals are then ranked. A defensive goal with only one relevant move is considered more important than one with several options, for instance. The focus of attention is also used here. The program favours (other things being equal) play in the neighbourhood of either the opponent's or its own last move.

WHAT HAS BEEN ACHIEVED

Previous programs to play Go, until recently, have concentrated primarily on tactical aspects of the game, and have shown that this approach can lead to a program able to play a complete game (though only at the novice level). Strategy had been largely ignored. The previous work also explored the kinds of 'perceptual' organisation which are useful in playing Go.

Kyu has built on the earlier approaches to describing a board position in terms of strings and groups, and has attempted to integrate this with a top-down strategic (goal-directed) approach to move generation. Kyu has also attempted to bring into the program some sense of following a coherent strategy over a series of moves.

So far, the program has only been developed far enough to play the opening game (and further development has been discontinued, unfortunately). Our assessment is that the program plays an acceptable opening, albeit a conservative and unimaginative one. Kyu builds a reasonable position with which to enter the mid-game.

Kyu does guide its moves according to sets of strategies which remain constant through series of moves and counter-moves. However, the selection of which goal to pursue at a particular move is less than satisfactory. The ranking of goals in two priority levels, with use of focus of attention, does not necessarily lead to following of consistent goals from one move to the next. It appears to operate reasonably well in the opening game. But we anticipate that as the board fills up the interaction between strategic aims and tactical considerations needs to become more complex.

It is interesting to compare the approach described here with that reported in Reitman and Wilcox (1979). Both approaches combine a sense of 'strategy' with a 'tactical' component (though by different mechanisms), and a multi-level structured representation system for board positions. It does not appear that INTERIM.2 uses specific *descriptions* of the tactics and strategies it is following. It obtains coherent play (it seems) rather by maintaining within its focus of attention all groups which were important to recent previous tactics considered. The design method was to create a move-generating program first (INTERIM.1 – as described by Reitman and Wilcox (1978)) and then to add the 'strategy following' mechanisms afterwards in its move planner PROBE.

In contrast, Kyu was designed specifically to operate top-down, and the strategic component is intrinsic to its functioning. We believe that our organisation, if further developed, would ultimately permit more sensitive play, since the strategic and tactical routines alike can have access to encoded descriptions of what has been going on. The information is explicitly available within the program. However, actually building routines which can use such descriptions productively is a very different matter of course.

We offer this description of Kyu in the expectation that many 'expert' systems involving perceptions and responses can fruitfully be organised in a similar manner. The key elements are a multi-level structured data representation, with a hierarchically organised planning system in which explicit encodings of strategies and goals are used. We believe the organisation summarised in Fig. 4 can be adapted for many different problem domains. We hope that the principles of Kyu's organisation have been identified clearly enough here that others will be able to adapt them in different domains.

The distinction made here between strategies ('Goal generators') and Goals is perhaps reminiscent of the distinction made by Davis and Buchanan (1977) between rules and 'meta-rules', and is close to the concepts of 'goals' and 'goal generators' as presented by Sloman (1978).

POSSIBLE FUTURE DEVELOPMENTS

In the present program, the set of *strategies* is not determined very flexibly. The program sticks with a fixed set for a given period of time (and declares that it has no strategies after the 25th move!). Of course, not all of its strategies have instantiations (goals) in a particular case. The strategies are ranked at any time into two priority levels.

This system obviously invites the use of 'smoothly varying application coefficients', i.e. smoothly changing priority levels, as described by Berliner (1980) for his backgammon program. This would avoid sharp discontinuities in the program's play as the game progresses through the various stages of board development.

Continuity of *goals* (as well as of *strategies*), of course, can be obtained by keeping a list of goals pursued at previous moves, and giving some preference to (re)activating a current goal possibility if it appears in that list.

The interaction between strategies and tactics is harder to develop. We should want to introduce a way of taking into account the effect of a move on the global situation (e.g. 'capturing this group would relieve pressure on that group over there'). That interaction is not fully captured by a preference for 'multi-function' moves; the interaction as such is never *described* and therefore cannot contribute *strategically* in generating following moves. This insight suggests that when a generated move turns out to fulfil several functions, then a strategic analysis program might be triggered (a 'demon' perhaps) to attempt to describe the interaction involved. Presumably only certain patterns of interactions (yet to be enumerated) deserved such descriptions. It seems probable that this development would incur further elaboration of the existing bottom-up position analysis routines.

Another avenue for future development of the program lies in having it develop a model of the opponent's goals and strategies. When it is the opponent's move, Kyu could perform a move analysis from the opponent's point of view, constructing a strategy list, goals, etc., in the normal way. Then, seeing which move was actually made, Kyu could infer which strategies and goals the opponent might be pursuing.

Such an inference might be in error, or course, because the program would assume that the opponent has the same set of possible strategies (and weights) as itself. However, making such an inference would create a refined notion of *focus*, not as meaning a local geographical area on the board to attend to but rather as indicating a group or army that should receive attention.

REFERENCES

Berliner, H. J. (1977), A representation and some mechanisms for a problem-solving chess program, in *Advances in Computer Chess 1* (ed. M. R. B. Clarke), Edinburgh University Press, Edinburgh.

Berliner, H. J. (1980), Computer Backgammon, *Scientific American,* **242**(6), 64–72.

Burstall, R. M., Collins, J. S. and Popplestone, R. J. (1971), *Programming in POP-2,* Edinburgh University Press, Edinburgh.

Davies, D. J. M. (1976), POP-10 User's Manual, Technical Report No. 25, Dept. of Computer Science, University of Western Ontario, London, Canada.

Davis, R. and Buchanan, B. G. (1977), Meta-level knowledge: overview and applications, *Proc. 5th Internat. Joint Conf. Artificial Intelligence,* Cambridge, Mass. pp. 920–927.

Reitman, W. and Wilcox, B. (1978), Pattern recognition and pattern-directed inference in a program for playing Go, in *Pattern-directed Inference Systems,* (ed. F. Hayes-Roth), Academic Press, New York.

Reitman, W. and Wilcox, B. (1979), The structure and performance of the INTERIM.2 Go program, *Proc. 6th Internat. Joint Conf. on Artificial Intelligence,* Tokyo, pp. 711–719.

Ryder, J. L. (1971), Heuristic analysis of large trees as generated in the game of Go, Stanford University, Microfilm No. 72-11,654.

Sander, P. T. (1979), A Strategic Approach to the Game of Go, M.Sc. Thesis, University of Western Ontario, Department of Computer Science.

Sloman, A. (1978), *The Computer Revolution in Philosophy,* Harvester Press, Hassocks, Sussex.

Zobrist, A. L. (1970), Feature extraction and representation for pattern recognition and the game of Go. University of Wisconsin.

APPENDIX

Annotated *Fuseki* by Kyu

The following is an annotated *fuseki* played by Kyu. The program was black, and moved first.

1 (d16) Standard *hoshi* opening
2 (p17)
3 (q4) Standard corner *hoshi*
4 (e3)
5 (d5) Standard *kakari* against white corner stone
6 (r16)
7 (d7) Reinforces black stones in corner and begins to extend toward black stone in upper left corner
8 (c2)
9 (g4) Threatens to cut white group off from the centre and also reaches toward black stone at lower right
10 (j4)
11 (c10) There is more territory to be made by stretching this group out than by replying to white's last move
12 (d14)
13 (g17) When attacked on one side, slip away on the other!
14 (l16)
15 (q13) Play is too close to white strength, leaving side open for. . . .
16 (q6)
17 (r9) Some help to black's threatened stone at upper right; also threatens to go under white at lower right
18 (o3)

19 (r5) Begins to work out corner shape; also threatens to join other black stones alongside
20 (r6)
21 (h4) Opening strategies beginning to give out – this does nothing.
22 (h3)
23 (d15)
24 Quit

As Fig. 1 shows, Kyu has done quite a reasonable job in the twenty-odd moves of the opening. Its territories are beginning to take shape on the left side of the board. The combination of the upper left corner and the left side could lead to a large territory, especially as the way to the centre is open. The black groups along the right side could lead to a good gain for black and much harassment of white if played correctly (something out of Kyu's reach). White is in control in the upper right corner and along the lower edge.

The above moves took approximately 6 seconds each on a DECsystem-10 with an ancient KA10 processor.

11

Strategic planning in Go†

Paul E. Lehner
Par Technology Corporation,
P.O. Box 2005, Reston, VA 22090, USA

ABSTRACT

In Go, there are often a large number of move sequences that are consistent with a strategic plan, all of which will have the same basic positional effects on the board. By examining just one of these sequences, information can be derived about the other sequences consistent with a plan. This type of strategic look-ahead is called a representative search, and is frequently exhibited by Go players. A program for doing representative searches is described and evaluated. In addition, a general approach to representing both tactical and strategic plans is presented.

INTRODUCTION

Writing a Go program is, in many ways, an even greater challenge than programming chess. In chess, there are usually between twenty and thirty legal moves in a position; in Go, there are usually two to three hundred. In addition, even a relative beginner will sometimes exhibit simple look-ahead twenty moves deep. Procedures for pruning search trees are therefore even more valuable in Go than chess.

One approach to pruning a search tree is to look only at moves which (are hoped to) result in satisfying a pre-defined goal. The tactics analyser of the Reitman and Wilcox (1979) Go program, for example, operates by maintaining a goal stack for each colour. In each new position during a look-ahead, new subgoals are added or deleted from the stacks depending on whether satisfying them will help achieve the higher level goals already in the stacks. Only moves which help achieve the most recently added subgoal for the side on the move are then examined. Berliner (1974) and Wilkins (1979) have both applied a similar approach in chess.

†Support for this work under NSF Grant MCS77-0880 is gratefully acknowledged. I would also like to thank Walter Reitman for his many helpful comments and guidance.

These programs are designed to handle tactical look-ahead problems, that is, problems where even 'minor' deviations from a correct move sequence can lead to failure. This paper extends this work by demonstrating that this approach is also appropriate for higher level strategic planning in Go.

REPRESENTATIVE SEARCHING

In playing Go, it is often possible to formulate a plan simply on the basis of the perceptual characteristics of a position, that is, without any look-ahead. Perceptual analysis of this type is usually insufficient to evaluate a plan adequately. Often, a perceptually based proposed plan will generate unexpected side-effects. Consequently, in order to evaluate a strategic plan effectively, some type of look-ahead is necessary. Go players, however, often find it impossible to evaluate a strategic plan with the type of precise move-by-move look-ahead that is characteristic of a tactical analysis. This is because at each node in the search tree there are generally several reasonable moves which are consistent with the plan. In addition, in handicapped games, the difference in the playing strength of the two players is such that the weaker player is often unable to determine his opponent's precise responses.

Despite these problems, it is clear that some type of strategic look-ahead does take place. Consider, for example, the position in Fig. 1. In this position, which occurs frequently in handicapped games, most players would recognise that the one-stone group on K4 is loosely surrounded by the three white stones

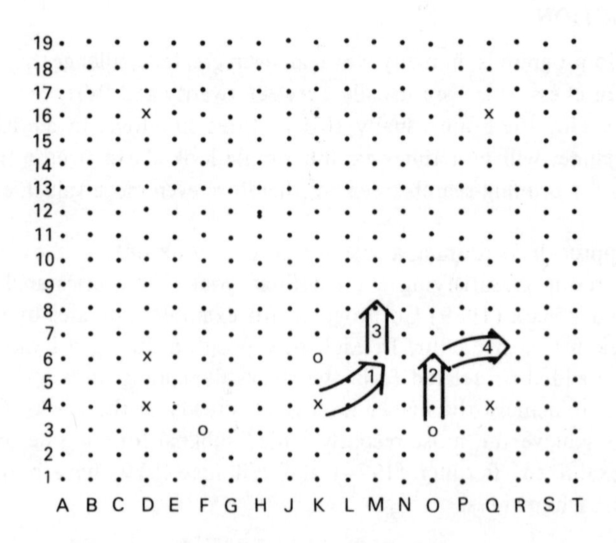

Fig. 1 – Illustration of strategic look-ahead

on F3, K6 and O3. Furthermore, since this group has no base (enough territory to make two eyes), it may be captured if white manages to enclose it with linkages. Consequently, unless a sacrifice is being considered, black should try to prevent his group from being enclosed. Black can do this by running out (i.e. playing a sequence of stones) between the white stones F3 and K6 or the white stones O3 and K6.

If Black runs out in the O3-K6 direction, e.g. by making the move M5, white can force black to make at least one more running move by extending from O3 toward the centre (say O5) and threatening to link across to K6. After forcing black to make one or more running moves, white can then switch directions by enclosing and attacking the handicap stone in the bottom right corner. For black, this attack on the handicap stone is a very undesirable result. Running in the F4-K6 direction leads to a similar result; however, in this case, the attack on the stones in the lower left is not nearly so devastating as the attack on the lower right handicap stone.

As can be seen from this example, some form of loose look-ahead can be done to determine the likely effects of running out in either the O3-K6 or the F4-K6 direction. What makes this type of look-ahead possible is that all sequences of moves which follow the pattern in Fig. 1 have the same basic positional side-effects. Or, equivalently, any sequences of moves which followed this basic pattern is representative, strategically, of all the possible sequences. Consequently, it is possible to determine some of the consequences of the proposed plan of running out in the O3-K6 direction by examining a few move sequences. This type of look-ahead will be referred to as a 'representative search'.

Apparently, representative searching is something that Go players do a great deal of. In the Go protocol in Kerwin and Reitman (1973), for instance, the player frequently talks about playing a move 'in the area of', 'around', or 'in the direction of' some specific board point.

CONTINGENCY PLAN GOAL TREES

One way to represent the sequence of moves and goals generated during a look-ahead is with a set of Contingency Plan Goal Trees (CPGT). For each move sequence, a CPGT can be created by (1) recording the goal stacks that lead to each move, (2) combining opposing goals from the two goal stacks into a single goal–countergoal pair, and (3) combining identical goal pairs into a single node in a hierarchical goal tree structure. To illustrate, the CPGT in Fig. 2 corresponds to the look-ahead in Fig. 1. The move sequence can be recovered by reading the bottom nodes from left to right. The goals that lead to each move are contained in each move's ancestors. For example, black's first move at M5 was played to prevent white from enclosing black's stone. This ESCAPE goal is a subgoal of the SAVE group goal which, in turn, is a subgoal of the global WIN goal.

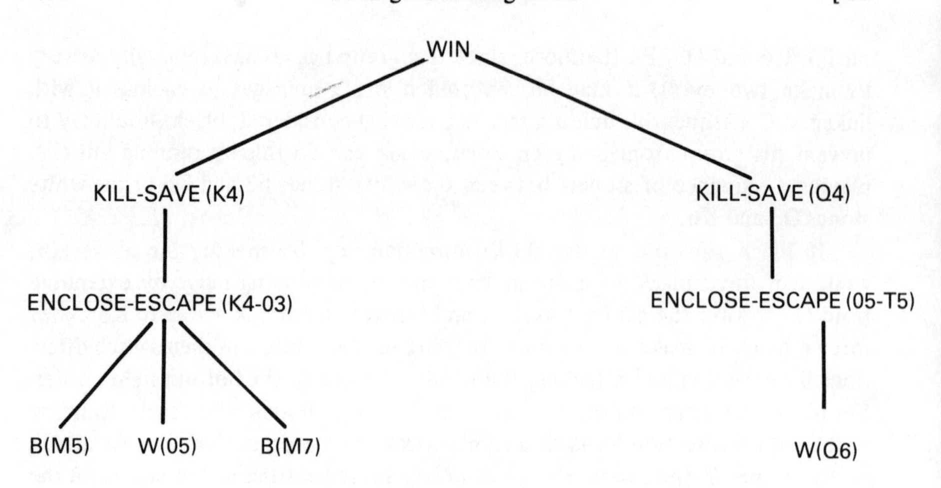

Fig. 2 – Contingency plan goal tree.

The CPGT representation is convenient for representing the goal and move sequence in both strategic and tactical look-aheads. In the case of a representative search, the upper-level goals are relatively insensitive to the lower-level goals and moves. That is, different move sequences will have identical upper level goals in their corresponding CPGTs. In a tactical look-ahead, on the other hand, it is necessary to pay careful attention to precisely which moves are played. A 'small' mistake can completely invalidate a plan.

A REPRESENTATIVE SEARCH PROGRAM

A representative search program for analysing running sequences, such as the one displayed in Fig. 1, was implemented. Although the program was designed so that it could eventually be incorporated into the Reitman and Wilcox program, this has not been done up to now. Since the program was designed primarily to test the feasibility of the representative search concept as a basis for strategic planning, the program does only a minimum amount of tactical analysis. Indeed, it avoids moves that may lead to tactical complications. A brief description of the program follows.

A representative search is initiated with a call to the routine ENCLOSE–ESCAPE, which is passed the following information: the group under attack, the endpoints of the farthest attacking sector line†, the side on the move and the attacker's groups which do not have a secure base. Routines for calculating these parameters are already resident in the Reitman and Wilcox program.

†Any two unlinked stones which are not 'permanently' separated by an opposing linkage or string form the endpoints of a sector line (Wilcox). Any sector line has the potential of being connected by a chain of linkages. The farthest attacking sector line is the sector line which a group must cross in order to escape enclosure.

If it is the defender's turn, the routine ESCAPE–FAIL? is called to see if the escaping group has already been enclosed by linkages. If it has been enclosed, then the search ends immediately, because the escape goal has failed. On the other hand, if there are no attacking sector lines, then the group is assumed to have escaped. In this case, information about potential follow-up (described below) is recorded. This is followed by a one move back-up to see if an alternative attacking move exists.

If ESCAPE–FAIL? does not return a stopping condition, the routine ESCAPE is called to generate an escape move. The move is always a one-point jump (i.e. an *ikken-tobi* or *kogeima* linkage extension) from the stone in the defender's group which is closest to the centre of the farthest attacking sector line. In most cases, this is either (1) an *ikken-tobi* jump which crosses all of the attacking sector lines or, if none is found, (2) an *ikken-tobi* or *kogeima* extension toward the centre of the farthest attacking sector line.

Note that the ESCAPE routine only generates one move. This reflects the strategic assumption that all of the possible escape moves have a number of effects which are common to all of them. It is these invariant effects which are being searched for.

If it is the attacker's turn, the first routine called, ENCLOSE, checks to see if the defending group is within the attacker's sector lines. If it is, then the routine ENCLOSE–LINE is called to see if there is a move which will link up the two endpoints of the farthest attacking sector line. If such a move exists, ENCLOSE returns that move. Otherwise, the routine ENCLOSE–THREAT is called twice to generate a pair of moves which (1) are one point extensions from each side of the sector line, and (2) permit black to enclose the defending group on the next move.

If the defender has already crossed the attacker's sector lines, then the only way for the attacker to continue is by creating new attacking sector lines. The routine CREATE–LINE does this by looking for *ikken-tobi* jumps from the endpoints of the previous attacking sector line which will create new attacking sector lines.

If no attacking move exists, the strategic consequence information is recorded. This is followed by a two-move back-up to determine if an alternative attack continuation exists.

In most cases, the ENCLOSE routine returns two moves, one extension from each side of the farthest attacking sector line. This reflects the assumption that all extensions from one endpoint are qualitatively similar, while extensions from opposite sides are qualitatively distinct (i.e. result in different strategic side-effects).

There are several restrictions on this move-generating system. First, the system avoids contact fight moves (i.e. a move directly adjacent to an enemy stone). Contact fight moves often lead to local tactical complications which the program cannot handle. In particular, if an ENCLOSE–THREAT move is a contact fight move, it is replaced by a CREATE–LINE extension. Furthermore, if the CREATE–LINE *ikken-tobi* extension is a contact fight, or if the *ikken-tobi* linkage can easily be cut, then it is replaced by either a *kogeima* or *kosumi* extension.

Another restriction occurs in situations in which after the defender has made an escape move, one of the attacker's weak groups is itself in danger of being enclosed. In this situation, in order to avoid a counterattack, the ENCLOSE routine will only return an extension from the side of the attacking group that is endangered with enclosure.

For an example of how the move-generating system operates, consider Fig. 3. The white group at O4 is surrounded by linkages and the sector line going from K4 to Q6. ENCLOSE–ESCAPE is called with black, the attacker, on the move. Since the white group has not crossed the attacking sector line, ENCLOSE calls ENCLOSE–THREAT, which generates two moves to be examined, O6 and L6. After the first candidate, O6, is placed on the board, it is white's turn. L6 will be tried later. The attacking sector line is now K4–O6, and ESCAPE returns the move M5, which is a one-point jump toward the centre of this sector line.

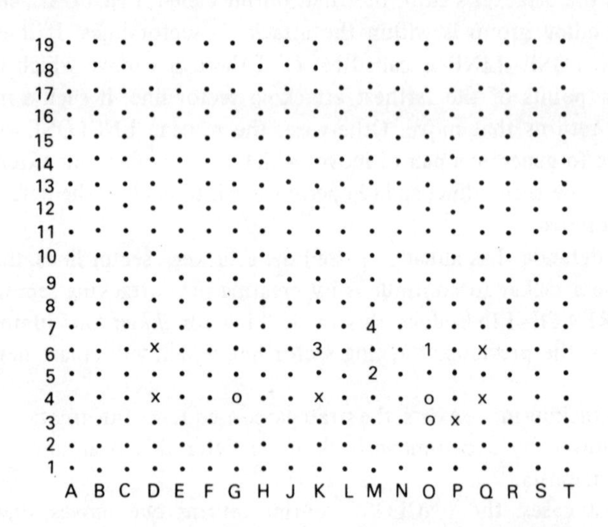

Fig. 3 – Sample search sequence from representative search program

After the white play at M5, attempting to enclose the K4-O6 sector line is no longer feasible. Consequently, ENCLOSE calls CREATE–LINE to create a new attacking sector line. CREATE–LINE returns two options, K6 and O8. However, since the K4 group is itself now under attack (note the sector line G4-M5), only the K6 option is tried. After the K6 move, white responds with an *ikken-tobi* jump to M7 which crosses the K6-O6 sector line. This ends this search branch.

For each branch in the search tree in which the defender escapes, a CPGT is generated. This is done by recording the goal stack associated with each move.

Each CPGT will have an ENCLOSE–ESCAPE goal as the first subgoal of the global WIN goal. Defending moves serve this subgoal directly. Therefore, on the defender's turn no subgoals are added to the goal stack. Attacking moves, on the other hand, will usually serve some function other than attempting to enclose the defending group. Information about these additional functions is maintained by adding subgoals to the attacker's goal stack. Table 1 lists the available subgoals.

Table 1
Attacker subgoals available

Subgoal	Explanation
PUSHLEFT (PUSHRIGHT)	Force defender to run out toward left side of sector line.
BUILDLEFTWALL (BUILDRIGHTWALL)	Create new attacking sector line by extending from left side of old sector line.
BUILDMOYOLEFT (BUILDMOYORIGHT)	Build a *moyo* by extending from left side of sector line.
NEWTER	Increase the size of or create a new territory.
ESCAPE	Prevent an attacking group from being enclosed.

Whenever a search branch terminates, the routine ENCFOLLOWUP is called to determine the strategic effects that have occurred. It does this by listing the strategic plans which have become more playable as a result of the search moves. In the present program, three classes of plans are noted (see Table 2).

Figure 4 contains the CPGT that corresponds to the move sequence in Fig. 3. Since the program generates a representative search, the move sequences examined are not likely to contain the most reasonable lines of play. Consequently, the move information is not very useful. However, the information contained in the CPGTs about strategic effects should be useful even if the moves played in the game differ. If, for example, a CPGT contains a BUILDMOYOLEFT subgoal, then any attack from the left side should result in a *moyo* being built. This type of invariance should also be true for the NEWTER subgoal and all of the follow-up in Table 2.

Table 2
Follow-up goals

Goal	Explanation
INVADE	Play inside enemy territory or *moyo*.
EXTEND/SQUEEZE	Side extension which forces opponent to run because he cannot make a base.
ENCLOSE	Enclose a group with linkages. Only used if group has no base.

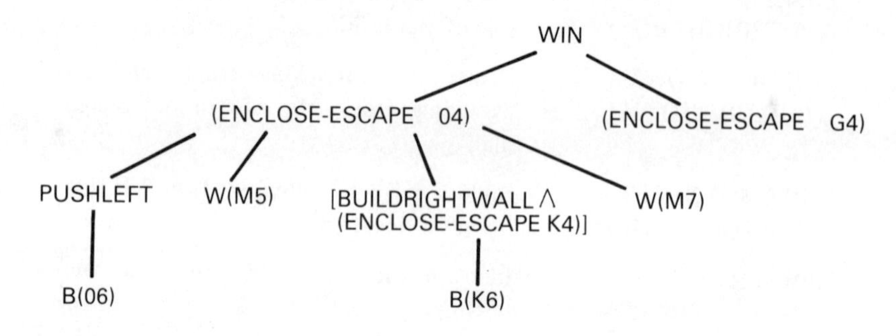

Fig. 4 – CPGT from representative search program

PROGRAM EVALUATION

In order to evaluate the program, it was tested on forty positions taken from professional games. By comparing the program's play with the relatively 'ideal sequences' that a professional either played or suggested in the game commentary, it is possible to determine the accuracy of the program's analysis. In particular, it was interesting to see if the strategic consequences predicted by the program actually occurred in the corresponding ideal sequence.

Comparison of the program's CPGT to the ideal sequence was achieved by examining the following features: territory formation, *moyo* formation, follow-up enclosure attacks and invasion or extend/squeeze attacks. Table 3 indicates the percentage of agreement between the program's analysis and the ideal sequence.

Table 3

Strategic side-effect	Percentage agreement with ideal sequence
Territory formed	95%
Moyo formed	92.5%
Enclosure attack	82.5%
Invasion or extend/squeeze attack	75%

For the most part, the professional evaluation (taken from the game commentaries) and the program's predictions of important strategic side-effects agreed. Most of the errors which did occur were attributable to the program's failure to detect significant side-effects accurately, and not to the representativeness of the move sequences played. A more detailed evaluation of this program is given in Lehner (1981).

DISCUSSION

Overall, the program test results support the initial proposition that it is possible to gain information about the side-effects of a strategic plan by examining only a small number of the move sequences that are consistent with that plan. However, the representative search program was often far better at identifying these strategic effects than it was at evaluating their significance. Frequently the significance of a strategic side-effect depended, to a large extent, on exactly which move sequence was played.

This result suggests that a representative look-ahead is not, by itself, sufficient to evaluate a strategic plan. Strategically bad plans can be rejected quickly, but once a plan passes this first test, a more precise search, taking into account tactical considerations, is needed. Ideally, a Go program would utilise the results of the representative search to guide this more precise look-ahead by trying to maximise the positive side-effects and minimise the negative ones.

REFERENCES

Berliner, H. (1974), Chess as problem solving: The development of a tactics analyser. Unpublished doctoral thesis, Carnegie-Mellon University.

Kerwin, J. and Reitman, W. (1973), Video Game #3: A Go protocol with comments. Unpublished paper, University of Michigan, Mental Health Research Institute.

Lehner, P. E. (1981), Planning in adversity: A computational model of strategic planning in the game of Go. Ph.D Dissertation, University of Michigan.

Reitman, W. and Wilcox, B. (1979), Modelling tactical analysis and problem solving in Go. *Proceedings of the Tenth Annual Pittsburgh Conference on Modelling and Simulation,* pp. 2133–2148.

Wilcox, B., Instant Go, *The American Go Journal,* 12(5), 7–28.

Wilkins, D. (1979), Using patterns and plans to solve problems and control search. Unpublished doctoral thesis, Stanford University.

12

Seeing is believing (or how to make *Sabaki*)

David J. H. Brown
Logica Ltd, Cobham Park, Cobham, Surrey, England

ABSTRACT

Deciding which move to make when playing Go (or any other game) is a matter of translating the board position and the sequence of plays that led to it into a set of belief structures concerning the state of the game, in both an objective and a subjective sense. The latter sense refers to inferences made about the opponent's own perception of the game and his probable plans.

INTRODUCTION

It has been claimed (Brown and Dowsey (1979)) that the game of Go is not susceptible to brute-force search. A more subtle (and perhaps intelligent) technique is required. Indeed, Berliner (1978) has suggested that perhaps Go will replace chess as the intellectual task *par excellence* for Artificial Intelligence.

The approach advocated here has much in common with efforts to develop knowledge structures suitable for mechanical chess playing in both the endgame (e.g. Bratko, Kopec and Michie (1978)) and the middle game (e.g. Wilkins (1979)). Such work may be described as aiming toward competence, in contrast with the performance objectives of programs which play 'across the board' games.

SEEING

Fundamental to the problem of decision-making is that of perception. A mechanism can only reason about a problem in terms that it can perceive.

Much of human perception is concerned with inference; that is, it is difficult to be 100% sure that what one sees is actually there. Many of our visual processes depend largely upon expectations of what we will see, which in turn depends upon our beliefs of what things are. Hence the oft-mentioned phenomenon of a visual illusion. So it is with machines (programs) that reason at higher, more abstract levels than that of the lowest level of information in their perceptual fields. Abstraction implies inference, and much of inference is inductive which in turn leads to the possibility of misinterpretation.

This phenomenon suggests that any formal problem solving system (e.g. a computer program) operating on a external task domain must be capable of non-monotonic reasoning; that is, the system must be able to keep track of the inference chain used in forming a hypothesis in order that should it be subsequently discovered that the hypothesis is erroneous, underlying hypotheses may themselves be scrutinised for their continuing validity.

BELIEVING

Conjecture: 'Before a system can perceive an object it must be capable of believing in it'.

By 'object' is meant anything in the real world (e.g. a Go game, the players, their actions and intentions) which can be designated (Newell (1980)).

By 'capable of believing in' is meant that a system has a designation prototype for each of the kinds of objects in which it can believe.

Thus 'belief' and 'knowledge' are here treated as synonymous.

Within the context of Go, such beliefs may be expressed in terms of some notation (McDermott (1978)). A difficulty arises in that the notation used may itself influence the semantic content of the system elements being depicted, and significantly the nature and extent of their manipulation. This latter point is not a conscious effect on the part of the designer, but rather an inherent limitation of his using any given representational formalism.

For example, RAG (Brown (1978)) is a reasoning system using a semantic network as the basic representation for describing both a game situation and inference rules operating on that situation. Now, it happens that semantic networks are not particularly convenient for representing procedural knowledge; thus many facts of a situation which could be dynamically computed (when a particular rule needing that information is triggered, for example) in fact have to be continually evaluated in order that the purely static matching of subgraphs can be performed.

Not only does this impose a considerable overhead on the system as it updates its belief structures when moves are made and/or hypotheses are formed but because such updates are themselves ad hoc, the designer is encouraged to 'short-cut' inference chains by programming tricks. Such tricks can play havoc with a less than perfect design and perhaps ought to be avoided.

Consequently, a new representation system is being considered for RAG. It retains the same expressive capability for the representation of declarative information and is enhanced by the attachment of procedural tests within inference rules.

Briefly, inference rules take the form:

(GOAL, CONDITION) → ACTION

Previously, CONDITION elements comprised a subgraph linking together the OBJECTs of the GOAL and ACTION. In its new form, the subgraph is replaced by a set of patterns to be matched such that a consistent set of variable instantiations is obtained. The efficiency of this matching process is sensitive to the order of presentation of the various patterns in the CONDITION. In Fig. 1, for example, (HORIZON horizon web) should not be used to instantiate 'web' because it would turn up too many unreasonable candidates because it does not contain the information that only webs of FRIEND-GROUPS are of interest. Additionally, assignations have been introduced; this enables the OBJECTs of ACTIONs to be created at rule-matching time (e.g. 'region' in Fig. 1).

```
(INVADE – FRAMEWORK
    (GOAL               (INTENT INVADE)
                        (OBJECT framework)
    (ACTION             (INTENT MAKE-SABAKI)
                        (OBJECT region)
    (CONDITION          (ELEMENT group FRIEND-GROUPS)
                        (STRENGTH group STRONG)
                        (WEB web group)
                        (BOUNDARY sector-line framework)
                        (CROSSES web sector-line)
                        (HORIZON horizon web)
                        (ASSIGN region (INTERSECTION
                        horizon framework))))))
```

Fig. 1 – *When to MAKE-SABAKI.* Lower case atoms denote variables to be matched with features of a given position. ASSIGN is a pseudo-predicate which causes a new object to be created.

This is illustrated in the following discussion; no formal definition of this representation has been developed as yet. One of the primary obstructions to using a 'standard' representation such as AMORD (de Kleer *et al.* (1978)) is the need to provide partial-matching capabilities. A discussion of this requirement is, however, outside the scope of this paper.

SABAKI

This is a very difficult concept to describe. To this author's knowledge, no program or theory has been developed which encapsulates its essential features.

Numerous teaching texts refer to it, but usually only by means of a profusion of examples.

Briefly, *sabaki* means development; it is thought of as a 'light and flexible' way of forming a position, usually within the confines of an enemy framework just before the door is closed. It is also used (*sabaki katachi*) to describe the shape of a group of stones resulting from such a development. Figure 2 gives a classical example (Nagahara (1972)).

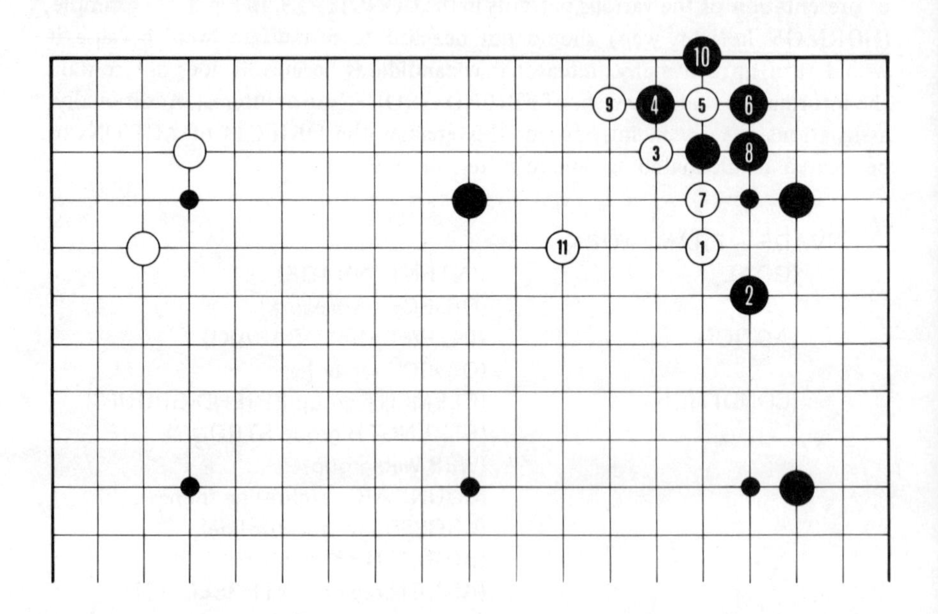

Fig. 2 – A *sabaki* sequence.

Superficially, *sabaki katachi* is characterised by a certain 'airiness' in the shape; stones are not tightly clustered together and many cutting points are left behind. In point of fact, *sabaki* sequences usually involve sacrificing stones to gain a position (as it requires more stones to capture a group than are being captured it is actually a very efficient technique in the group).

It is to be contrasted with *korigatachi* (frozen shape) in which stones are lumped together in an inefficient shape. A difficulty arises in distinguishing *korigatachi* – which is highly undesirable – from thickness, which is highly desirable (sic), but this will not be elaborated here.

Sabaki is however to be contrasted with wall building since the idea of a wall is something solid that the opponent can be squeezed against, whereas *sabaki katachi* is what the player seeks when he is in danger of being squeezed. It allows the opponent to pick off bits of the position – with little profit in doing so – without substantially remedying the fact that his framework has been intruded upon.

How to achieve *sabaki* is a problem which may be amenable to solution by a 'generate and test' method. In this case, it is sequences that are being generated and the test component relates to a static pattern analysis which is performed at the conclusion of a sequence. There are therefore three subproblems to consider:

(1) how to generate plausible moves,
(2) how to use these to form (heuristically) reasonable sequences of moves,
(3) how to evaluate the resulting shapes.

Before these are discussed, it should be emphasised that *sabaki* shapes are weak shapes; they are not useful for the purposes of establishing strength and influence, merely for dealing with it. Consequently, it is imperative that they be employed only within the terms of a reasoning system capable of deciding where and when such sequences are desirable. Within the context of RAG, this decision could be made by the rule depicted in Fig. 1 whose meaning might be expressed as:

> 'MAKE-SABAKI within the region defined by the INTERSECTION of an enemy framework to be INVADEd and the horizon of the web of a STRONG FRIEND-GROUP which CROSSES the sector line BOUNDARY of that framework'.

The concepts of webs and sector lines are due to Reitman and Wilcox (1978). Figure 3 illustrates their meanings in the present example. Returning to the discussion, the first subproblem can be tackled using 'generalised moves'. These are descriptions of moves in terms of points having certain relationships to (strings of) stones. In Fig. 2, for example, the initial generalised move is described by RAG as

((PART-OF SHIMARI S1) (PART-OF SHIMARI S2) (IKKEN-TOBI move S1) (KEIMA move S2))	For the purposes of exposition, only the essential features are shown. SHIMARI is a standard term for 2-stone corner enclosures; IKKEN-TOBI and KEIMA are relations between stones.

Many 'standard' tree sequences of such moves can be identified for various tactical purposes (Brown (1979)). However, for the development of *sabaki* it would be impractical to have a declarative representation of these. Consequently, it is necessary to search (pruned) trees of instantiated moves. The goal-seeking mechanism described by Reitman and Wilcox (1979) would be suitable in this

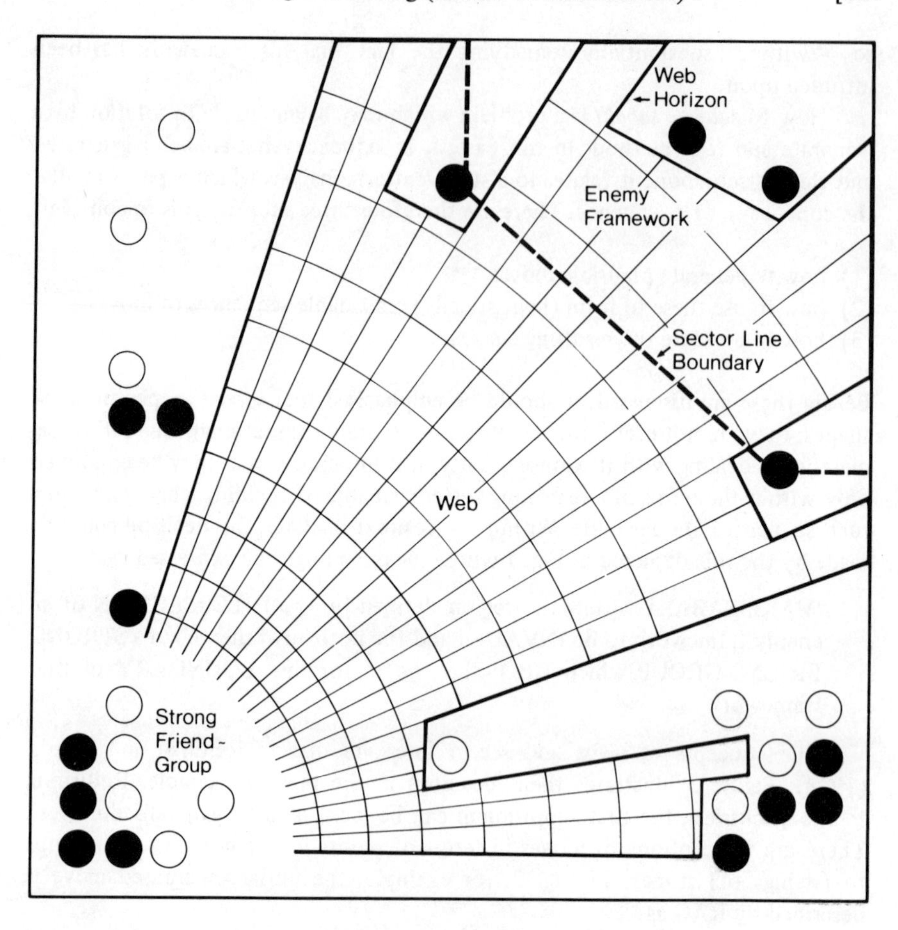

Fig. 3 – The interaction of webs and sector lines.

regard if one could identify moves as being typical of *sabaki* sequences and thereby be able to generate them. However, it is as yet unclear whether in fact there is a sufficiently small subset of generalised moves which could be identified as appropriate.

Fortunately, one can apply their notion of refuting moves which do not satisfy certain constraints as a means of performing a heuristic prune of the search tree; i.e. generate and test. Thus, the solution to the second subproblem is dependent upon the third, viz. identifying whether the resultant shape has the characteristic qualities of *sabaki katachi.* There is an implicit assumption of transitivity here; if a shape is *sabaki,* then so are each of the sub-spaces produced by a sequence which generates it.

It can be seen that the utility of the technique discussed here depends greatly on the effectiveness of the *sabaki katachi* recogniser, described next.

DANGOSITY

A *dango* is the ultimate in inefficient shapes; a useless inefficient clump of stones. The influence measure proposed by Zobrist (1970) is a means of obtaining a whole board view of stone placement efficiency. It corresponds in spirit with mobility measures for evaluating chess positions (e.g. Atkin and Witten (1973)). However, it is inappropriate for measuring local *dangos* and one must resort to less intuitively appealing measures, such as:

$$\text{dangosity} = \frac{\text{number of stones in a string}}{\text{number of potential liberties of that string}}$$

It is a well known theorem that the maximum area bounded by a given perimeter is that described by a circle. Consequently, it can be seen that greater clumping of stones leads to increased dangosity using the above definition.

SABAKI KATACHI

Applying the above principle to the strings constituting a group provides one component for measuring lightness. A second component is obtained by considering the area bounded by a group in relation to the number of stones it constitutes. For example, white 11 in Fig. 2 is described by Nagahara as 'the essence of what is called *Karui Sabaki* (light *sabaki*)'. Although black can capture white 3 and 9, whilst he is doing so white will gain a thicker and more stable position in the course of forcing black to complete his capture. Of course, this raises a very serious question of how to decide when to stop a *sabaki* sequence and go for thickness but that question will have to remain unanswered for the present. This leads us to a definition of group lightness (*karusa*):

$$\textit{karusa} = \frac{\text{area bounded by a group}}{\text{number of stones in that group}}$$

We can now define

$$\textit{sabaki katachi} \text{ of a group } G \text{ of strings } S = f\Big(\sum_{S \in G} \text{dangosity } (S), \textit{karusa}(G)\Big)$$

'*f*' is deliberately left open at this stage, awaiting the results of empirical investigation.

SUMMARY

The two themes of this paper are:

(1) the relationship between designational richness and perceptual facility is one of interdependence;

(2) when such richness is lacking, it is necessary to resort to search methods employing coarse evaulations; whilst these limit the explanation capabilities of a problem-solving system, they have nevertheless found considerable success in other domains, such as chess. It should be emphasised that the approach is feasible only within the context of local objectives in the case of Go.

REFERENCES

Atkin, R. H. and Witten, I. (1973), Mathematical relations in chess, in Bell, A. G. (ed.) *Computer Chess,* Atlas Computer Laboratory, pp. 37–80.

Berliner, H. J. (1978), A chronology of computer chess and its literature. *Artificial Intelligence,* **10**, 201–214.

Bratko, I., Kopec, D. and Michie, D. (1978), Pattern-based representation of chess end-game knowledge. *Computer Journal,* **21**(2), 149–153.

Brown, D J. H. (1978), Reasoning about games. *AISB Newsletter,* **32**, 14–17.

Brown, D. J. H. (1979), Hierarchical reasoning and the game of Go. *Proc. IJCAI-6,* 114–116.

Brown, D. J. H. and Dowsey, S. (1979), The challenge of Go. *New Scientist,* **81**, 303–305.

de Kleer, J. *et al.* (1978), AMORD–a deductive procedure system. *AIM-435.* Massachusetts Institute of Technology.

McDermott, D. V. (1978), Notational engineering. *Proc. AISB-GI Conference.*

Nagahara, Y. (1972), *Strategic Concepts of Go.* Ishii Press.

Newell, A. (1980), Physical symbol systems, CMU-CS-80-110, Carnegie-Mellon University.

Reitman, W. and Wilcox, B. (1978), Pattern recognition and pattern-directed inference in a program for playing Go, in Waterman, D. and Hayes-Roth, F. (eds.) *Pattern-directed Inference Systems,* Academic Press, pp. 503–523.

Reitman, W. and Wilcox, B. (1979), the structure and performance of the INTERIM.2 Go program. *Proc. IJCAI-6,* 711–719.

Wilkins, D. (1979), Using plans in chess. *Proc. IJCAI-6,* 960–967.

Zobrist, A. L. (1970), Feature extraction and representation for pattern recognition and the game of Go. Ph.D. thesis, University of Wisconsin.

PART IV – OTHER GAMES

INTRODUCTION

M. R. B. Clarke
Department of Computer Science and Statistics, Queen Mary College,
University of London, Mile End Road, London E1 4NS.

A glance at the literature of artificial intelligence shows that much of its methodology has been developed and tested on a wide variety of games and otherwise idealised and unworldly situations. The distinction between what is a game and what is not a game, even if necessary, is not as clear-cut as it seems at first sight. Where for example does one draw the line between a program that tells you how to invest on the stock exchange and one that tells you how to bet at poker? If we say that what distinguishes a game is that its rules and the environment in which they apply can be written down in a reasonably small space then good scientific method indicates that theories should be developed and tested in simple settings such as these where only their essential features are at issue.

Previous sections have dealt with theories of search and their application or irrelevance for two widely known but difficult games. Because of their highly developed culture, Chess and Go are often considered to merit the greatest attention, but deep though these games are they do not necessarily expose in their purest form all the problems that one might wish to study. Chess in particular is open to criticism for the comparative complication and inelegance of its rules and apparatus. Supporters of chess would say that in practice these are only minor programming inconveniences to be balanced against the deep principles needed for good play and lack of mystery that surrounds them. One advantage possessed by games with simpler rules than chess is that they can often be parameterised to provide a natural continuum of difficulty, although it must be said that the same effect can also be obtained by investigating progressively simpler endgames in chess or small localised problems in Go. Neither chess nor Go, being games of perfect information, can model situations containing uncertainty, a common feature of the real world, unless something like a model of suboptimal opposing play is included.

The first two papers in this section are concerned with Othello, a game whose setting has superficial similarities to Go but whose play is very different. Unlike Go, conventional tree-searching methods of the kind developed for chess seem to work rather well for Othello which has a considerably smaller average branching factor. Topologically the three games are quite distinct, but there seems no hard evidence yet that the search problems they pose are qualitatively different. On the contrary a plausible conjecture is that tree-searching is a powerful tool for any sufficiently simple two-person game of perfect information but one that with current technology reaches the limit of its usefulness at just below the branching factor of chess.

It is interesting to consider what view would be taken of search based programs if the whole world agreed that only one of these games was worth working on. If Othello was the choice it would be concluded that brute-force search was the key to strong play, whereas Go would indicate that it was virtually useless. This seems to show that there is not much more to be learnt from programming games like Othello that yield comparatively easily to brute-force methods. Some people would put chess in this category as well but never those who know enough about the game to realise how badly the current programs play.

Scrabble at first sight poses completely different problems. One is the purely technical but nevertheless very interesting task of devising an efficient organisation of the lexicon. Shapiro's paper shows one approach to this problem which is fundamental to Scrabble in the same way that an efficient move generator is to a chess-playing program. The existence of strong human players means that there is quite a lot of information about promising strategies, but it's not clear how to order or deal with interactions between them. Being combinatorially rather large Scrabble seems to lie in the experimentally fruitful region where brute-force is ineffective.

New Eleusis satisfies the criterion of simplicity for the study of induction. It is a modern card game in which an undisclosed rule for the generation of sequences is specified and the participants perform experiments to form and test hypotheses about the unknown law by playing cards to test the next member of the sequence. The induction of rules from examples is a well-studied and still far from solved problem of artificial intelligence that is receiving increasing attention in the literature. It is also a fundamental component of human knowledge acquisition. Anyone who has tried for example to incorporate human knowledge into a chess program knows that the rules and concepts in the books are almost never defined in precise and explicit terms but nearly always by presenting a small number of typical examples from which the reader is presumed to infer the general case without difficulty.

If New Eleusis provides a paradigm of theory formation in science, poker contains all the elements of decision-making in the real political and economic world, where uncertain information, bluffing and the estimation of expectations and probabilities all play a part. In its context poker is probably as difficult a game as chess and a strong program would be a major achievement.

Plan formation is another important problem more usually studied in a robotics context (e.g. Nilsson (1980)). The last paper of the collection tackles it in one of the most original settings one could envisage, three-cushion billiards.

One idea introduced in this paper, possibly for the first time in the planning literature, is the notion that a proposed play, though theoretically the best, may be too difficult to execute. Many of us find this to be a dominant feature of the zero-cushion version of the game.

REFERENCE

Nilsson, N. (1980), *Principles of Artificial Intelligence.* Tioga, Palo Alto, California.

13

Reversi: An experiment in game-playing programs

Stephen L. Stepoway
Department of Computer Science and Engineering, Southern Methodist University, Dallas, Texas 75275, USA

ABSTRACT

The game of Reversi, also known as Othello, is one of the simplest of board games to learn, yet it is almost impossible to master. This paper describes a program, written in Pascal, which plays the game against a human opponent. The basic algorithms used are standard for game-playing programs: a depth-first tree search utilising minimaxing and alpha-beta pruning. Instead of a fixed bound, however, the program uses a variable bound on the search depth which is adjusted for deeper or shallower searches depending on the time required to find the previous move. Because of the restrictions on the first few moves of both players, it is practicable to use table look-up techniques for the early game. Evaluation of board positions is based on well-known heuristics for the game, which involve both positional information about board configurations and net strength counts. The history and current status of the program are discussed, along with planned modifications.

INTRODUCTION

Among board games, one of the simplest to learn is Reversi (Gardner (1966)), a game very similar to Othello (Gardner (1977)). The game may be learned quickly, yet such dramatic changes occur during the course of play that it is extremely difficult to determine which player, if either, has the advantage at any point in the game. The simplicity of the rules coupled with the difficulty of mastering the game create a significant challenge to the author of a Reversi-playing computer program. This paper will describe a program which plays one side of the game against a human opponent.

First the game rules and some suggested tactics will be briefly described. Then the program, which uses fairly standard game-playing techniques, will be described. Finally, some of the shortcomings of the program and contemplated modifications will be considered.

THE GAME

The game of Reversi is played on an 8 by 8 board; the colours of the squares do not matter. There are 64 markers which have contrasting colours on their opposite sides, say red and black. Initially the board is empty. One player has 32 markers turned red side up; the other has 32 turned black side up. The players alternately place a single marker on the board according to the following rules:

(1) The first four markers must be placed in the central four squares.
(2) After the four central squares have been filled, the players continue to alternate in placing markers on the board in unoccupied squares. Each must be placed so that it is adjacent to an enemy marker, either orthogonally or diagonally. In addition, the marker must be placed in line with a friendly marker and separated from it by one or more enemy markers (and no empty spaces). All enemy markers so flanked are reversed so that they become friendly markers. Markers remain fixed during a game, but a marker may be reversed any number of times.
(3) If the placing of a marker simultaneously captures two or more chains of enemy markers, the markers in all captured chains are reversed.
(4) Pieces may be captured only by the placing of a marker. Enemy markers flanked at both ends as the result of other causes (such as the reversal of some marker) are not captured.
(5) If a player cannot make a legal move he loses his turn. He continues to lose his turn until a legal move becomes possible for him.
(6) The game ends when all 64 squares are filled, or when neither player can move (either because no legal move is possible or because all markers are gone). The winner is the player with the most markers on the board.

As an example of these rules see Fig. 1(a) and 1(b). In Fig. 1(a), if red plays on square (3,6) he reverses six markers: (3,5), (4,5), (5,4), (4,6), (5,6), and (6,6). As a result, (1(b)), the board becomes mostly red, whereas before play it was predominantly black.

Although the rules for Reversi are simple, the task of finding good moves is so large and complex that no well-defined procedure exists. Experience has shown that some tactics are more successful than others; some suggestions are presented here.

At the beginning of the game it is best for the first player to place his second marker above, below, or beside his first, rather than diagonally adjacent. By the same token it is wise for the second player not to play diagonally opposite his opponent's first move. By not placing his first marker diagonally opposite the first player's first move he gives the first player the opportunity to make the strategically inferior diagonal move.

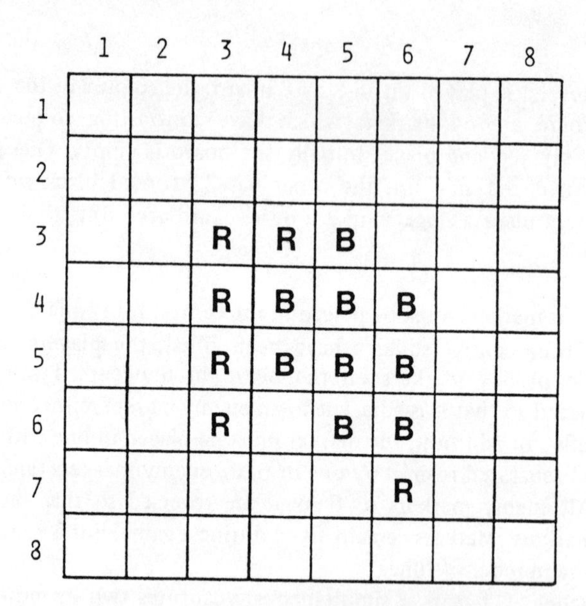

Fig. 1(a) – Before red move at (3,6).

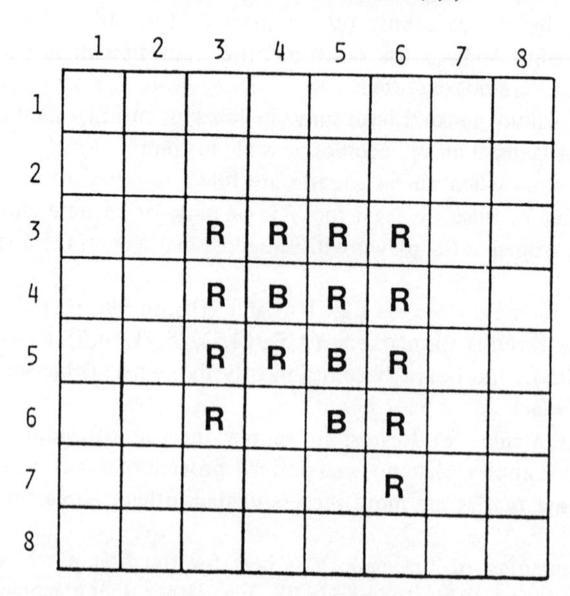

Fig. 1(b) – After red move at (3,6).

If possible, the early game should be confined to the central 16 squares. Special efforts should be made to occupy squares (3,3), (3,6), (6,3), and (6,6). The first player forced outside this area is usually placed at a disadvantage. Outside the central 16, the most important squares to occupy are the corners. For this reason it is important not to place markers in the squares adjacent to the corners, as this would give the opponent the opportunity to take them. Other squares which are important to occupy are those squares at a distance of two from the corners; they should be taken whenever possible. As a summary, in Fig. 2 those squares beneficial for a player to occupy are indicated by a '+', those that are disadvantageous by a '–'.

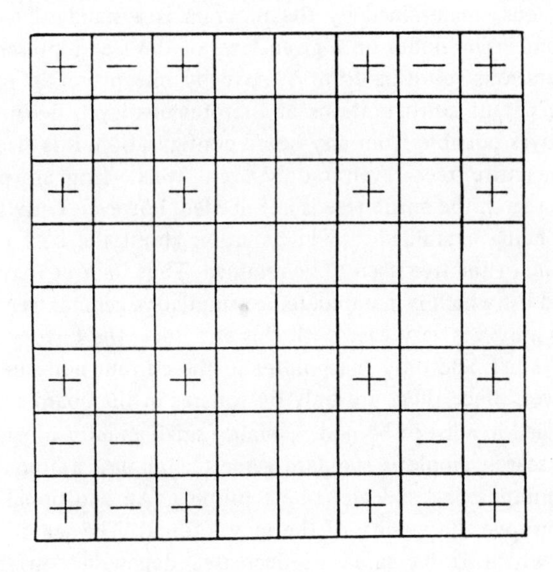

Fig. 2 – Squares given special examination in evaluation function.

THE PROGRAM

The program plays one side of a game of Reversi against a human opponent. The program selects its moves using standard game-playing techniques (Nilsson (1971)). It verifies that the moves entered by the human player are legal, and it accepts several special commands. Some of the more interesting features are described here.

The board is constructed as an 8 by 8 array and addressed using (row, column) pairs as in the earlier example. The human player inputs moves in the form:

X X

where each X is some integer number. The program first determines if the move typed is a legal one. If the move is not legal an error message is printed, and the player is given the opportunity to select another move. If the move is legal the program prints a list of all the board positions which have been reversed by that move.

The program recognises a move of 0 0 as a special command. The program outputs prompts to determine if the player wishes to have the current board configuration printed on the terminal, to revoke a pair of moves (the program's last and the player's previous), or to forfeit a move. If the request is to print the board or to retract a pair of moves the player is then given the opportunity to input a new move.

The data base maintained by the program is a standard tree model of a two-person game. The nodes on a given level of the tree represent the possible board configurations resulting from a move by one player in response to the corresponding parent configurations at the previous level. Because of the large number of moves possible from any board configuration, it is clearly impossible to generate the entire tree – even to only a few levels – from any point in a game. In such a tree search the entire tree is not needed, however. Only the path to the current node being examined and information about the best move found so far at each level of the tree need to be retained. Thus the tree may be implemented by a linked list which is manipulated to simulate a general tree.

Revoking moves is very easy with this structure; the history of the game is maintained in a list, and only the pointer to the current node must be changed to revoke moves. Since there are only 64 squares in the board a complete game may be contained in a list of 64 nodes, a fairly small amount of space.

The tree search employs standard game techniques: a bounded depth-first search using minimaxing and alpha-beta pruning. An additional mechanism is included to improve the quality of the moves found. The search uses a variable depth-bound which is increased or decreased depending on the amount of time required to find the previous move. If finding one move uses only a short amount of time, the next move the program is required to find (after the opponent's response) will use a deeper depth-bound. In a similar manner the depth-bound will be decreased if the previous move required too much computation. The trigger points (critical times) for this mechanism are constants within the program. This mechanism is useful for tree search problems in which the fan-out of the tree does not change drastically from one level to the next. For the middle game in Reversi the fan-out is uniform enough for this technique to work.

The generation of moves in a game-playing program is rarely conceptually complex, but it often requires a great deal of computation. Such is the case with the move generation routine used in this program. Moves are generated by scanning the board for empty squares and then determining if a move to that square would be a legal one. This requires, in the worst case, examining all 8 neighbouring squares for enemy markers and perhaps following a line of enemy markers in a given direction to determine if placing a marker in the empty square under consideration would fulfil the requirements of rule (2) above.

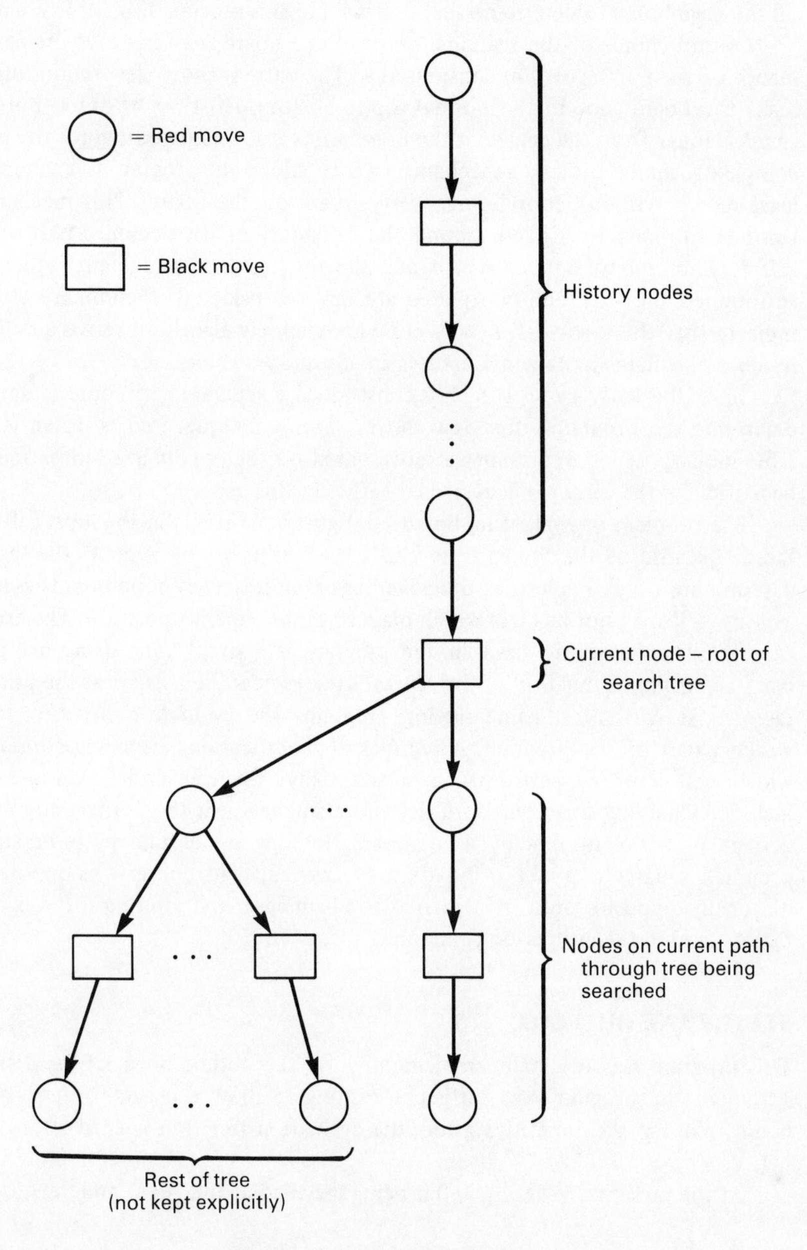

Fig. 3 – Program tree structure.

Although this algorithm is simple, it may be very slow because it requires the examination of many squares which cannot be legal moves. For example, if an empty square has 8 empty neighbours it is necessary, in general, to examine all the neighbours to determine that no legal move is possible using this square.

Careful choice of the scanning order of the board may improve the performance of such an algorithm substantially. The current move generation routine scans the board, not in the normal top-to-bottom, left-to-right order, but in a spiral manner from the centre of the board outward. Compensating for the more complex scanning order is a mechanism which allows the program to examine all legal moves without considering every square on the board. This mechanism restricts the scan to a band around the boundary of the occupied part of the board. Thus many squares which are already occupied and many which are surrounded only by empty squares are never considered. Preliminary studies indicate that this trade-off, a more complex scanning algorithm versus a reduced number of squares to be considered, is an advantageous one.

Since the early game is highly constrained a separate procedure is used to determine the program's first few moves. The technique used is essentially a table look-up which determines a move based on the opponent's moves and the heuristics for the early game described earlier in this paper.

The problem of evaluating board configurations is by far the most difficult faced. Because of the dramatic reversals that occur during a game, the task of determining which player has the advantage is not easy; even on boards as small as 4 by 4 it may not be clear which player has the superior position. The evaluation function currently used in the program is a simple one using net piece counts and the occupation of the critical squares near the corners as the primary factors. As with most game-playing programs the evaluation function is the weakest part of the program. A number of modifications are being considered which will improve performance substantially. Changes under consideration include examining for special priority more squares near the corners and at the corners of the central 4 by 4 sub-board, looking for certain patterns among occupied squares (e.g. the occupation of two adjacent corners, as opposed to diagonally opposite ones, is a particular advantage), and altering the weighting factors used in the evaluation function.

STATUS AND OUTLOOK

This program was originally implemented by the author on a DECsystem-10. Although the program was sufficiently stong to draw the game out to a full board, playing a competitive game, the evaluation function needed strengthening.

At the present a VAX-11/780 is being installed at this site†, and the program

†A reference to the author's previous affiliation, the University of Texas at Dallas. [Editor]

is being transported to the new machine. In addition to moving the program, some major modifications are being contemplated. As previously mentioned, the evaluation function is being revised in an attempt to improve the performance of the program in the middle part of the game, the area in which it is weakest. An investigation is also being made into improvements in the move-generation routine. An incremental approach which would maintain a list of legal moves, modifying the list as necessary after each move, is being considered. This technique may not be feasible for Reversi, however, because of the dramatic changes resulting from a single move.

Little effort was made to optimise any part of the program. It was designed and constructed in a highly modular form which greatly simplified its debugging. Now that the framwork of the program is functioning, attempts to optimise it are being considered.

An ambitious change is being considered for the user interface. A Genisco frame-buffer graphics system and associated data tablet will be available on the new machine. It would be desirable to use the frame buffer to display the current board configuration and let the player use the data tablet to indicate which square he wishes to occupy. A menu-driven system will allow the player to revoke moves or request that the program suggest a move. To do this, however, will require a considerable investment of time; therefore the graphics interface will not be implemented in the immediate future.

CONCLUSIONS

In this paper a PASCAL program has been described which plays Reversi against a human opponent. A number of well-known game-playing techniques are used in the program, which is based on a minimaxing tree search using alpha-beta pruning. To improve the quality of moves found a variable bound on the search depth is used, the mechanism attempting to use a uniform amount of time to find each move.

As experience with the program has accumulated, a number of weaknesses in it have become apparent. Modifications to the evaluation function and move generation routine are currently being designed which will not only improve its play but also increase the speed of the program.

Through careful design a flexible framework has been constructed which can easily be modified and expanded upon. Although game-playing programs are sometimes large group efforts, this system shows that small efforts can produce game-playing programs of considerable skill.

ACKNOWLEDGEMENTS

The author would like to thank Roy Earle for his many valuable comments on an earlier draft of this work.

REFERENCES

Gardner, M. (1966), *Martin Gardner's New Mathematical Diversions from Scientific American,* Simon and Schuster, New York, 75–81.

Gardner, M. (1977), *Scientific American,* April, p. 134.

Nilsson, N. J. (1971), *Problem Solving Methods in Artificial Intelligence,* McGraw-Hill, Chapter 5.

14

Brand – an Othello program

Anders Kierulf
Im Haegeler 1,5453, Remetschwil, Switzerland

ABSTRACT

Othello is a game which is well suited to programming. Because of its extremely simple rules, writing an Othello program is easy, but writing a program which plays well is quite another matter. There is no trivial winning strategy and to beginners the outcome of the game may seem quite random, because the disc-count may change dramatically during the last few moves. As many players are unaware of the fundamental strategies, some of the widely accepted strategies and how they can be used in a program are described.

Othello is then compared with chess, as there are differences in the game tree and in the importance of material.

After that the Brand Othello program is described. Because it uses the well-known brute-force strategy, some important details will be emphasised, in particular the evaluation functions which are the most important parts of the program.

The current performance of Brand is demonstrated with some game positions to show what the program recognises, and suggestions for further improvement are made.

RULES OF OTHELLO

The rules of Othello are similar to those of Reversi. Othello is played with an 8 × 8 board and 64 discs which are black on one side and white on the other. The starting position is shown in Fig. 1: four discs at the centre of the board. Black always starts; he must place a black disc (that is, black side up) where it encloses a white disc between the disc he is setting down and a black disc which was on the board before. The enclosed white disc is turned, so it becomes black.

An example: if black plays d3 (note that the notation used is not consistent with algebraic chess notation), he encloses the disc on d4 between d5 and d3, so the disc on d4 is flipped (Fig. 2). Then white has the options e3, c3 and c5, turning e4, d4 or d5, respectively.

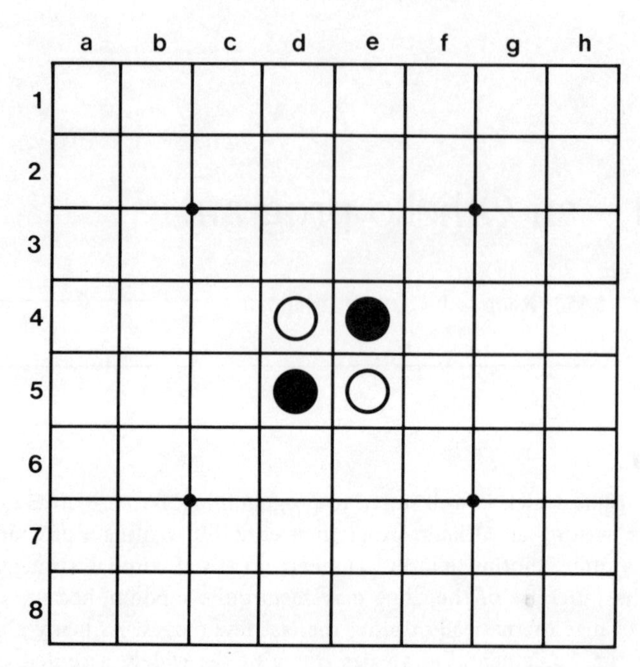

Fig. 1

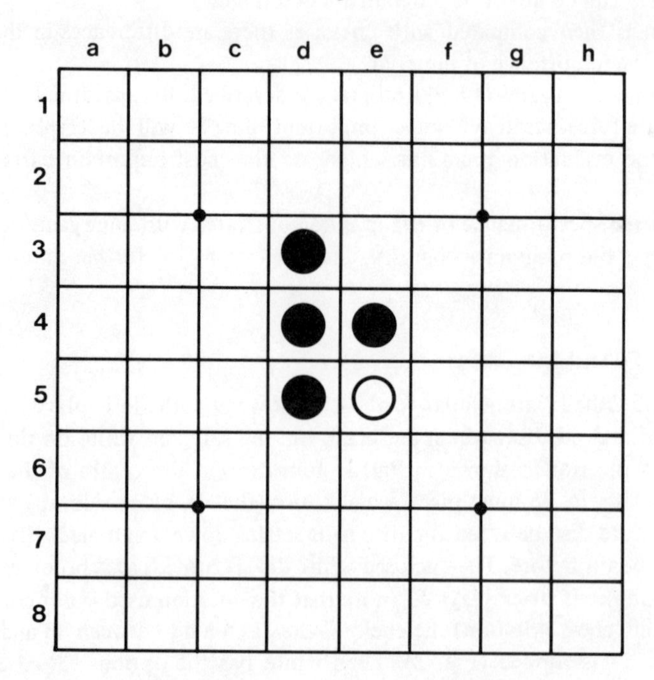

Fig. 2

More than one disc may be turned in one move. If several discs of the same colour aligned in a straight, unbroken line are enclosed, all these discs must be turned, and if several directions (diagonals are valid too) are possible, all discs in all directions must be turned.

Consider Fig. 3 (taken from a game between Jonathan Cerf (black) and Takuya Mimura, played at the 1980 world championship): it is black to play, and Cerf chose h6, flipping the disc at g5. Suppose he had gone to d1: he would have flipped the discs at d2, d3 and e2, f3. Or with b3, he would have flipped all the white discs from c3 to f3.

If a player has no move that encloses an enemy line, he has to pass; if both players have to pass, the game is over and the player with more discs wins (usually, that is when the board is full).

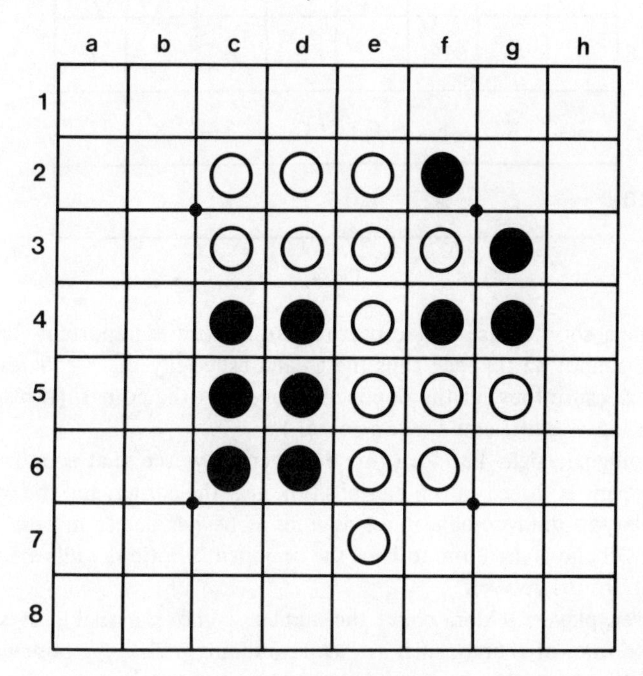

Fig. 3 – Black to play.

STRATEGY

For ease of explanation, a notation will be introduced which is commonly used in Othello, namely the concept of the square type (see Fig. 4). So all squares like b1, g1, a2, h2, etc. are referred to as the C-squares, b2, b7 etc. as the X-squares and so on. (A, B, C and X are standard symbols, the others are needed later on.)

Many players are unaware of the fundamental strategies. The one presented here is general enough to be useful in many situations; many other techniques are widely disputed.

	a	b	c	d	e	f	g	h
1	corner	C	A	B	B	A	C	corner
2	C	X	F	G	G	F	X	C
3	A	F	D	E	E	D	F	A
4	B	G	E	M	M	E	G	B
5	B	G	E	M	M	E	G	B
6	A	F	D	E	E	D	F	A
7	C	X	F	G	G	F	X	C
8	corner	C	A	B	B	A	C	corner

Fig. 4

Beginners soon realise that capturing the corners is important, because a corner disc cannot be flipped. Thus the C- and especially the X-squares may be dangerous, because they let the opponent move into the corner. (If black plays b2 or g7 in Fig. 3, white could take a corner.)

So a subgoal might be to capture a corner. However, that is only possible if the opponent is forced into a bad position near the corner, and the opponent will not play an unfavourable move as long as he has better moves. The key strategy in Othello is therefore to limit the opponent's options while maintaining enough options for yourself.

However, players seldom count the number of moves available. It is simpler to use some rules of thumb, such as: 'avoid building walls!'. Suppose white had to move in Fig. 3: moving to c7 would be suicide, because white builds a wall and eliminates all his options at the western side of the board at one blow. This example indicates why a high disc-count is not important until the very end of the game: if you try to maximise your disc-count during the midgame, you will get a lot of discs, but also a lot of walls and few options, so during the endgame your opponent will control the game and flip your discs again (remember that a single move may turn up to 18 discs!). In a computer program, the endgame is no problem: with a microcomputer, approximately the last 12 moves can be played perfectly under tournament conditions, and that's the only time disc-count is important.

Disc-count may be used sometimes if only the stable discs are counted. A stable disc is a disc which cannot be flipped any longer, no matter where the players move. A corner disc is always stable, and a whole edge is stable too.

For a computer, it is simpler to count the options than to look for walls. Other rules of thumb such as setting where the opponent has options, keeping your discs clustered rather than scattered and so on are difficult to implement, but they might add some favourable long-time effects to the program.

STATISTICS IN OTHELLO GAMES

To find some heuristics to use in the program, 80 tournament games were analysed. The results were not exact, but they showed some qualitative differences.

The significance of the number of options available was confirmed: the average branching factor is between 11 and 12 for moves 15 to 28, about 8 at move 42, and falls down to 1 at move 60. After move 25, the winner has an average of about 3 to 4 options more than the loser.

A uniform tree with height 60 and branching factor 7 would have about the same number of nodes as the complete Othello tree. This seems rather too much, because in the games analysed the players tried to maximise their mobility, and random games would have a smaller branching factor.

In these games, moves which turned discs in only one direction were preferred; the average number of directions actually taken was about 1.1 at move 10 and increased to 1.5 at move 50. If every option is considered (not only those selected), the average is about 0.1 directions higher.

COMPARISONS BETWEEN OTHELLO AND CHESS

A comparison is made here between Othello and chess because there is much more programming experience with chess than with Othello, and nearly all literature about game-playing programs concentrates on chess.

The branching factor is much higher in chess than in Othello: in the mid-game about 11 in Othello, and 38 in typical chess positions. I think a brute-force approach might work better in Othello than in chess, because it is possible to analyse deeper.

Squares in Othello can be treated about the same way as material in chess. If the squares occupied get points, that is analogous to giving points for queen, rook, etc.; it even faces much the same problems. As with material in chess, the values of the squares in Othello depend heavily on the situation: the corners are not always good, and X-squares may be extremely good moves. Consider Fig. 5 (taken from a game between Mark Weinberg and John Stoner): White has an excellent move at b7, because he can play a5 next time and get the a1 corner no matter what black does. So this approach faces the same problems as the material approach in chess does; a queen may be worth nothing at all if she is poorly placed.

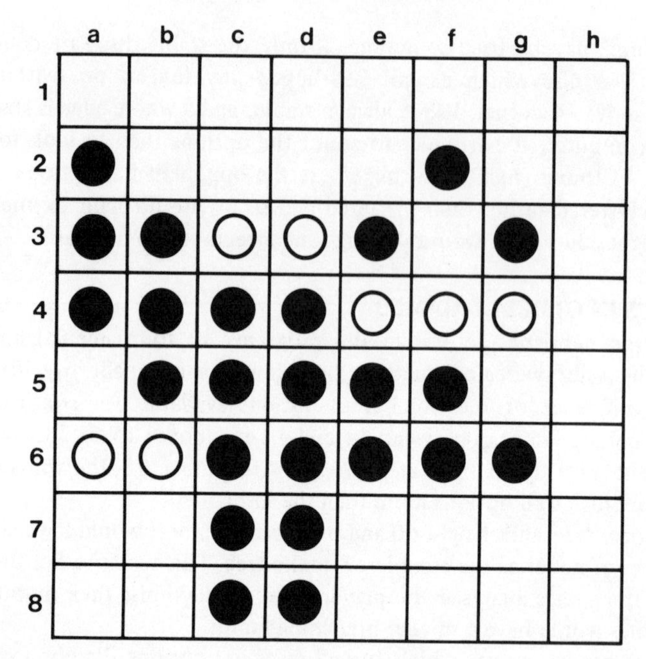

Fig. 5 – White to play.

THE BRAND OTHELLO PROGRAM

Brand 2.2 is a brute-force Othello program. The tree-search is as usual conducted depth-first, with alpha-beta cutoffs and 'killers' to speed it up.

The quiescence search is very rudimentary, but it improved the performance quite a lot. The value of a corner is subtracted if the opponent can capture a corner; this has the effect that moves which lead to an immediate corner-capture are refuted, and most corner-attacks are seen with one ply less – that means in about a third of the time. The approach is comparable with the 'checks and captures' technique used in many chess programs.

Time-control is achieved by a very simple rule: starting with a 2-ply search, the program searches each depth until the time used is greater than or equal to a quarter of the time currently available. That works fine, because searching one ply deeper uses three to four times more time. The only problem encountered is that Brand sometimes conducts a 10-ply search when there are 11 empty squares and does not increment the search depth one further; it should be given a little more time as soon as it can reach the end of the game.

All moves are generated before they are executed, but except at depth 1, they are not sorted; they are executed in the same order in which they are generated. However, there are two 'killers' at each depth which are tried first. Then the other squares are checked to see if they are legal: corners first, then A-, B-, D-, E-, G-, F-, C- and finally the X-squares. This method is quite efficient, because corners (if possible) are most likely to be good moves. This search order is taken from Frey (1980).

THE EVALUATION FUNCTION

The evaluation of a position is computed by adding the evaluations of the moves leading to that position. Each move is rated with respect to 4 components:

(1) the 'mobility' at the corresponding node (i.e. position);
(2) the value of the square occupied;
(3) the values of the discs flipped;
(4) the number of directions in which discs are flipped.

Each of the components will be described in some detail, because they are the central part of the program: they determine the 'playing style' of Brand 2.2. Experiments have been conducted with different values, and doubtless the values given below could be improved. So regard them as estimates and experiment yourself.

(1) Mobility

The mobility at any node is computed by giving 40 to 50 points for each option available to the player to move. X-square options are not counted unless the corresponding corner is occupied, and C-square moves are counted as 20 to 25 points if the corner is empty, normal otherwise.

Each option is rated higher if there are few options than if there are many; but if there is only one option (forced move), that is as bad as if there were no options at all.

To compute the mobility, all options at a node must be computed before any of them is executed, but that is not a great drawback: although some of the moves generated will never be executed (because of cutoffs), the increase in computing time is small. In Brand 2.1, the subroutine which looks if a move is legal or not is 500 bytes long (6502), and does not contain any overhead at all. If none of the adjacent squares contain an enemy disc, execution time is 92 microseconds, including call and return! So most of the time is spent in the routine which executes a move and evaluates it.

In Brand 2.1, the mobility was added to the evaluation at all depths; in version 2.2, mobility in a 6-ply search is only evaluated at depth 5 and 6. This change was made because the program was sometimes distracted by a temporary loss or gain of mobility, which would vanish with the next move.

(2) Square Occupied

Each type of square is rated differently, and the rating depends on the content of some squares nearby. Thus the X-squares score negative values if the corresponding corner is empty, positive values if it is occupied.

Because the values are computed after the move is executed and not before, the values depend on the new position.

The algorithms below refer to specific squares; in the program, the algorithms are location-independent. This is achieved by chaining all squares together, once clockwise (Fig. 6) and once anticlockwise (the mirror image of Fig. 6).

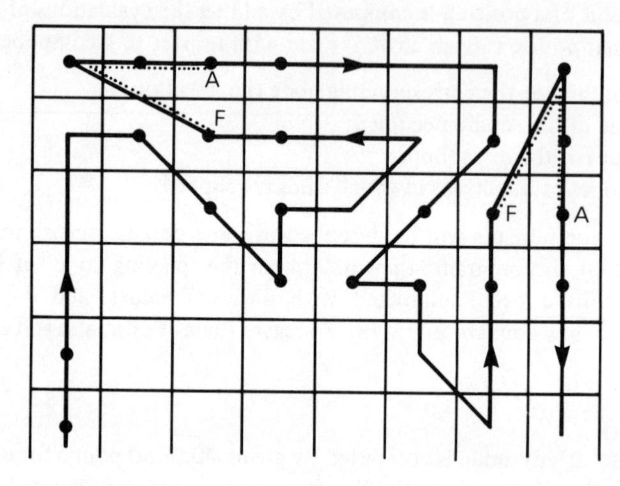

Fig. 6

A square is then referred to by first looking up the index for that square, then using that index plus an offset to look up the square in the chain. As an example, the F-square which is adjacent to a given A-square (see dotted lines in Fig. 6) can be located for all A-squares with the instructions i: = index [square given] ; square wanted: = chain [i-3] . In Fig. 6, the clockwise chain is responsible for all marked squares; the others are handled by the counter-clockwise chain.

The computation is quite complicated, so it will be presented in a modula-2-like language which should be easy to understand. Own and opp mean occupied by own or opponent's disc, respectively; emp means empty. The keyword 'RETURN' returns the value and exits from the procedure.

C-square (b1):

```
    IF a1 = own  THEN RETURN    175  END;
    IF a1 = opp  THEN RETURN      2  END;
    IF c1 = emp  THEN RETURN  - 150  END;
    IF c1 = opp  THEN RETURN  - 100  END;
    IF d1 = emp  THEN RETURN  - 150  END;
    IF d1 = opp  THEN RETURN  - 100  END;
    IF e1 = emp  THEN IF d2 = opp  THEN RETURN 10
                                   ELSE RETURN - 150
                      END
```

```
END;
IF e1 =  opp   THEN RETURN   - 100   END;
IF f1 =  emp   THEN RETURN      10   END;
IF f1 =  opp   THEN RETURN   - 100   END;
IF g1 =  emp   THEN IF f2 = own  THEN RETURN  - 225
                                 ELSE  RETURN     10
                 END
END;
IF g1 =  opp   THEN RETURN   - 100   END;
IF h1 =  opp   THEN RETURN   - 100   END;
RETURN 175.

A-square (c1):
    IF d1 <> emp
    THEN IF  c2 =  emp   THEN RETURN 35 END
    ELSE IF   e1 =  opp   THEN RETURN 25
         ELSIF (e1 = emp) AND (f1 = own) THEN
                                  RETURN 35 END
         END
    END;
    RETURN 12.

B-square (d1):
    IF e1 =  emp
    THEN IF  f1 =  opp   THEN RETURN 30
    ELSE IF   e1 =  c1     THEN RETURN 30
    END;
    RETURN 12.

X-square (b2):
    IF a1 =  own   THEN RETURN      100   END;
    IF a1 =  opp   THEN RETURN        2   END;
    IF (g1 = opp) OR (a7 = opp)  THEN RETURN  - 100
                                        END;
    RETURN  - 200.

F-square (c2):
    IF (c1 <> emp) AND (b1 <> emp) THEN RETURN 25 END;
    IF d2 =  opp   THEN RETURN          5   END;
    RETURN  - 5.

G-square (d2):
    If (c2 <>  emp) OR (e2 <> emp) THEN RETURN 30 END;
    RETURN 18.
```

```
D-square (c3):
    IF (d3 <> emp) AND (c4 <> emp) THEN RETURN 50 END;
    RETURN 20.

E-square (d3):
    IF (c3 <> emp) OR (d2 <> emp) THEN RETURN 40 END;
    RETURN 20.

Corner (a1):
    IF (b1 = emp) AND (c1 = own) AND (c2 = own)
    THEN IF g1 = own THEN RETURN 100
                     ELSE  RETURN 150
         END
    END;
    IF (a2 = emp) AND (a3 = own) AND (b3 = own)
    THEN IF a7 = own THEN RETURN 100
                     ELSE  RETURN 150
         END
    END;
    IF (b1 <> emp) OR (a2 <> emp) THEN RETURN 400 END;
    RETURN 255.
```

(3) Discs Flipped

Discs flipped get a value which does not depend on the situation. The only exceptions are the A-squares: they get a high value if both corner and C-square are occupied by own discs. The values given to the squares are as follows:

M: 20, C: 255, A: 2 OR 150, B: 5, X: 0, F: –10, G: 2, D: –5, E: 2.

(4) Number of Directions

If discs are turned in two directions, –5 is added to the evaluation; –15 for three directions, and –20 for more than three directions. This gives a small, position-dependent bias towards moves which turn discs in only one direction.

IMPLEMENTATIONS AND THEIR PERFORMANCE

Brand 2.1 is implemented on the Commodore CBM 3016/32 and on an extended KIM-1. The whole program is written in 6502 assembly language and requires about 3K bytes excluding input/output.

Brand 2.1 was placed seventh out of 20 contestants at the Santa Cruz Open Machine Othello Tournament. Each program was allowed 30 minutes per game in which to make all moves. That gave about 60 seconds per move, which allowed a search depth of 6 plies during the midgame.

The current version, Brand 2.2, is implemented on the Lilith personal computer built at the ETH Zurich. It is written in Modula-2 and consists of about 500 program lines (again excluding input/output). The speed is approximately the same as in 6502 machine language.

In games between versions 2.2 and 2.1, 2.2 won by 47-17, 34-30, 62-1 and 52-12, so it is clear that the new version plays better.

It is interesting to compare the moves selected by Brand with the moves selected by good players. Looking 5 plies ahead, about 35% of the moves would be the same, about 55% were among the two and 70% among the three best evaluations.

In the position of Fig. 3, Cerf as black did not want to play to d7 because that would allow white a cheap move at g6; both f1 and h6 appear to be good moves. And what does Brand mean? At all depths, d7 gets the highest evaluation, while f1 and h6 become better with increasing depth. The evaluations for depth 6/7 are: d7: 14/45, h6: 5/6, f1: 13/–28. The evaluations for h6 and f1 are acceptable, but for d7 they are wrong. It was thought that this might be because the mobility is not evaluated at depth 2 and the new option at g6 is not counted. However, when this was changed, d7 was still best at all depths, while h6 and f1 got worse. Instead b3, which allows White a cheap move at h3, is considered quite good. So Brand is convinced that d7 is a good move; but this is certainly not clear.

In Fig. 5, the good move at b7 is recognised with search depths of 6 plies and more. With 2-, 4- and 5-ply searches, b7 is quite bad. In the 3-ply search, b7 is second-best. At all depths smaller than 6, f3 is selected: a reasonable choice, but not the best. It would be interesting to know what other programs do with that position; b7 should probably be selected by looking 5 plies ahead, because of the uninterruptible sequence b7 - ? - a5 - ? - a1.

FUTURE IMPROVEMENTS

Here is a collection of ideas which might improve the program's playing strength, but which are not yet implemented.

The mobility should be computed quite differently. Consider Fig. 5: White has three options which turn the disc at e3: d2, e2 and f3 (and g1, but that one is too poor to consider). The program does not see that all three options vanish if any of them is executed. So in that part of the board, only one move should be counted.

Paul Rosenbloom, the winner of the Santa Cruz Tournament, used the concept of 'Surround' to measure the mobility; he counted discs adjacent to empty squares (see *Othello Quarterly* (Spring 1981)). It was probably this concept which led to his victory.

More knowledge about Othello should be incorporated in the evaluation function. A slight improvement in the move-evaluation (which can be considered as a 1-ply search) might result in gross changes in a 6-ply search.

It happens that Brand captures a corner early in the game and then fails to find the right continuation. It should increase its number of stable discs by playing near that corner; instead it tampers with the situation at another part of the board. So stable discs should be included in the evaluation function to get far-sighted moves.

While these improvements will undoubtedly lead to better play, it is unlikely that master level play in Othello can be reached by using the brute-force approach. Although the program may find the correct move in situations such as Fig. 5, it does not know how to develop such positions; a much deeper search would be necessary to do that. However, that is only possible if some kind of selective search is used.

Jonathan Cerf (the current world champion) recently stated that the top programs from Santa Cruz are about equal (if not superior) to the best human players. So it may be that the brute-force method is good enough if far-sighted evaluation functions are used. However, this argument will not be convincing until Cerf has really lost against such a program.

REFERENCES AND BIBLIOGRAPHY

Frey, Peter W. (1980), Simulating human decision-making on a personal computer, *BYTE,* July, 56–72.

Knuth, Donald E. and Moore, Ronald W. L. (1975), An analysis of alpha-beta pruning, *Artificial Intelligence,* **6**, 293–326.

Maggs, Peter B. (1979), Programming strategies in the game of Reversi, *BYTE,* November, 66–79.

Othello Quarterly, published by the United States Othello Association, P.O. Box 342, Falls Church, VA 22046, USA. [Probably the best non-Japanese publication about Othello.]

15

A competitive Scrabble program

Peter J. Turcan
Department of Computer Science, The University of Reading,
Whiteknights Park, Reading RG6 2AX England

ABSTRACT

Scrabble is the world's most popular word game. It contains skill, judgement, knowledge of words and an element of luck. National championships have been organised in a number of countries for some years and the game has risen to near the level of chess. This paper outlines a program which plays Scrabble on a microcomputer.

The design of the program can be divided into two main stages: the search for words and the strategies of play. My thesis concentrates on the former. This paper is the first in what I hope is a series, describing the implementation and testing of strategies involved. An overview of the current system and its performance to date is also given. No evidence has been found that a comparable program exists and considerable enthusiasm has been shown by the Scrabble world in its development.

PROGRAM DESIGN

The program consists of two main sections. One, the controller, handles the human player's moves, the drawing of the board on the VDU screen, the random selection of letters, scoring and all other facilities required to model the game. The second section, the program-player selects the computer's move from a given vocabulary.

Unlike other word games (e.g. 'Lexicon') an anagram search using the letters held in hand is of little use unless the words found can be connected to the structure of words on the board. Also many words can be played which use letters already placed on the board. In fact, the only time an anagram search is appropriate is when making the first word, when the board is empty! Much depends on the structure of words placed. The search system developed considered, in parallel, the information held by the board structure, the program's 'rack' of

7 letters and the known vocabulary. The search has the general capability that it will find every move possible given the following information:

(1) a vocabulary of words, of any size, in any language;
(2) a set of letters held in the program's rack (any number and any selection);
(3) any situation on the board, no matter how complicated;
(4) any board size, with any distribution of premium squares.

To make the program independent of the vocabulary size, a WINDOW and BLOCK-READ system was implemented. The window can be of any size that the machine can hold but is typically 256 or 512 words. The vocabulary is held in separate files, one for each word length. So if there are 2345 words in the seven-letter word file, then four blocks of size 512, followed by one of size 297 are read in. After each block is read in it is scanned to find possible plays which can be made. If one found is considered 'better' than the best one found so far, then this 'better' one is stored as the 'best-so-far'. The vocabulary is searched in decreasing order of size, under the assumption that a long word would be of more value than a short one. This was done in case it was necessary, owing to time restraints, to stop the search when a word of sufficient value was found. However, in practice, the program was sufficiently efficient to search the entire vocabulary (nearly 9,000 words of between 2 and 8 letters) in a reasonable length of time (around 2 minutes per move).

Only one word is stored outside of the window (other than those on the board): that one considered the 'best-so-far', which is stored along with its coordinates and score.

PLAYER-A

The program-player used as the basis for future testing and comparison has the following basic strategy (called Player-A):

(1) play the word with the highest score;
(2) if NO word can be found at all, then exchange all 7 letters with a fresh 7 from the pack of remaining letters.

Despite the apparent simplicity of this strategy, there are some underlying features of it which make its playing characteristics more complicated than might appear at first sight.

CHARACTERISTICS OF PLAYER-A

(1) Single letter extensions

The importance of words which can be extended by a single letter is a major concept of Scrabble. The most common letter used in an extension is 'S' but all allowable extensions are of use. Their value lies in the fact that it is only possible to make more than one word in a single move if words already on the board are extended by one of the letters from the word being placed. The score for these cross-generated words is added to the score of the placed word. It would seem that the more words that are made, the higher the total score for that move.

The importance of two-letter words in Scrabble (especially obscure ones) is their use when forming a longer word, which needs to make cross-words to fit the prevailing word structure. Figure 1 shows a striking example of this use.

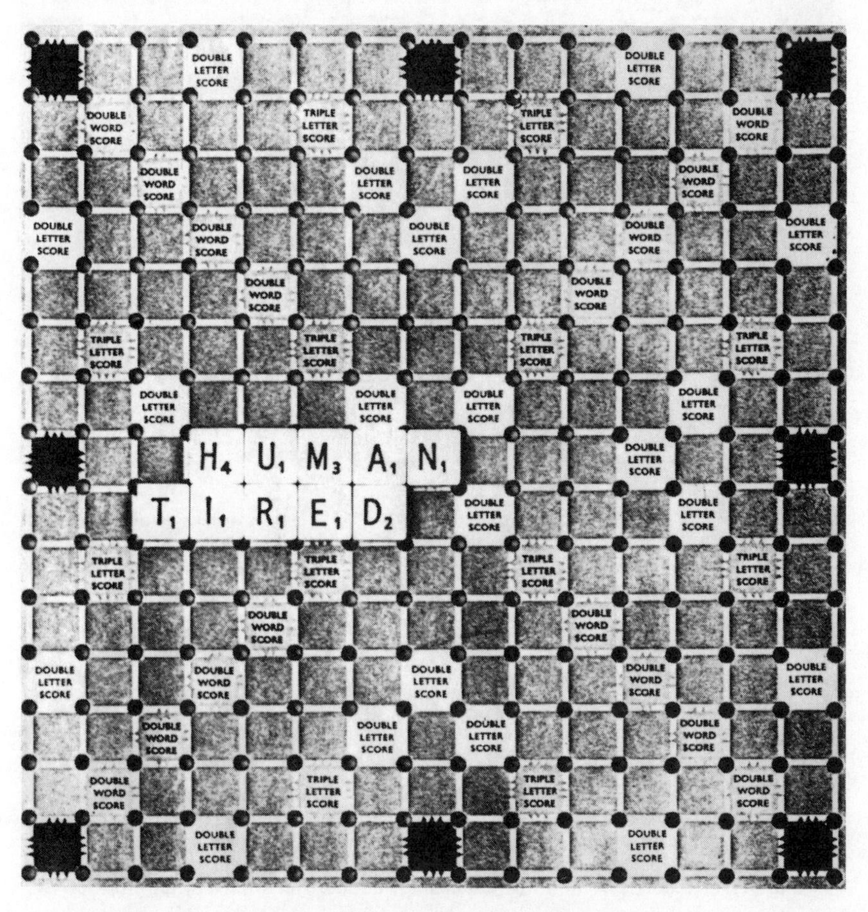

Fig. 1 – The first player placed HUMAN (for 28 points). The second player placed TIRED, to form four 2-letter words (HI – calling attention, UR – expression of hesitation, ME – the accusative of I, AD – colloquial for advertisment).

It follows from this that words can be formed on the board which were not themselves placed, but were entirely or partially cross-generated. As these words lead to high scores their occurrence in the vocabulary significantly affects the performance of the player and the structure on the board. Figure 2 shows an example of a very 'tight' game where many cross-words were formed, some up to 5 letters long. The maximum word length currently held is 8 letters although the program is perfectly capable of finding all words of greater word length, up to the maximum of 15 letters.

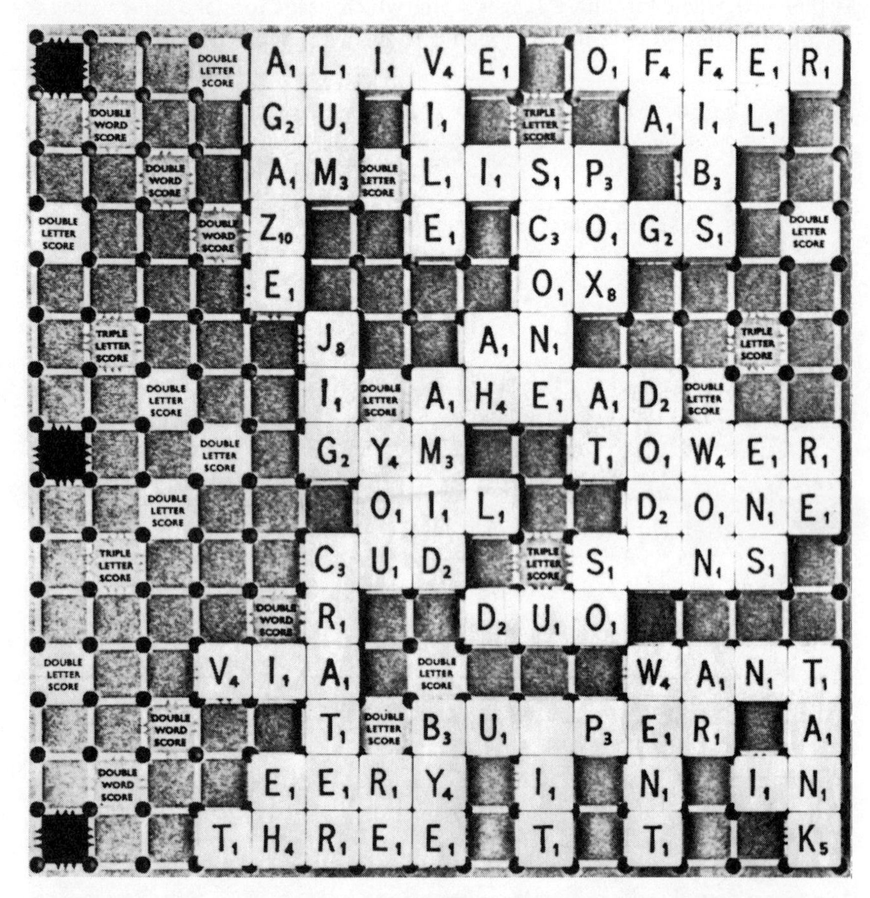

Fig. 2 – The words SCONE, AMID, DODO, WON, ENS and YOU were entirely cross-generated, along with many 2-letter words. This game was between 2 program players and shows one of the tightest board structures ever formed by the program.

Consider the word PRELATESS (a female high-ranking ecclesiastic). It could be entirely cross-generated, as the following are all words, being single letter extensions of the preceding one: AT, ATE, LATE, ELATE (puffed up with success), RELATE, PRELATE (a high-ranking ecclesiastic), PRELATES (plural of prelate), and so to PRELATESS! So far, however, the longest recorded entirely cross-generated words are of 5 letters.

Typical extensions made include QUA to QUAD to SQUAD to SQUADS, where the D, S and S respectively are contained in words placed at right angles to QUA. Figure 2 shows a number of these sequences.

(2) Bonus Scoring Words

Placing all 7 letters held results in a bonus of 50 points added to the score for that move. These plays are often game winners, but are difficult for a human to

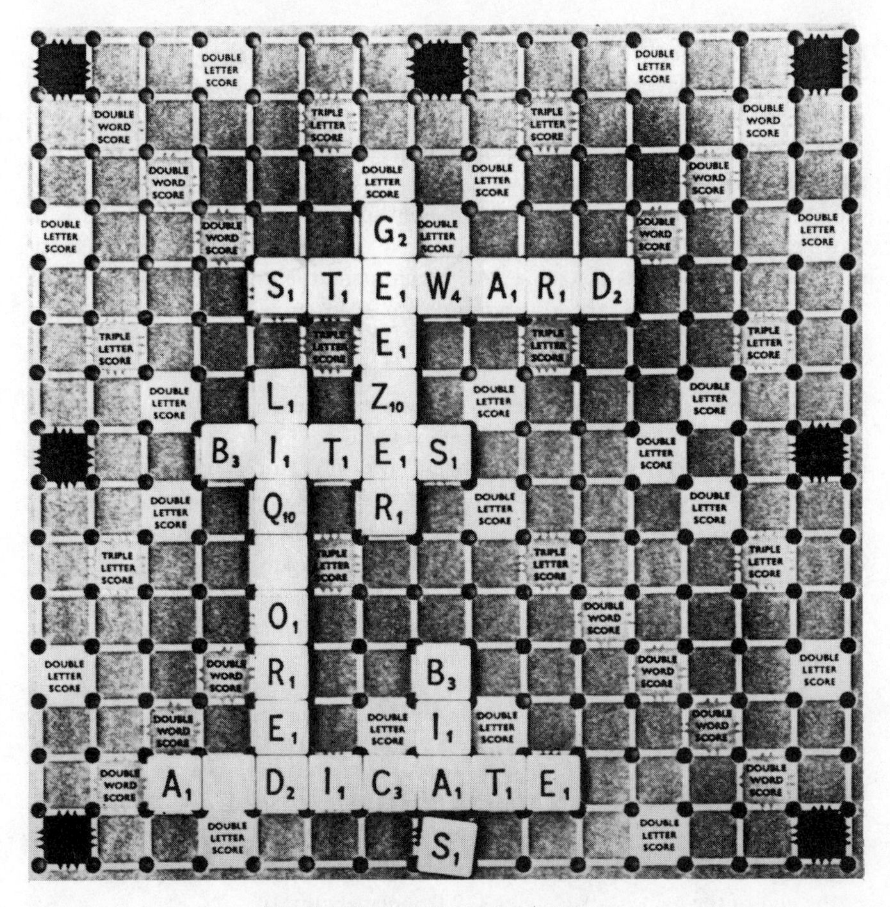

Fig. 3 – The play proceeded as follows:

Player 1:	BITES	20 points
Player 2:	GEEZER	27
Player 1:	LIQUORED	84
Player 2:	STEWARD	44
Player 1:	ABDICATE	64
Player 2:	BIAS	27

find. The program has no such difficulty, if one exists in its vocabulary, and plays one, on average, every 2 or 3 games. The record so far is two in the same game. The main restriction here is the limited number of 7/8-letter words known. To place all 7 letters, either a 7-letter word must be found and 'hooked' onto the board structure by means of a single letter extension to a placed word, or an 8-letter word can be played using one letter already present on the board. Figure 3 shows one of the more spectacular examples of the latter case. The record highest-scoring bonus word to date is AQUEOUS (the Q on a triple-letter square) for 91 points.

(3) Competitiveness

The ability of Player-A was judged both from observations made of games played against human opponents, and on the basis of a series of 20 games, when the program played both sides. In each case, the individual moves, scores and final results were recorded.

Against human opposition, the program played consistently well and won most games played against interested fellow students. It very rarely passed, averaged over 20 points per move, and often made the board too 'tight' for the human player to see high-scoring opportunities. However, it suffered from a few notable shortcomings.

(a) It opened up triple-word-squares for the opponent (but the program was quick to make use of them if its opponent did not).
(b) It occasionally wasted an 'S' or 'blank' for only 1 or 2 extra points, when they were better saved.
(c) It was occasionally left with the Q unplayable at the end of the game.
(d) It did not usually finish first, being left with a few unplaced letters.
(e) Although it rarely scored less than 10 points in a move, it always made the move, rather than the possibly more beneficial choice of exchanging all its letters, especially if it had a rack full of vowels.

PLAYER-A v. PLAYER-A

From a series of 20 games the following results were obtained:

average score for a player at the end of the game	= 322.0	lowest combined total (both players total)	= 565
average combined score (both players total) is thus	= 644.0	longest game (in moves)	= 36
average number of moves in a game for the starter	= 15.4	shortest game (in moves)	= 25

average number of moves for the second player	= 14.9	total number of times any player exchanged letters	= 0
average score for a single move	= 21.3	total number of bonus scoring words played (GASOLINE-65, OMITTED-67, NUMERAL-67, STOUTLY-72, ACQUIRES-74, EDGEWAYS-75)	= 6
highest score for a player at the end of the game	= 404	average number of triple-word-squares reached	= 5
highest combined score (both players total)	= 706	average score of words using triple-word-squares	= 26.0
highest individual move score	= 78		
lowest score for a player at the end of a game	= 265		

(vocabulary size: 8750 words of from 2 to 8 letters in length.)

NOTES ON STATISTICAL ANALYSIS

As with all measurements and assessments made in experiments involving an element of luck, a sufficiently large sample should be taken to ensure a reasonable degree of confidence in the results. However, there is a vast amount of collectable data from the game Scrabble, each requiring a different size of sample to be confident of the results. For example, to give an average move score, 20 games (approximately 600 moves) should give an accurate assessment, whereas to find the significance of the letter 'X' may require a sample of 100+ games, or to find the significance of an individual word in the vocabulary may take thousands of games.

The policy adopted was to take a sample large enough to be confident of the average scores achieved, but to be content with merely tentative observations of the significance of strategies, words in the vocabulary, letters held, and other interesting but complicated factors which would require a huge sample of games to assess reliably. This policy is justifiable as the combination of score analysis and observation can be the basis of the tuning and refinement of the playing strategies.

IMPLEMENTING STRATEGIES – THE SCRABBLE EQUATION

To implement any strategy within the program requires both a clear definition of the strategy and a method for taking it into account, possibly with relation to other strategies also relevant to a particular play. For example, a word may waste an 'S' but avoid using a 'U' when the 'Q' is held. Some method of combining the effect of strategies is required; this combined with any given word's score should give a good indication of its usefulness.

To give values to any strategy, numerical figures must be calculable, as direct comparisons must be made. The usefulness of each word found can be assessed by an equation of the form:

VALUE(⟨word⟩) = SCORE + S1 + S2 + S3. . . + SN

where Si is the numerical value (positive, negative or zero) for the word's usefulness with respect to strategy Si. The VALUE is called the 'PLAY-VALUE' (PV) of the word. Thus the 'best' word can be chosen as the one with the highest PLAY-VALUE found.

THE DEVELOPMENT OF PLAYER-B

The deficiencies of Player-A can be roughly divided into three areas: letter control, positioning and the endgame. The following summarises an initial investigation into the theory behind each, and their inclusion in the Scrabble Equation.

(1) Letter Control

To save an 'S' or a 'blank' for later use, when it only accounts for 1 or 2 points in the current move, a negative value is given for each one used. For example, 3 points could be deducted from the PV for each 'S' played in a particular word.

PV(⟨word⟩) = SCORE − 3 (number of S's used)

This has the effect of saving the S if another word scoring a few points less but not using it has been found.

For example PV(STUMP) = SCORE(say, 20)−3(1) = 17
PV(PLUM) = SCORE(say, 18)−3(0) = 18

So PLUM, scoring 18, is played in preference to STUMP scoring 20.

The worst sin of Player-A was when holding a Q and a U, to play the U, but not include the Q as a higher scoring word could be made without it. A 'Q' is worth −20 points at the end of the game if it is not played, so it is worth getting rid of. A heavy penalty is therefore imposed if a U is played off in this situation, and a small bonus gained if the Q is played. For example, if the rack held: Q U L A I N T and, say, UNLIT scores 25 and QUAINT scores 15, then

PV(UNLIT) = 25 − 12(use of U) = 13
PV(QUAINT) = 15 + 3(use of Q) = 18

So QUAINT would be played unless another word found scored more than 18 points and used neither the U nor the Q.

(2) Positioning

This is the most complicated of the problems, concerning only the triple-word-score (TWS) squares in this initial study.

There are three different ways of opening up a TWS, defined as follows.

(a) Direct. A word opens up a TWS directly if by use of one of its letters a TWS can be reached (e.g. placing a word in column 3, starting in row 1).

(b) Indirect. A TWS is opened indirectly if a second 'hook' word is required to reach it (e.g. a word placed in column 3, row 2).

(c) Extension. If a word can be extended, by say ING, on to a TWS , then the TWS has been opened.

There is a considerable problem in working out whether a word does or does not open up a TWS. It depends on a number of factors, including the 'opening' letter or letters, whether the opening is direct, indirect or by extension, and the structure of words around it. For example, a word is harmless, even if it enters say column 1, if there are words already there blocking access to any TWS. In practice, most of the TWS squares were obtained directly so only this case is considered here.

To indicate whether a square can be used to reach a TWS, there are two flags (UP and DOWN, or LEFT and RIGHT) indicating which, if any, TWS squares can be reached directly from it. The flags are set on initialisation and reset on the following conditions:

– a letter is placed on the appropriate TWS square;
– a letter is placed adjacent to this square;
– a word is placed between this square and the TWS blocking the path to it.

At any one time a square may have 0, 1 or 2 set flags. It follows that a value can be deducted from a word's PV, for each set flag it covers. A value could also be added if a TWS is reached, thus preventing its use by the opponent.

PV(⟨word⟩) = SCORE − 3(number of TWS flags covered)

or

PV(⟨word⟩) = SCORE + 3(for each TWS obtained)

(3) The Endgame

In the closing stages of the game the emphasis changes from making high-scoring words to getting rid of all the letters held. This is to gain extra points for the opponent's remaining letters. A simple strategy could be to put a small value on each letter placed, and a large value on getting rid of ALL the letters held when there are none left to refill with (i.e. so that the game ends). If the pack of remaining letters is empty (or at least nearly empty) then:

- nullify the effect of the previous strategies (except the QU one)
- calculate PV(⟨word⟩) = SCORE + 1(number of letters placed) + 10 (if all letters placed).

ASSESSMENT OF THE SCRABBLE EQUATION

In the process of trial and error in refining the devised strategies, over 100 games were played and observed, both for dual program players and with human opponents. One of the most important assessments is, of course, how well the PV system works when two or more 'special cases' prevail at the same time. When a combination of considerations apply to one given situation, the PV must balance properly to make the right decision: combining strategies is one of the most difficult situations to deal with successfully in programming games. A variation by just one point in the values given can significantly adjust the playing characteristics of the program. In general, the heuristics which performed best were those in the two clear-cut cases:

- withholding the U for the Q;
- playing a word which used ALL the remaining letters.

In these two cases, the alteration to the PV is so dominant as to force its occurrence. However, the other strategies, although making reasonable decisions in some instances, suffered from some hindering side-effects, some of which are noted here.

The 'S' is of most use in a widely developed game, which the program does not play. It is also of use in getting rid of vowels (as in the words GEESE, LIAISON, LOOSE, etc.). If the 'S' value is set too high then they are collected instead of played, and an accumulation of vowels may develop.

The positioning heuristic suffers because of the sheer complexity of deciding whether a word can be used to link to a TWS. It is in the nature of the game for there to be high-scoring 'areas' on the board, where a number of good words can be placed. Sometimes when this area is near one of the edges the program avoids placing one on to the edge but places one within one square of it, which could be extended to a TWS anyway. This implies that a good positioning heuristic would require consideration of the very complex area of indirect openings of the TWS squares.

The simple device of adding one for each letter placed in the endgame has an undesirable feature. The most easily placed letters are all disposed of quickly (e.g. the A, E or T) but the more difficult letters (e.g. V) are left unplayable.

This leads to the conclusion that, in the more subtle strategies of play, a device less rigid than the Scrabble Equation is required. One recurrent problem was the variance in usability of the letters. This could partially be overcome by ordering the vocabulary so that words using the least-playable letters come first, and the most-playable letters (including the S) last. Where two words scored the same, this would have the effect of choosing the one with the least-playable letters, simply because it was found first. This could be done without any explicit strategy within the program.

The endgame is one of the very few areas in Scrabble where a look-ahead search is feasible. So if a word cannot be found which uses up all the remaining letters, find the shortest sequence of moves which will. There is of course the confusing factor of the opponent's moves to be considered.

PLAYER-A v. PLAYER-B

The results here are from a series of 20 games, with each player starting first in 10 of the games:

number of games won by Player-B	= 13	highest game score achieved in the series by Player-A	= 351
number of games won by Player-A	= 7	number of games where Player-B finished first	= 13
average end of game score for Player-B	= 321.6	number of games where Player-A finished first	= 5
average end of game score for Player-A	= 299.1	number of games where neither player could finish	= 2
highest game score achieved in the series by Player-B	= 410		

CONCLUSION

The complete search of all possible moves results in a powerful player, which is difficult to genuinely improve on. Clear-cut special case situations can be adequately expressed quantitatively in the form of a Scrabble Equation, but the more subtle areas require a less rigid device. The problems found in trying to quantify these areas of judgement indicate how complicated the game really is. The power of the program lies in its ability to make 2, 3 or more words in a single move, which has the effect of producing high scores, and using its letters to good advantage. It also makes the board difficult for a human opponent to play. Its current vocabulary is small (8775 words) compared with that of a good human player. The current area of research is into the ordering and content of the vocabulary files. Some top Scrabble players, from the London Scrabble League, have made some suggestions regarding the development of strategies and the vocabulary. It is possible that a simple 'find-highest-scoring-word' heuristic, with a minimum of special cases, but with a larger more carefully selected vocabulary would simply overpower a good human player. Not-so-good players are overpowered as it is.

ACKNOWLEDGEMENTS

Supervisor, Dr J. Roberts

J. W. Spear Ltd, for use of the name 'Scrabble'.†

The London Scrabble League, in anticipation of further suggestions.

BIBLIOGRAPHY

Orleans and Jacobson, *How to Win at Scrabble,* Hodder and Stoughton.

Hinch, *The Scrabble Book,* Pan.

† SCRABBLE is a trade mark of Selchow and Richter in North America.

16

Scrabble crossword game-playing programs

Stuart C. Shapiro
Department of Computer Science, State University of New York at Buffalo
Amherst, New York 14226 USA

HISTORY OF THE PROJECT

In the period of 1973–79, I headed a series of projects to write programs to play the Scrabble† crossword game. These projects culminated in three programmed players which played at a fair human level. In 1973–74, Margaret Ambrose, Barbara Rasche, Ben Schneiderman and I did the preliminary basic design. My primary interest was the design of a Scrabble oriented lexicon data structure. Margaret and Barbara implemented a version of the lexicon in SNOBOL 4. In 1976, Howard Smith and I refined the lexicon structure and the lexicon search algorithm and Howard implemented a player in SIMULA67. This player played several respectable games interactively against human opponents, although its lexicon never exceeded 1500 words. These projects were carried out in the Computer Science Department of Indiana University. In 1978 at the Department of Computer Science, SUNY at Buffalo, Karl Schimpf and Michael Morris implemented the game manager and lexicon routines in Pascal and each wrote a player. The Pascal lexicon never exceeded 2150 words. These players played a few games each, but since they ran on a large university computer which swaps out a program whenever it accesses the disc, they were not usable interactively. These efforts were summarised in a paper presented at the Sixth IJCAI in 1979. The project has been dormant since then.

THE LEXICON

As mentioned above, my primary interest in the Scrabble project was the lexicon as a design problem in algorithms and data structures. I saw the central problem as: given a set of letters find all the words that can be made from any combination

†SCRABBLE is a trade mark of Selchow and Richter in North America.

and permutation of them, and find them in approximately the order of their value in the Scrabble game. I decided to make other issues of play, tactics and strategy secondary to this one.

The lexicon data structure decided on is a letter table, or *trie,* in which each node, n, contains a letter, l, a list of words, w, a success pointer to a sub-trie, and a fail pointer to a sub-trie. If L is the sequence of letters contained in all nodes on the success path from the root to but not including n, w contains all words that are permutations of the letters in Ll, the success sub-trie contains all words formed from Ll plus some other letters, and the fail sub-trie contains all words formed from L and some other letters but not l. The order of letters on both success and fail paths is a canonical order whose major sort is on the value of the letter in Scrabble, whose secondary sort is on the frequency of the letter in the game set, and whose tertiary sort is on the frequency of the letter in English. To keep the trie smaller, 'S' is placed last. The order is QZXJKHFY WVCMPBGDLUTNRIOAES. Figure 1 (taken from Shapiro (1979)) shows an example trie.

The bigger the lexicon, the more efficient this structure is. The first 151 words in the Pascal lexicon required 453 nodes (approximately 3 nodes per word). When the lexicon grew to 2125 words, 4257 nodes were needed (approximately 2 nodes per word). However, each word is stored explicitly in a word list, as well as being implicitly stored in the trie. The following idea can shorten the word lists. Each word list is on a node at the end of a success path of k nodes and contains words which are permutations of the k letters in the nodes on that path. Instead of using k characters to represent the normal spelling of a word, we only need k binary numbers, each of $\lceil \log_2 k \rceil$ bits. For example, in Fig. 1, the list BREAK, BAKER, BRAKE is at the end of the path K-B-R-A-E. BREAK consists of the 2nd, 3rd, 5th, 4th, then 1st letters on the path and can be coded as the binary numbers 001, 010, 100, 011, 000. Since we know that each word on this list uses five three-bit numbers, the entire list can be coded as the octal digit sequence: 124301304212304. Similarly, the correct spelling of each fifteen-letter word (the longest we need for Scrabble) needs only $15 \times 4 = 60$ bits to store.

The lexicon is searched by taking the letters on the rack and the letters at the proposed board location, putting them in canonical order, and doing a backtrack search of the lexicon trie with the following characteristics:

(1) Every word found contains all the letters from the board.
(2) Words are found using all possible combinations of letters from the rack.
(3) Blanks from the rack may match any letter – words returned indicate how the blank is to be used.
(4) If letter L1 is more valuable than letter L2, words using L1 but not using L2 will be found before words using L2 and not using L1.
(5) Words using a set of letters will be found before words using a subset of those letters.

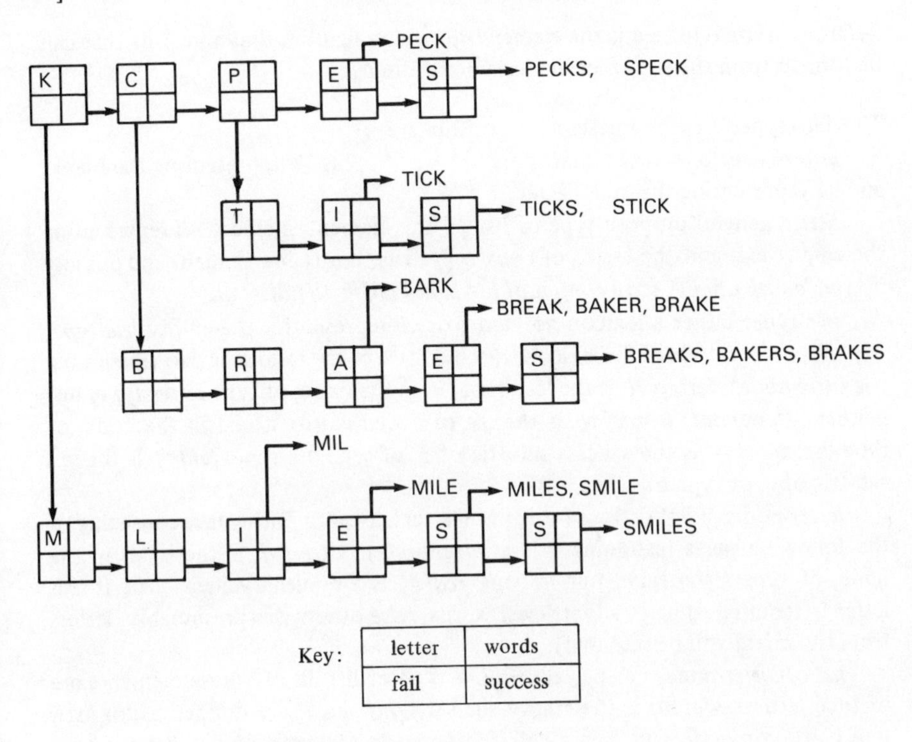

Fig. 1 – An example lexicon trie.

The search was designed so that it could be terminated before it finished with good assurance that the highest-scoring words have been found first. However, since the order of letters from the board was not retained, not all words found were playable. The search algorithm is presented below.

THE LEXICON SEARCH ALGORITHM

The algorithm presented in this section is a revision of the function *findwords2* in Shapiro and Smith (1977). The major revision is a change from a detachable coroutine to a resumable generator.

The search is performed by a generator function that provides a list of words each time it is run. Initially, the function *findwords* is called with a lexicon trie, a list of letter nodes, and an empty list of 'pairs' whose purpose will be explained below. *Findwords* returns a data structure called a *letter-pair-type* from which the list of words may be retrieved. This *letter-pair-type* can be given to the function *resume,* which will call *findwords* appropriately to produce the *letter-pair-type* containing the next list of words. This can be repeated until the *letter-pair-type* returned is the element *nil*, which signifies that all words that can be formed from the list of letters have been found.

The data types used by the search algorithm are:

letter-type: one of the characters '*A*'... '*Z*', plus '#' representing the blank, and *nil* representing the 'null' letter.

list: a general purpose type of list of any element; includes *nil* representing the empty list, and the result of *cons[*α,β*]*, where α is any element and β is any list; *hd[cons[*α,β*]]* = α; *tl[cons[*α,β*]]* = β; *hd[nil]* = *tl[nil]* = *nil.*

trie-type: either a lexicon *trie-node,* or *nil* representing the empty *trie-type.*

trie-node: a node of the lexicon trie consisting of the following parts (assuming τ is a *trie-node*): *letter[*τ*]* is the letter stored in the node, of type *letter-type,* but neither '#' nor *nil; words[*τ*]* is the list of coded words stored in the node, of type *list; succ[*τ*]* is the success sub-trie of τ, of type *trie-type; fail[*τ*]* is the fail sub-trie of τ, of type *trie-type.*

letter-node: a data structure for the letters given to *findwords,* consisting of the following parts (assuming ν is a *letter-node*): *letter[*ν*]* is the letter in the node, of type *letter-type,* but not *nil; req[*ν*]* is a boolean value – *true* if this letter is required to be in all retrieved words, *false* otherwise (presumably, letters from the board will be required).

list-of-letter-nodes: a special purpose type of list all of whose elements are of type *letter-node; nil* is the empty such list; *hd* and *tl* are defined as for *lists;* if ν is a *letter-node* and β is a *list-of-letter-nodes, insert[*ν,β*]* is a *list-of-letter-nodes* containing ν as well as all the elements in β all ordered in the canonical order, and *remove[*ν,β*]* is a *list-of-letter-nodes* which contains all the elements of β except for ν.

pair-type: a data type used to associate a letter from the input list of letters with a node of the lexicon trie; if α is a *letter-node,* and β is a *trie-type, letter-trie-pair[*α,β*]* is a *pair-type* γ, *letter-of-pair[*γ*]* is α, and *trie-of-pair[*γ*]* is β.

letter-pair-type: the data type returned by *findwords* and input to *resume;* if α is a *list-of-letter-nodes,* and β is a *list* of *pair-types, letters-pairs[*α,β*]* is a *letter-pair-type* γ, such that *letters-of[*γ*]* is α and *pairs-of[*γ*]* is β; if γ is a *letter-pair-type, words[trie-of-pair[hd[pairs-of[*γ*]]]]* is a coded list of words that can be formed from the input list of letters, the sub-sequence of *pairs-of[*γ*]* formed by including only those pairs whose *trie-of-pair* is not *nil* is the reverse of the success path from the root to the current node and its length is the number of letters in each of the words.

In addition, *nil* is a possible element of all these data types, and any function of one argument given above will return *nil* if its argument is *nil.*

Additional auxiliary functions are:

before[let1,let2:letter-type] :boolean – returns *true* if *let1* comes before *let2* in the canonical order, *false* otherwise; the current order is *#QZXJKHFY WVCMPBGDLUTNRIOAESnil.*

done[letters:list-of-letter-nodes] :boolean – returns ***true*** if *letters=nil* or if *req[v]=false* for all *letter-nodes v* on *letters, false* otherwise.

next-let-nodel[letters:list-of-letter-nodes] :letter-node – returns the first *letter-node* on *letters* whose *letter* is not '#', *nil* if there is no such *letter-node.*

next-let[letters:list-of-letter-nodes] :letter-type ⇐ *letter[next-let-node [letters]].*

remove-next-let[letters:list-of-letter-nodes] :list-of-letter-nodes ⇐ *remove [next-let-node[letters] ;letters].*

Finally, the function *findwords* is:

```
function findwords[ trie :trie-type;
                    letters: list-of-letter-nodes;
                    pairs: list of pair-type] : letter-pair-type;
begin
  while not(trie=nil and pairs=nil) do
    if trie ≠ nil then {searching forwards}
      if letters = nil then {the trie node we've found is in hd[pairs]}
        if pairs = nil then
          return[nil] {the original letters and pairs were both nil}
        else if words[trie-of-pair[hd[pairs]]] = nil then
          trie ← nil {no words here, prepare to backtrack}
        else return[letters-pairs[letters,pairs]] {have found some words}
      else if letter[trie] = next-let[letters] then
        begin {the trie-node matches the first non-# letter}
          pairs ← cons[letter-trie-pair[next-let-node[letters] ;trie] ;pairs] ;
          letters ← remove-next-let[letters] ;
          trie ← succ[tree]
        end
      else if letter[hd[letters]] = '#' then
        begin {'#' matches the trie-node}
          pairs ← cons[letter-trie-pair[hd[letters] ;trie] ;pairs] ;
          letters ← tl[letters] ;
          trie ← succ[trie]
        end
      else if before[letter[hd[letters]],letter[trie]] then
        {the first letter is not in the trie rooted at this node}
        if req[hd[letters]] then trie ← nil {cannot ignore a required letter}
        else begin         {ignore this letter, but stack it in pairs
                            with a null trie-node for backtracking}
              pairs ← cons[letter-trie-pair[hd[letters] ;nil] ;pairs] ;
              letters ← tl[letters]
          end
```

```
        else trie ← fail[trie] {this trie-node doesn't match;
                                follow the fail path}
    else {trie=nil;pairs≠nil; we've gone as far as we can go;
      current node in hd[pairs] }
        if done[letters] then
            {no required letters left unmatched}
          if trie-of-pair[hd[pairs]] ≠ nil then {the last letter matched a node}
            if words[trie-of-pair[hd[pairs]]] ≠ nil then {report these words}
              return[letters-pairs[letters,pairs]]
            else {this node had no words}
              if letter[letter-of-pair[hd[pairs]]] = '#' then
                begin {'#' can match another node on the fail path}
                  trie ← fail[trie-of-pair[hd[pairs]]];
                  letters ← insert[letter-of-pair[hd[pairs]];letters];
                  pairs ← tl[pairs]
                end
            else {the letter matching this node was not '#'}
                begin {now try the search ignoring this letter,but save it in
                pairs for further backtracking}
                  trie ← fail[trie-of-pair[hd[pairs]]];
                  pairs ← cons[letter-trie-pair[letter-of-pair[hd[pairs]];nil];
                  tl[pairs]];
                end
            else {trie-of-pair[hd[pairs]]=nil; backtrack past an ignored letter}
                begin
                  letters ← insert[letter-of-pair[hd[pairs]];letters];
                  trie ← nil; {= trie-of-pair[hd[pairs]] }
                  pairs ← tl[pairs]
                end
    else {trie=nil; pairs≠nil; letters≠nil; done[letters]=false}
        begin
          while pairs ≠ nil and trie-of-pairs[hd[pairs]] = nil do
            begin {backtrack past ignored letters}
              letters ← insert[letter-of-pair[hd[pairs]];letters];
              pairs ← tl[pairs]
            end;
          {trie=nil; letters≠nil; done[letters]=false}
          if pairs ≠ nil then
            begin {have already searched success path;
                  can't report any words here; search fail path}
              trie ← fail[trie-of-pair[hd[pairs]]];
              if letter[letter-of-pair[hd[pairs]]] = '#' then
                begin {'#' can match another node on the fail path}
```

```
                    letters ← insert[letter-of-pair[hd[pairs]];letters];
                    pairs ← tl[pairs]
                  end
              else {ignore the letter that previously matched this node}
                  pairs ← cons[letter-trie-pair[letter-of-pair[hd[pairs]];nil];
                  tl[pairs]]
          end
      end;
    {trie=nil and pairs=nil; can neither search forward nor backtrack}
    return[nil]
end findwords
```

In the original call to *findwords, trie* should be the root of the lexicon trie, *letters* should be the original *list-of-letter-nodes* properly ordered, and *pairs* should be *nil. Findwords* will return either *nil* if no words can be formed from the given letters, or a *letter-pair-type* containing the first coded list of words. If additional words are required, this *letter-pair-type* should be passed to *resume,* defined below.

```
function resume[l-p: letter-pair-type]: letter-pair-type;
  var letters: list-of-letter-nodes;
      pairs: list of pair-type;
  begin
      if l-p = nil then return[nil]; {can't resume – already done}
      letters ← letters-of[l-p];
      pairs ← pairs-of[l-p];
      {since we're resuming, pairs≠nil,
      hd[pairs] has a trie-node with words in it which we've just reported,
      and the success subtrie has already been searched}
      if letter[letter-of-pair[hd[pairs]]] = '#' then
          {'#' can match another node on the fail path}
          return[findwords[fail[trie-of-pair[hd[pairs]]];
                              cons[letter-of-pair[hd[pairs]];letters];
                              tl[pairs]]]
      else {ignore the last letter that matched, but save it for backtracking}
          return[findwords[fail[trie-of-pair[hd[pairs]]];
                          letters;
                              cons[letter-trie-pair[letter-of-pair[hd[pairs]];nil];
                                  tl[pairs]]]]
end resume
```

RESULTS

The lexicon performed as expected, with the players quickly taking advantage of high-valued tiles. They did pass frequently because of the small lexicon and because we severely restricted the number of playing positions and the number of words they would consider. The strategy and tactics were also very primitive – the SIMULA player did not even consider parallel or extension plays. Nevertheless, in its two full, recorded games with humans, it only lost by scores of 339–208 and 212–198. Its average scores per word played were 13.13 and 14.07 while the humans' were 13.88 and 12.00 respectively. It would be interesting to see how such a player would perform with sophisticated tactics and a large vocabulary.

REFERENCES AND BIBLIOGRAPHY

Ambrose, M. and Rasche, B. (1974), A computerized Scrabble player. Unpublished project report, Computer Science Department, Indiana University, Bloomington, IN.

Morris, M. J. (1979), An implementation of a Scrabble crossword game playing program. Unpublished project report, Department of Computer Science, SUNY at Buffalo, Amherst, NY.

Schimpf, K. M. (1979), SCRAP: Scrabble Crossword Automated Program. Unpublished project report, Department of Computer Science, SUNY at Buffalo, Amherst, NY.

Shapiro, S. C. (1979), A Scrabble crossword game playing program. *Proc. Sixth IJCAI,* Computer Science Department, Stanford University, Stanford, CA, pp. 797–799.

Shapiro, S. C. and Smith, H. R. (1977), A Scrabble crossword game playing program. *Technical Report No. 119,* Department of Computer Science, SUNY at Buffalo, Amherst, NY.

Smith, H. (1976), A Scrabble playing program. Unpublished project report, Computer Science Department, Indiana University, Bloomington, IN.

17

A multi-strategy gaming environment

Nicholas V. Findler†, George L. Sicherman and Bede McCall
Group for Computer Studies of Strategies, Department of Computer Science, State University of New York at Buffalo, 4226 Ridge Lea Road, Amherst, NY14226, USA

ABSTRACT

Together with a large and varying number of collaborators the authors have been engaged in a long-term project aimed at investigating how decisions are and should be made under uncertainty and risk. Learning programs of different types have come to the centre of our attention, both in the course of trying to simulate human cognitive behaviour and in constructing wholly machine intelligence-oriented competitive strategies. We describe an interactive environment in which an arbitrary number of human and machine strategies, up to a total of eight, can be pitted against each other. The game of Draw Poker was selected as the vehicle of these studies since it shares many characteristics with real-life decision-making tasks.

This project has come to an end. We also describe our current work on automatic analysis and synthesis of strategies. Although the systems being developed are highly context-independent, we are able to utilise our experience gained in the previous project.

INTRODUCTION

Both Artificial Intelligence and its first domain of activity, automatic game-playing, preceded the advent of computers. Although some of this activity was fake (e.g. von Kempelen's Chess Automaton), some algorithms effectively were implemented in 'hardware' (e.g. Torres y Quevedo's King and Rook versus King mechanical Chess player). Even Turing's and Shannon's celebrated chess programs were not run on an actual computer.

It is outside the scope of this paper to discuss the reasons and motivations for game-playing programs. We feel that, apart from the intellectual challenge, the by-products of such research justify the effort and resources invested.

†Dr. Findler's address is now: Computer Science Department, Arizona State University, Tempe, Arizona AZ85287, USA.

In this chapter, we describe a long-term project aimed at studying decision-making under uncertainty and risk, and machine learning. We have used the game of Draw Poker as the vehicle of our investigations. As a conceptual and, to a fairly large degree, technical continuation of these efforts, we have engaged in more general, context-independent studies on automatic analysis and synthesis of strategies. (For further information, see the papers by Findler and by Findler *et al.* in the references and bibliography at the end of this chapter.)

We first provide an updated version of two surveys of our work published several years ago (Findler (1977) and Findler (1979)). It is followed by a brief description of our current activity.

DRAW POKER AND ITS DECISION PROCESSES

The vehicle for studying decision-making must be realistically complex, whether one wants to simulate – and not caricature – human cognitive processes or to produce intelligent systems whose performance may surpass that of man. In contrast with one-person vs. Nature or two-person confrontations, a multi-person game allows several strategies to be compared with one another or with some appropriate baseline measure. Furthermore, several human players (situated possibly in different rooms) can compete with machine strategies. Such a laboratory environment enables one to hypothesize and verify theories of human decision-making, problem-solving and learning processes inexpensively. It also allows Turing tests of a sort to be conducted in which the subjects are asked to distinguish human competitors from programs. Fig. 1 depicts the graphic display at a moment during the confrontation between a human player and seven machine strategies.

These were some of our reasons for choosing to study Draw Poker, a game popular in many countries. For information on the game, see, for example, Crawford (1961), Jacoby (1947), Morehead (1964), Morehead, Frey and Mott-Smith (1964), Wallace (1968), Yardley (1961) and Zadeh (1974). Its simple rules (summarised in the Appendix to this chapter) and limited range of actions, coupled with the depth of analytical reasoning required of any meaningful strategy, render the programming effort invested in a large system 'cost-effective'. Human players construct and continually modify mathematical models of the game and psychological models of the opponents. Eliciting information on these from them serves the whole range of our research objectives, from generating a sufficiency theory of human behaviour to establishing wholly machine intelligence-oriented competitive strategies. We believe that games of imperfect information and those involving both chance and skill are more useful for certain studies in Artificial Intelligence than games of pure skill and perfect information – without trying to belittle the intellectual challenge, the depth and breadth of the efforts needed for programming games in the latter category, such as Chess or Go.

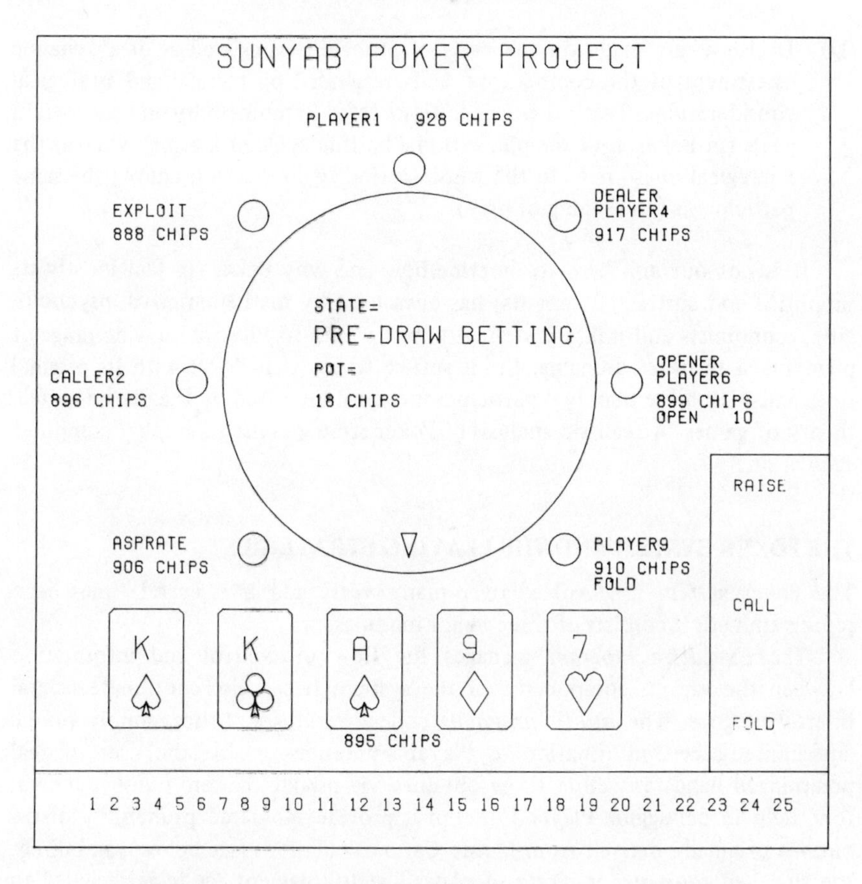

Fig. 1 – The graphics display used as the interactive environment.

Poker shares many important features of decision-making with 'real-life' problems.

(A) In evaluating *alternative courses of action* the player assumes
  (i) a likely 'state of nature' based on subjective probabilities;
  (ii) plausible (not necessarily rational) actions by the other participants.

(B) The player can *manipulate information* by
  (i) 'buying' information about the others' situations;
  (ii) giving away misleading information about his own situation.

(C) Each player has limited financial resources, which he has to manage optimally in the long run. His strategy is the visible projection of his *resource management style.* His 'policy decisions' (concerning, for example, investment for the benefit of projecting a particular style) have obvious analogues in commercial enterprises and political campaigns.

(D) Decisions are made on the basis of probabilities as well as of a dynamic assessment of the competitors, and are guided by tactical and strategical considerations. Tactical considerations refer to momentary and short-term goals (in Poker, for example, within a betting cycle or a game) whereas the strategical ones apply to the whole period of interaction among the same participants (an evening of play).

It is not our aim here to describe how and why Poker (in fact mostly its simplified and abstracted variants) has been used by mathematicians, psychologists, economists and military strategists *per se* and to illustrate a wide range of phenomena in other domains. Let it suffice to say that Poker with its original rules and with more than two participants cannot be solved by the mathematical theory of games. A realistic analysis of Poker strategies has to employ computer simulation.

THE POKER SYSTEM AND THE PLAYING STRATEGIES

The Poker system has evolved over many years and has several times been reprogrammed. It consists of three major modules.

The *Executive Program* manages the flow of control and information between the various components of the system. It can also coordinate several interacting jobs. The *utility programs* collect various statistics, supply public and limited-access information to Player Functions, enable the user to deal prearranged hands as well as those obtained via pseudo-random number generators, help in debugging Player Functions, provide tabulated probability distributions originally derived from Monte Carlo calculations (see below), and direct the so-called *tournament mode* of play. The tournament mode is designed to eliminate the effects of runs of good or bad hands and of biased seating patterns, similarly to the Duplicate System used in Bridge tournaments. Suppose six players are seated around the table at random and each is dealt a hand at random. Altogether 6!5! = 86,400 different hand-player-seat *arrangements* are possible since one player can be anchored to a constant seat. A *tournament* consists of a user-specified number of games of different arrangements selected at random without replacement from the 86,400 possible ones.

The *Player Functions* take the part of the players. They interact with the Executive Program and the Utility Programs by responding to game situations according to the different ordered sets of decision components. A game situation is determined by a player's own hand, and the past and current betting and drawing behaviour of all players. The consequences of a game situation, of course, vary among Player Functions. The game situation space can be partitioned according to a structure pattern provided either in advance by the user or, as described later on, by several of the learning programs. The automation of partitioning or, in other words, of the formation of equivalence classes is fundamentally important. We expand on this issue in our account of the Bayesian players below. At the outset of the project we ran Monte Carlo calculations to tabulate various distributions of hands, to derive a provisional partitioning of Poker hand classes, and to obtain initial values for certain heuristic parameters for some of the learning strategies. In the following, we discuss the most interesting player functions out of over 40 strategies we tested. Several of these have not been reported on in Findler (1977) and Findler (1979).

Static Players

The static machine players can be characterised as rigid control structures whose responses depend exclusively upon the game process rather than upon the behaviour of the opponents. The decision trees constructed for these players implement heuristics taken from the Poker literature or established by our Monte Carlo runs. There are, however, some additional static players. We single out the RH-player (named after two graduate students, Jean Rachlin and Gary Higgins) and the family of Mathematically Fair Players.

The *RH-player* follows the principle that a bet should be directly proportional to the tablepot (TABLEPOT) and inversely proportional to the number of people still alive in the game (LIVE), to the number of raises which have occurred (RAISECOUNT), to the number of opponents still having a chance to say something after him (FOLLOWERS), and to the amount he has to put in the pot to stay in the game (RAISE). Jean Rachlin and Gary Higgins found experimentally the characteristic distribution of a measure of the probability of winning,

$$\mathrm{RH} = \frac{\mathrm{TABLEPOT}}{\mathrm{LIVE*(RAISECOUNT+1)*FOLLOWERS*RAISE}} \tag{1}$$

and the optimum partitions for Poker hands, in which an approximately constant value of *RH* calls for a given action in the game.

In order to establish a basis of comparison and a starting point for some of the learning programs, we developed a family of players relying on the Mathematically Fair Strategy (*MFS*). The *fair bet* is computed by equating the expected value of losses:

$$p_j \,.\, B_o\,(j,k) = (1-p_j)\,.\left[\sum_{m=1}^{k-1} B_a\,(j,m) + B_f\,(j,k)\right] \tag{2}$$

Here, p_j is the probability of player j's winning a given hand; $B_o(j,k)$ is the total contribution of player j's opponents to the pot up to the kth betting cycle; $B_a(j,m)$ is player j's bet in the betting cycle m; and $B_f(j,k)$ is the fair bet to be made by player j in the kth betting cycle.

As can be seen, this strategy ignores all the second-order effects of the game-situational variables (number of players folding, checking and raising; seat arrangements; nature of opponents and games, etc.) and is obviously incapable of bluffing. This is a serious deficiency against sophisticated human and machine players and the Statistically Fair Player (see below) amends this problem. Bluffing is an essential part of Poker and has a multi-purpose role. First, bluffing has a direct, short-term monetary goal within a single game. By under-representing a strong hand ('sandbagging'), the player tries to keep other players in the game so as to increase the size of the pot. Over-representing a weak hand may result in gain over stronger opponents; it can also *buy* information about the other players. That is to say, showdowns provide the bluffing player with snapshots of the relationship between the strength of the opponent's hands and their betting behaviour. (No showdown takes place if all players but one fold. The bluffing player can force a showdown by paying the price of calling.) Deciding when and how far to bluff with a given hand and a given history of play against a given set of opponents is one of the key issues in long-term money management. Another major objective of bluffing is to obscure and distort one's strategy and thereby to keep the communication channels noisy.

As said before, Equation (2) leads to a *family* of the Mathematically Fair Players (*MFP*'s). Many Poker experts recommend, for example, 'not to throw good money after bad'. That is, a player should consider only the utility of his *current* investment, an idea which is equivalent to ignoring the summation term in the brackets on the right-hand side of Equation (2). The respective fair bet values are returned by the function FBET (full equation) and FBET2 (summation term omitted). Note that player functions that use FBET2 play more aggressively. Table 1 also contains FBET3 and FBET4. FBET3 returns a bet one chip larger than FBET, and FBET4 lies between FBET and FBET2.

Another distinction among the *MFP*s is the source of the probability values, p_j. If they come from tables obtained in the Monte Carlo runs (PROB in Table 1), these empirical values grow less accurate as the number of players still in the game diminishes. Certain efficient combinatorial calculations, performed by TROB, a utility routine of our system, provide theoretical probability values during the pre-draw phase of the game. An extension of this calculation also takes into consideration the number of cards drawn by each opponent, and computes the theoretical probability of winning for the post-draw hands (PWIN).

The 18 *MFP*s have been tested against a set of standard opponents in runs of 15,000 games each. The runs were made using the Tournament Mode of the system, and players were reseated every 50 games. In each run, two copies of the *MFP* being tested participated to reduce further the undesirable 'neighbour effects'.

The selection of the opponents was based on the speed, memory requirement and stability of the strategies considered rather than their skill and sophistication. We have therefore fixed a set of four static and two learning players for the 18

Table 1
The definition of the 18 variants of the Mathematically Fair Strategy

Name	Pre-draw functions		Post-draw functions	
	Betting	Probability	Betting	Probability
MFP1	FBET	PROB	FBET	PROB
MFP2	FBET	TPROB	FBET	PROB
MFP3	FBET	TPROB	FBET	PWIN
MFP4	FBET2	TPROB	FBET	PROB
MFP5	FBET	PROB	FBET	PWIN
MFP6	FBET2	PROB	FBET2	PROB
MFP7	FBET2	TPROB	FBET2	PWIN
MFP8	FBET2	PROB	FBET2	PWIN
MFP9	FBET2	TPROB	FBET2	PROB
MFP10	FBET	PROB	FBET2	PROB
MFP11	FBET2	PROB	FBET	PROB
MFP12	FBET	TPROB	FBET2	PWIN
MFP13	FBET2	TPROB	FBET	PWIN
MFP14	FBET	PROB	FBET2	PWIN
MFP15	FBET	TPROB	FBET2	PROB
MFP16	FBET2	PROB	FBET	PWIN
MFP17	FBET3	PROB	FBET3	PROB
MFP18	FBET4	PROB	FBET4	PROB

runs to compare the *MFP*s. Figure 2 shows for each *MFP* five measures of quality:

- the final purse size after 15,000 games;
- the average purse size;
- the average win (or loss) per game;
- the 'raw win', the percentage of games won by the player;
- the 'win ratio', the percentage of showdowns won by the player.

Each of these measures are given as *deviations* from the respective values averaged over the 18 players so as to make it easier to compare them.
We have classified the 18 *MFP*s into 28 classes according to the betting functions used and the source of the probability values. It would be informative to compare quantitatively the performance of these classes but the figures and tables necessary for it would make this chapter intolerably long. Suffice it to say that, as we expected, those *MFP*s that use theoretical probability values, particularly after the draw, outperform those that use empirical ones. Furthermore, an aggressive strategy based on FBET2 before the draw, followed by a more cautious approach based on the FBET after the draw, seems superior to all other choices.

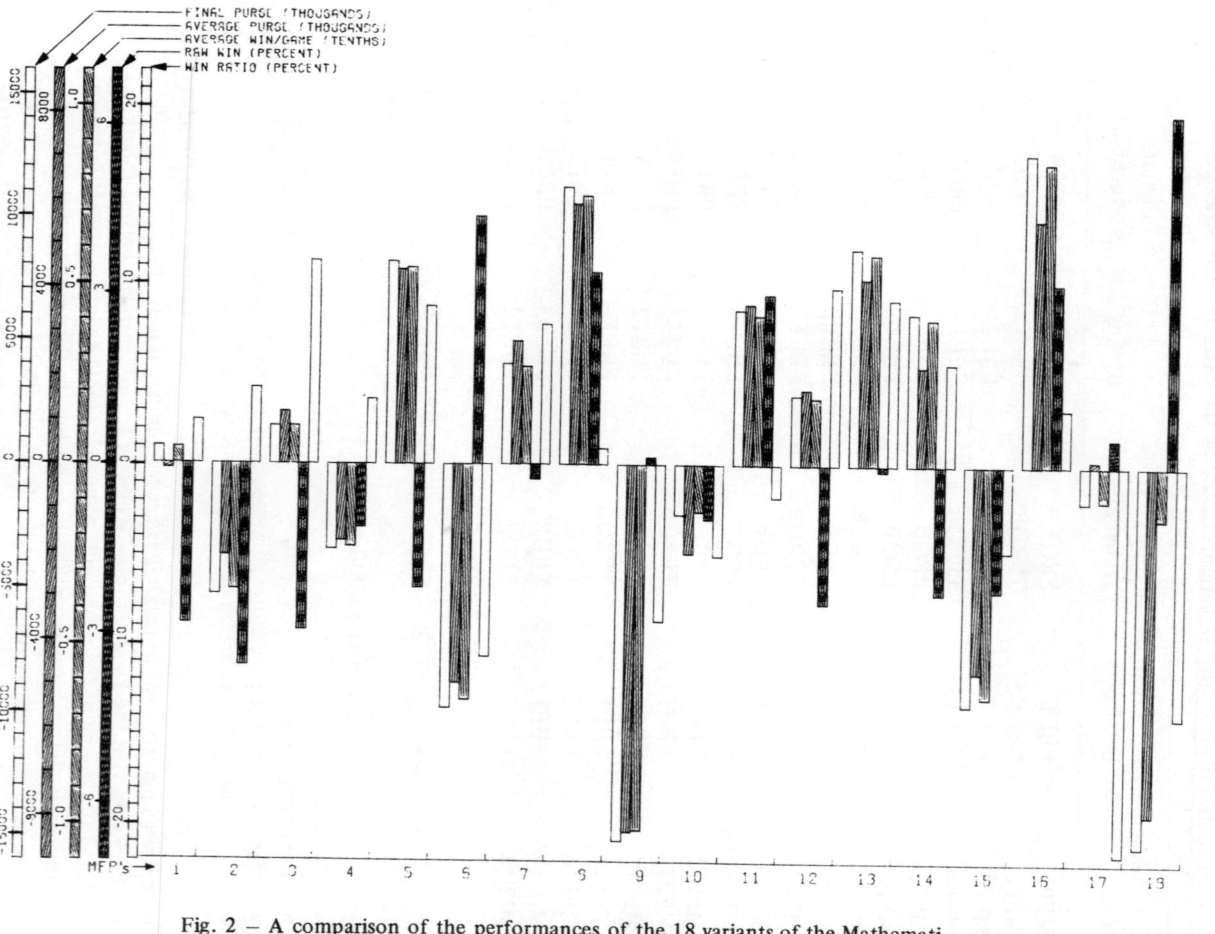

Fig. 2 – A comparison of the performances of the 18 variants of the Mathematically Fair Strategy according to the five criteria (see text).

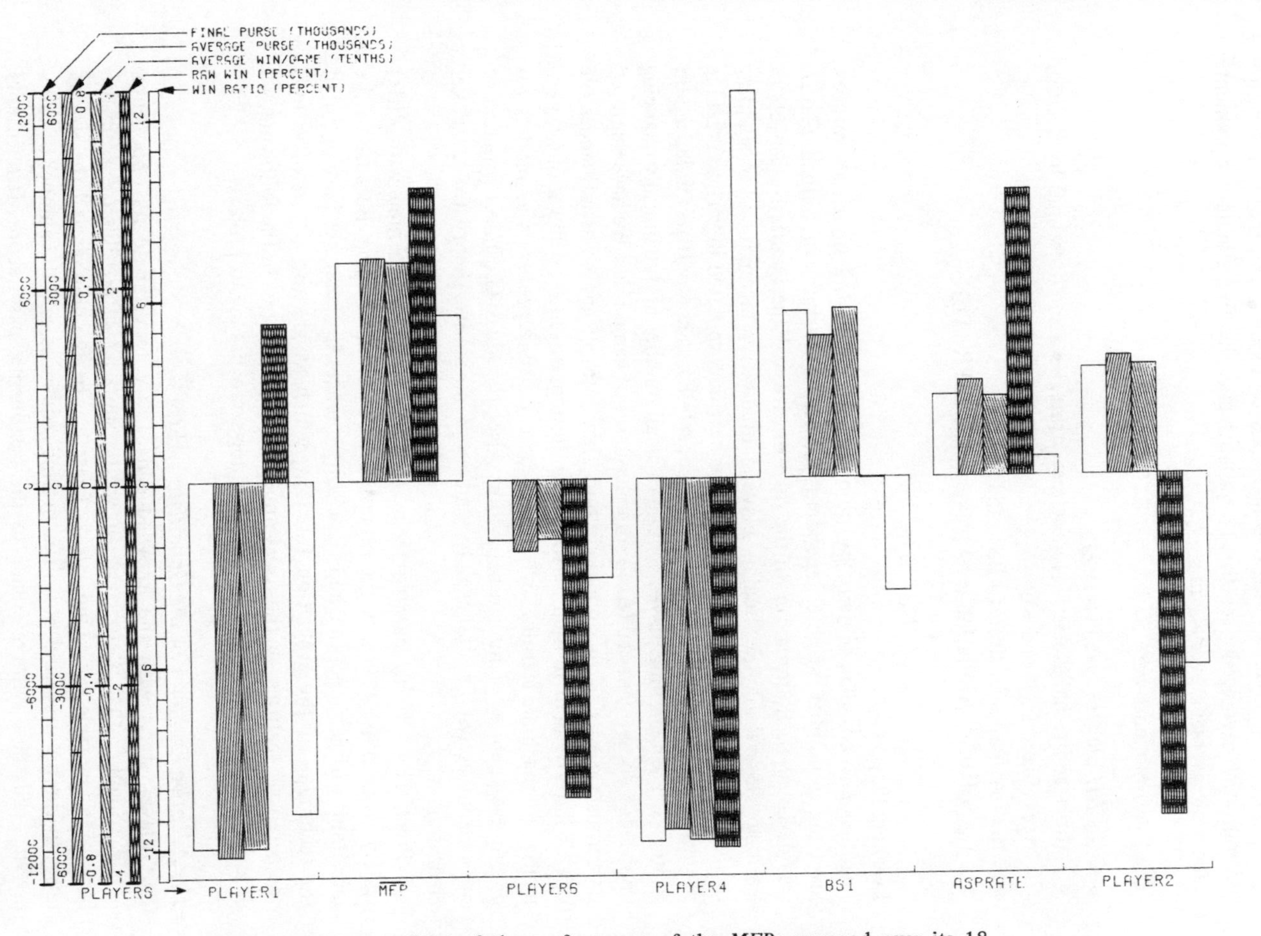

Fig. 3 – A comparison of the performance of the *MFP*s averaged over its 18 variants, *MFP*, and of the standard opponents, averaged over 18 runs (see text).

Finally, Fig. 3 shows the five measures of quality, as used in Fig. 2, for 'overall *MFP*' averaged over the 18 variants and the five standard opponents, each again averaged over all runs.

The five opponents were

- the *RH*-player (alias Player 1);
- three additional static players whose strategies are represented by decision trees (Players 2,4 and 6);
- the first Bayesian strategy BS1; and
- the Adaptive Aspiration level player (alias ASPRATE).

Learning Players

Learning any complex activity by humans is, in general, a multistage process involving a number of interdependent factors. Our study of human players was designed to illuminate both the quantitative and the qualitative aspects of learning. Several of the human players' qualitative techniques for adapting themselves to the game environment have been incorporated in various machine players. However, these should not be considered as competitive, independent strategies. Each learning player contains a small number of dynamically changing knowledge components added to some basic set of game rules. We have explored numerous variants of these, namely how they interact and what influences the rate of improvement in their performance. Besides our interest in various experiments on machine learning, we study these learning processes as models for descriptive theories of human behaviour. Also, the Quasi-Optimizer program of our current activity is designed to generate a normative theory for the Poker environment.

Practically all the learning techniques we have experimented with differ widely from those found in the literature on machine learning. Because of the uncertainty of game actions and their consequences in Poker, we have not used the technique of the evaluation function, which weighs the effects of various characteristic features, or the usual minimaxing procedure. In the following, we describe the essential elements of the learning strategies in our project.

The Adaptive Evaluator of the Opponents (AEO)

This player starts with the knowledge necessary to estimate its opponents' hands 'roughly'; that is, to come up with a short list of possible cases, on the basis of a few (selectable) indicators. These can be the number and the size of raises in the pre-draw and post-draw betting sequences, and the number of cards drawn – all these with reference to the opponents' past record. It refines its judgement of *each* of its opponents as their 'personalities' become better known. Every time there is a showdown, *AEO* updates a statistical database that correlates the opponents' post-draw betting sequence and their hands.

We have divided the range of all possible hands into 20 partitions, using the principle of equally distributed power of discrimination. Let $S(i,j)$ be some statistic (for example, the ratio of actual bet to fair bet) of player j, collected in partition i; and let $m(i,j)$ and $s(i,j)$ be its mean and standard deviation, respectively. *AEO* updates these values after each showdown. For reasons explained below, a number of statistics are collected, such as the ratio actual bet/fair bet, tablepot, last bet, total bet, tablepot-last bet, (tablepot-last bet)/tablepot, total bet-last bet, (total bet-last bet)/tablepot, total bet/tablepot, played pot odds/fair odds, and various moving averages of the above.

AEO's initial 'rough' estimate of an opponent's hand usually yields a small number of partitions in which the hand is likely to fall. A learning process along three dimensions can reduce this list of possibilities considerably. The *first dimension* of learning consists of collecting data for the above statistics. Initially, for lack of data, the Mathematically Fair Strategy is assumed and used for estimating hands. Later, but in the early stage of data collection, the statistical data are pooled over *all* partitions (of course, using each of the above type distributions separately) and compared with the current value, for possible match. As soon as enough observations are available in every partition, the current value of the statistic, S, is substituted into the predicate

$$|\hat{S} - m(i,j)| \leqslant w(i) \,.\, s(i,j) \tag{3}$$

for all likely partitions. Here, $w(i)$ is the weighting factor for partition i, initially 0.1. If (3) holds for one partition, that becomes the estimate of the hand. Otherwise, a learning process along the *second dimension* takes place. After the showdown, $w(i)$ is (A) reduced by 10% for all partitions incorrectly estimated as 'possible', and (B) increased by 10% for the correct but not predicted partition. The weighting factor thus converges to an optimum value in each partition.

We have found that for different opponents different statistical distributions work the best. This is because, although all strategies have the same long-term objective, namely to maximise monetary gain, they use different variables as controllers and indicators in deciding which subgoals to pursue and how to achieve them. The *third dimension* of the learning process consists of selecting the most effective from among the above statistics.

The combination of the three learning processes produces satisfactory estimates of the opponent's hand. The average, over all players, of the absolute value of the difference between the actual and estimated partitions is less than two – better for 'good' strategies and worse for quasi-random players. *AEO* also automatically selects heuristics for evaluation and playing, in a manner analogous to the 'Bayesian' approach discussed later.

The Adaptive Aspiration Level (AAL) Player

Experimental evidence, described in the psychological literature and also found in our studies with human subjects, indicates the existence of two complementary but not necessarily incompatible attitudes expressed in risk-taking environments. A situation or a sequence of events may 'turn on' either a loss-recovery (success-oriented) or a profit-protective (failure-avoidance) mode of operation. (We note here that an individual's behaviour may be guided by both needs, that is to achieve success and avoid failure, at the same time. We hypothesise, however, that the attendant anxiety would then disrupt any quasi-rational strategy.) The success-oriented mode of operation induces more aggressive game behaviour and (usually) higher bets. The failure-avoidance mode, on the other hand, induces more conservative behaviour and (usually) lower bets. However, we considered the change in purse size as a secondary variable whose effects on a player may depend on another, possibly latent variable that is the response to some stimulus configuration. This could be, for example, the difference between the expected and actual gain or loss. The *aspiration level* represents a cognitive balance between the cost of searching for better outcomes and the value of satisfaction with a safe current status. It is computed by comparing the expected losses incurred while modifying and testing response rules, with the expected long-term gains from improving one's play.

Our implementation was quite flexible in the following way. An 'activating mechanism' was established, which can be a function of the change in the financial status, of a significant violation of expectation (losing with a very good hand), or of any experimentally corroborated game-situational variable. The activating mechanism affects the aspiration level, which in turn participates in a two-stage decision process. The latter computes and modifies the mathematically fair bet upwards or downwards, depending on the aspiration level. In another variant of the program, the strategy alters its 'rough' estimate of the opponent's hands obtained by the technique of the *AEO* player before its learning process becomes active. *AAL* then makes its bets according to such altered estimates. In either case, a risk parameter appears in the formalism representing the betting behaviour. Different values of this parameter can describe behaviour ranging from very timid to extremely wild.

Selling and Buying Players' Images (SBI)

Better players are often willing to invest money in simulating a playing style (conservative, sucker, extravagent, etc.). It is an advertising expense, spent on selling a particular image over a certain number of games. The return on this investment is realised during critical games; the buyers of the image are misled and lose heavily.

With regard to the minimum required length of the selling phase during which stable, observable images are induced, there are some obvious starting points. The farther an image to be sold lies from the mathematically fair strategy, the longer the seller has to present it (more post-draw occurrences). In turn, a conservative player will take longer to buy an image than an adventurous one.

We now introduce a use for bluffing not mentioned previously. Whereas to reproduce a mathematically fair strategy is difficult even for an experienced player, to adhere to some broad playing style is relatively easy. Bluffing, as effected by its frequency and extent, is the most direct means of projecting such a strategy. In other words, the Mathematically Fair Strategy is modifed by a probabilistic component determined by the image this player wants to sell. Also, basic betting heuristics can override the fair bet action.

We have explored a number of ways to characterise the opponents. Two dimensions of playing style seem to suffice. The first is the *level of consistency*, the second the *level of cautiousness*. The two are not quite independent as our experience with human subjects showed. For example, a wild player is judged relatively consistent by the others within a much wider range of some indicator variable than a timid player. Or, one would expect a fair player to bet more consistently than an extravagent player would. With reference to the indicator variables, the average win per game and the average loss per game measures cautiousness whereas the scatter of the ratio between the actual and the fair bet reflects the consistency of a player. In another variant, we also tried to quantify the opponents' levels of cautiousness and consistency with the mean value and the standard deviation of the ratio between played pot odds and the fair odds, respectively. The advantage of using these statistics of a single variable as indicators is that we can easily express the relation between the two characteristic dimensions of card playing style.

The Family of 'Bayesian' Strategies (BS) That Make Inductive Inferences

In statistical decision theory, Bayes' criterion refers to the choice that minimises the average expected loss. In our terminology, a 'Bayesian' strategy continually readjusts its decision-making rules on the basis of the outcomes of its actions. It collects data on certain characteristics of situations and also on its average gains and losses with various actions in these situations. Finally, this player takes the most profitable action, as suggested by its knowledge base, and updates the respective entries in it. Such a technique should converge to an optimum strategy against non-learning opponents.

Because of limitations in computing time and memory space, only a few relevant features can be extracted from the situations. The first and simplest Bayesian strategy, *BS1*, observed only its hand and assigned it to one of 11 classes. Moreover, it could take only three 'actions', each a strategy for the entire game. Subsequent Bayesian players were extensions of *BS1: CALLER2* also observed which opponent was betting against it; *BS3* observed how many rounds of betting had taken place; and *SCHNE* (named for Bill Schneider, who programmed it) observed the value of the winning hand in each game, and the maximum and average pot with each hand value. All three players need larger tables of results than *BS1*.

Another problem with Bayesian players is controlling the amount of experimentation. In a given situation a player must try each action at least once.

BS1 tries each action once only, which sometimes causes a disorder that we call *Bayesian withdrawal.* As an example, suppose that the first time *BS1* holds a flush, it bets the limit, and is beaten by a full house. This suffices to deter *BS1* from ever betting the limit again with a flush, simply because its average gain (over one game!) is negative. In our early Bayesian players, the effect of Bayesian withdrawal was mitigated, though not eliminated, by averaging the past results for a class of hands with the results for neighbouring classes. *SCHNE* first plays a set number of games with a fixed strategy, and thereafter bases its strategy on its previous results.

During the past two years we have refined the Bayesian model with a view to training it for human competition. Our last model, *BS8*, incorporates several improvements over the old *BS3*. The most significant change was to observe how many cards the opponent draws instead of how many rounds of betting take place after the draw. We also rewrote the hand classifier to classify hands according to their '*D*-values' instead of their Poker ranks. The *D*-value is the probability of a hand's being better than a randomly dealt one.

The consequences of an action in an early round of betting are harder to judge than those in a late round. We therefore made *BS8* do more 'forced experimentation', i.e. deliberate deviations from recommended actions, early in the game rather than in its later stages. Since even this precaution will not necessarily prevent Bayesian withdrawal, we instructed *BS8* to continue making occasional experiments throughout a session. As a further precaution, we implemented *recency weighting,* whereby after each game the tables are multiplied by a factor slightly less than unity. This factor is called the *oblivion coefficient.*

We also eliminated the practice of drawing four cards to a high-card hand. The lore of Poker discourages drawing four cards as a sign of weakness; our tests confirmed this lore.

The great strategic weakness of the Bayesian model is that it cannot learn to bluff. The main purpose of bluffing with a poor hand is to encourage the opponents to bet when you have a good hand. The basic Bayesian model ignores such interactions. We therefore added a new module, the *Bluffing Supervisor,* to the Poker System. The Bluffing Supervisor maintains statistics on all bluffs during a session and computes how often a player ought to bluff. If turns a naive player function into a sophisticated bluffer.

These improvements caused *BS8* to play remarkably like a human player. We conjecture that by observing one more variable – the position of the dealer – *BS8*'s strategy would equal or surpass most human strategies. Of course, this change would multiply the size of *BS8*'s tables by the number of players. Instead, we introduced a more effective measure, the skill of the opponents. By monitoring its opponents' play, *BS8* classifies their strength as expert, average, or novice. For each strength, *BS8* maintains separate tables, each with different oblivion coefficients.

We are still awaiting the results of extensive human testing, which a private research group is performing. In our own tests with human volunteers, *BS8* held its own, eventually showing a profit after converging to a sound strategy.

The Statistically Fair Player

We noted previously that the Mathematically Fair Players do not bluff – a serious shortcoming against sophisticated opponents. They can, therefore, be outguessed by a strategy that recognises this fact. The Statistically Fair Player (*SFP*) implemented by Terence L. Roy (Roy (1976)) eliminates this deficiency. It can also identify *MFP* or near-*MFP* opponents and respond to them appropriately.

The *SFP* analyses the statistics gathered on the other players over all past games to adjust the frequency and amounts of its bluffs. It attempts to adopt a style similar to that of those opponents whose strategy is not near the mathematically fair one – a common recommendation in the Poker literature – and to bluff heavily and often against *MFP* and near-*MFP* strategies. (Such an approach makes sense because most Poker end games, in the laboratory and in real life, are two-person confrontations.)

The statistics collected are the mean value, m, and the standard deviation, s, of the ratio between the odds played and fair odds of each opponent. (The period over which the data are used is the most recent 300 bets, with the last 100 being weighted double. Thus *SFP* also adjusts to changes in the opponent's playing style.)

The program maps the relevant values of m and s into measures controlling the frequency and extent of bluffing so that *SFP* responds to *MFP* and non-*MFP* players as described above. This is a rather elegant and inexpensive technique for characterising the levels of cautiousness and consistency exhibited by the other players.

Finally, we note that when several opponents are still in the game, *SFP* weighs its response to them according to their current purse size. In other words, richer (and better) strategies are considered more important.

Programming the Zadeh Strategy

A member of our group, C. E. Pearson, implemented (Pearson, 1981) our first *comprehensive* strategy intended for humans as distinguished from the isolated techniques from Poker books adopted by most of our previous player functions. He decided to approximate a mathematically and psychologically well-founded strategy designed by Zadeh (Zadeh, 1974).

The cornerstone of Zadeh's strategy (indeed, of any sound strategy) is the observation of what each player opens with. Since the Poker System has no routines for doing this, Pearson had to design and write them. After he modified our 'mathematically fair' equation (2) to use information about what hands each player opens with, he obtained tables that agreed almost perfectly with Zadeh's tables of probabilities and recommended actions.

Zadeh distinguishes three eventualities during the betting: (1) all the opponents fold; (2) at least one opponent raises; and (3) at least one calls, but nobody raises. Pearson combined cases (2) and (3) to simplify the algebra. The expected gain from raising is then the sum of the opponents' contributions to the pot, multiplied by each opponent's probability of losing by (i) folding or (ii) being beaten in the showdown. The expected gain from calling can be computed similarly.

Another component of Zadeh's strategy is bluffing. Good players bluff rarely, but they do bluff. The Zadeh player function uses 'Reflective Bluffing', a strategy well-suited to a computer. According to the original proposal (Sicherman, 1979): 'Suppose a player wishes to bluff *b* percent of the time. If his hand lies in the *n*-th percentile from the bottom, where $n < b$, then . . . he would pretend that his hand is in the *n*-th percentile from the top'. This elegantly implements Zadeh's dictum: 'Bluff with your worst hands'. It also tends to deter opponents from calling a bluff; when a player who uses it seems to hold a very good hand, there is a 50% chance that he really holds it.

To consider its opponents' bluffing frequencies, the Zadeh function must recognise when an opponent has bluffed. Pearson's implementation simply counts the times an opponent shows a hand too weak to open with. Though it neglects the times an opponent folds or improves after having bluffed, it appears to be good enough for practical purposes.

The final function won against the static strategies convincingly. We could not obtain enough computer memory to test the Zadeh function against other learning strategies.

A Sample Run

Figure 4 shows the *change* in purse size vs. the game number for six competing strategies over 15,000 games. The participating players are:

- the Adaptive Evaluator of the Opponents (*AEO*), PLAYER9;
- the Adaptive Aspiration Level (*AAL*) player, ASPRATE;
- the strategy Selling and Buying Player's Images (*SBI*), EXPLOIT;
- the first Bayesian Strategy, *BS1*;
- the fourth Bayesian Strategy, *SCHNE;*
- the eighth Bayesian Strategy, *BS8*.

Some comments are necessary. *BS1* learns much faster than *BS8* but, asymptotically, it is inferior. (Note that *BS1* has reached a plateau after about 14,000 games whereas *BS8* monotonically improves after about 9,500 games.) *BS1* is 'egocentric', perceiving only its own hand as a situation-descriptor. Therefore, the type and number of the opponents and their actions do not matter. In contrast, *BS8* does observe the opponents' actions. However, to save memory space (and also because *BS8* was originally designed to play against a single human opponent), it does not distinguish between the other strategies. Of course, one has to pay a price for such an over-generalisation in *BS8*'s playing quality under such conditions. *BS8* does win 'hands down' when in its element, two-person games, after a sufficiently long training period.

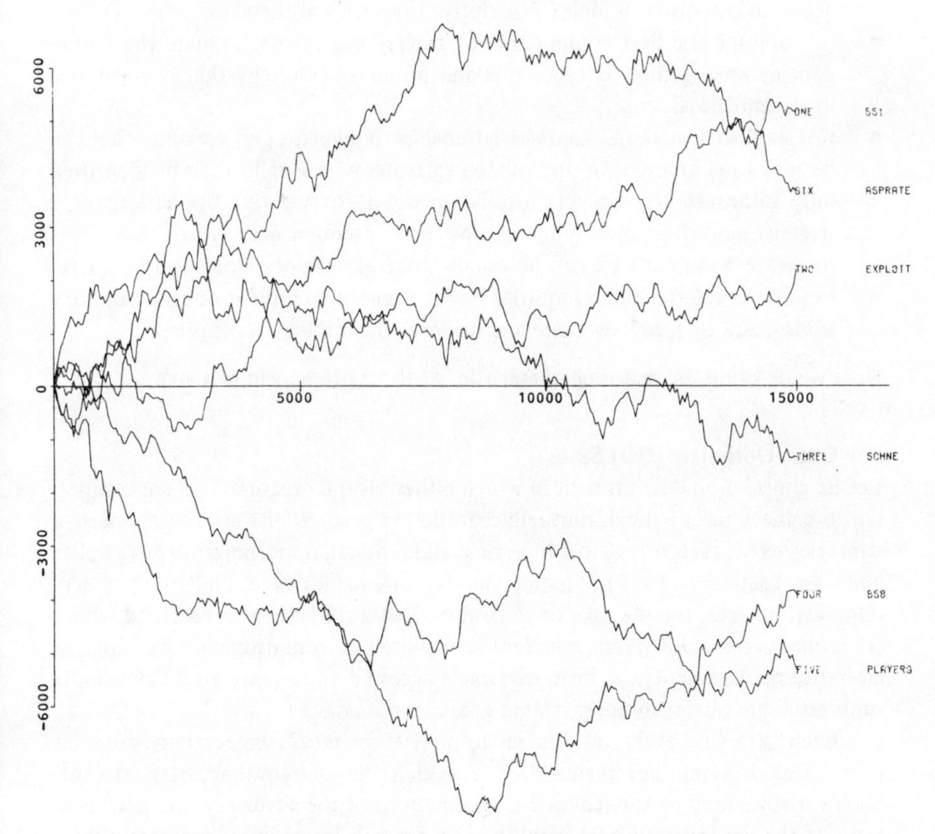

Fig. 4 – The change-in-purse-size vs. game number is shown for six competing strategies (see text).

OUR CURRENT ACTIVITY

Relying on the experience gained in the work described above, we are now engaged in a long-term effort aimed at automatic analysis and synthesis of strategies. Our objectives can be summarised as follows:

- to identify adequate computer representations of static and learning strategies, which representations can then be effectively and efficiently employed both in a simulated world and in direct interaction with the real world;
- to develop techniques which analyse strategies, measure their performance, and identify and evaluate their components ('credit assignment'), under most or all conditions;

- to observe strategies in action – either in a sequence of unperturbed confrontations with others or under 'laboratory conditions' when the environment is specified according to some experimental design – in order to generate computer models ('descriptive theories') of them;
- to combine the best components of several strategies, eliminate the redundancies among these components and produce a strategy that is normative in the statistical sense;
- to establish stochastic, causal relationships between open variables that can be measured at any time and hidden variables whose values can be identified only intermittently or periodically, in order to find out the actions of a strategy, and their underlying reasons and consequences;
- to create a system that can be taught strategies via principles and high-level examples, able to make inquiries about vague, incomplete or contradictory advice, and to apply, evaluate and improve the strategy so acquired.

Next we describe the major characteristics of three projects in this area.

The Quasi-Optimizer (QO) System

Let us consider an environment in which either several organisations are competing to achieve an identical, mutually conflicting goal, or else a set of alternative strategies exist, each trying to win against an identical, opposing strategy (Findler and van Leeuwen (1979), Findler and Martins (1980) and Findler (1982b)). (One can assume, for the sake of generality, that a *goal vector* is specified whose components need not be independent in real-life confrontations; for example, in air-battle management, the ratio of targets accessed and enemy air defence units suppressed are obviously inter-related goal components.)

Each strategy evaluates the environment by measuring certain variables (numerical or symbolic) available to it, which the strategy considers relevant. Such variables may be the real or assumed actions of the adversary, the perceived state of the confrontation, availability and capabilities of friendly forces, threat estimates, criticality and vulnerability of the adversary's and our resources, etc. An important component of a strategy is interpreting these measurements and incorporating them in the process of making decisions that can lead to goal achievement (and to prevent goal-achievement by the adversaries).

The environment as perceived by the strategy is unclear because some information may be unavailable, missing (risky or uncertain, according to whether or not the relevant *a priori* probability distributions are known, respectively) or obscured by noise (caused accidentally or by deliberate obfuscation). If the decisions based on such incomplete or inconsistent information are less sound than those of the adversaries, resources will be wasted and goal achievement will be farther removed.

Let us now consider how we could generate a new strategy. The system has to generate automatically a model (a *descriptive theory*) of every participating strategy through observation and measurements. It then has to assign to each component of the models some measure of quality; that is, an outcome-dependent *allocation of credit* must be made.

The strategy obtainable from the best components of the model strategies is a *normative theory* which is potentially the best of all available ones, on the basis of the information accessible by us. This normative strategy is in fact only *quasi-optimum* for four reasons. First, the resulting strategy is optimum only against the original set of strategies considered. Another set may well employ controllers and indicators for decision-making that are superior to any in the 'training' set. Second, the strategy is normative only in the statistical sense. Fluctuations in the adverse strategies, whether accidental or deliberate, impair the performance of the QO strategy. Third, the adverse strategies may change over time and some aspects of their dynamic behaviour may necessitate a change in the QO strategy. Finally, the generation of both the descriptive theories (models) and of the normative theory (the QO theory) is based on approximate and fallible measurements.

The system under development employs the following modules.

(i) The *QO-1* (Findler and Martins (1980)) assumes a monotonic strategy response surface and uses either exhaustive search or binary chopping to construct a descriptive theory of static (non-learning) strategies.

(ii) The *QO-2* (Findler, Mazur and McCall (1982)) extrapolates a finite sequence of learning trees, each representing the same strategy at different stages of development, and computes their asymptotic form. The latter will then be used in constructing the normative theory.

(iii) The *QO-3* (Findler (1982c)) minimises the total number of experiments QO-1 has to perform. It no longer assumes that the strategy response surface is monotonic and will eventually also deal with multi-dimensional responses. QO-3 starts with a balanced incomplete block design for experiments and computes dynamically the specifications for each subsequent experiment. In other words, the levels of the decision variables in any single experiment and the length of the sequence of experiments depend on the responses obtained in previous experiments.

(iv) The *QO-4* performs the credit assignment. That is, it identifies the components of a strategy and assigns to each a quality measure of the 'outcomes'. An outcome need not be only the immediate result of a sequence of actions prescribed by the strategy but can also involve long-range consequences of planned actions.

(v) The *QO-5* constructs a 'Super Strategy' by combining strategy components associated with outcomes of a quality above a threshold value.

(vi) The *QO-6* generates a Quasi-Optimum strategy from the Super Strategy by eliminating its inconsistencies and redundancies. It also tests and verifies the QO strategy for completeness.

The Advice Taker/Inquirer System (AT/I)

The objective of this system (Findler, Sicherman and Feuerstein (1979)) is to establish a man–machine environment in which a human adviser can teach strategies of confrontation on-line, through *principles* and high-level *examples.* The principles and examples normally consist of situations and recommended actions. (Principles describe rather general situations defined in a flexible manner whereas examples are specific and illustrate appropriate behaviour in a general situation by analogy with a particular one. Actions can either adhere to some general guidelines or follow a set of sharply defined prescriptions.) Whenever the system finds the advice given to be vague, incomplete or inconsistent with previously imparted knowledge, it makes inquiries and asks for clarification. The adviser can define and re-define the components of a principle at any time. He can also override temporarily the strategy taught so far by issuing an *order.*

The system does not start out with a blank memory. It knows the rules governing the confrontation, the variables, and the ranges of their values within the situation space. The adviser can at any time:

(i) define variables, functions, general and specific actions, confrontation-related adjectives, nouns and verbs – in terms of constants, confrontation parameters, current values, overall and moving averages of statistical values, basic confrontation actions, and Boolean and relational operators;
(ii) define principles of a strategy which connect a situation (specified as a Boolean combination of ranges of statistical variables – again current values, overall or moving averages) to some general or specific action;
(iii) give high-level examples by connecting sharply specified situations to direct confrontation actions;
(iv) make inquiries about definitions, principles, and values of statistical variables stored so far;
(v) issue an order which temporarily overrides the strategy acquired so far.

In turn, the system can

(a) ask for clarification whenever new definitions are vague or conflict with stored ones, or the strategy is incomplete in not covering the whole confrontation space;
(b) return exemplary actions in user-specified confrontation situations, in accordance with the strategy acquired;
(c) display definitions, principles, confrontation parameters, values of variables, etc.

Random number generators also have a role in defining game-theoretically mixed strategies. A sense of time has also to be incorporated in the 'tool kit' of definitions, whether it refers to real time or to an event counter.

We note two important facilities to be used in specifying principles. Let us call these *Adviser-Assigned* and *Adviser-Defined* Adversary Types (AAAT and ADAT, respectively). In the former case, the adviser *assigns* a certain adversary to one or more categories (Adversary Types) named by him. In the latter case, the adviser *defines* categories by Boolean combinations of ranges of statistical variables, which are regularly or continually collected over the adversary's actions. (The variables can refer to current values, or overall or moving averages.) At prescribed intervals, the system compares the adversary behaviour with the specifications of all ADATs. Accordingly, each adversary (at that time) may belong to various Adviser-Defined Adversary Types. Thus the principle can prescribe an action for all *such* adversaries that satisfy the definition conditions of the Adversary Type at hand.

Adviser-defined nouns can reasonably be required to be unambiguous. However, adjectives (and, to some extent, verbs) must often have different meanings when used to modify different types of nouns (compare a 'strong attack' with a 'strong concentration'). The AT/I system has to distinguish (at least) four different classes of instances:

(i) Patent: confrontation parameters, statistical variables, AT/I's own resources (e.g. 'If your air superiority is more than 2:1, seek air battles').
(ii) Interactive: the adversary's actions during current confrontation (e.g. 'If the adversary is bringing up additional resources, assume a holding position').
(iii) Statistical: accumulated data about the adversary's past behaviour (e.g. 'If the adversary is self-confident, make sudden attacks').
(iv) Inferential: assumptions about the intentions or events behind the adversary's behaviour (e.g. 'If the enemy appears to have received additional supplies, wait for confirmation').

This classification is neither exhaustive nor exclusive. If the Definition Manager, a part of the programming system, cannot decide unambiguously how to classify components of the definition, it has to consult the human adviser.

Another difficulty rests with the need to resolve a situation-dependent conflict between principles of global and momentary relevance. Furthermore, the system must be able to generate disambiguating questions whenever the adviser specifies inconsistent priorities for the principles.

Finally, we note that to teach a strategy by telling *how* to do things in general is more efficient and less error-prone than to tell *what* to do in every relevant situation. An AT/I-like system would have practical usefulness in doing this. Human experts would specify, via a sophisticated interaction with the machine, a number of alternative strategies. Other components, such as a QO-like system, would then generate uniformly structured models of each strategy. A prescriptive, quasi-optimum strategy would then finally be constructed from these.

The system under construction employs the following modules:

(i) The *AT/I-1* constructs the framework for the flow of information and control between the AT/I system and the adviser.
(ii) The *AT/I-2* converts the principles and high-level examples into a canonical form and stores them. Next it embeds them into an initially skeleton strategy which then becomes employable.
(iii) The *AT/I-3* eliminates inconsistencies and incompletenesses from the strategy acquired, in part by interacting with the adviser.
(iv) The *AT/I-4* tests (verifies) and evaluates the strategy constructed according to a metric which is independent of any particular strategy.

The Generalised Production Rules System (GPR)

The underlying motivations for the actions prescribed by a strategy, the actions themselves, and their consequences are not necessarily observable and measurable at any desired time. The values of such *hidden variables* can be identified only at certain times, either intermittently or periodically. At other times, their values have to be estimated. In contrast, the *open variables* are readily measurable at any time. The estimation is based on generalised production rules expressing stochastic, causal relations between open and hidden variables. Either can be cause or effect. The GPR system (Findler (1980b), Findler (1982a), Findler, Brown, Lo and You (1982), Findler (1983c)) is designed to provide decision support for expert systems in need of numerical estimates of hidden variable values.

A knowledge base is established over a period of measurements. It consists of an ordered set of generalised production rules of the form

$$W_r / M_{ijk} / T_{jm} \Rightarrow V_m(H_n) \quad : Q_r \tag{4}$$

Here W_r is the number of rules that have been pooled to form the rth rule. M_{ijk} is the ith combination of the parameters of the jth basic pattern (morph) (Findler and Morgado (1982)) describing the behaviour of the kth open variable (OV). T_{jm} is the difference in time (timelag) or in space (distance) between the start of the jth morph (in case of a trend) or its occurrence (in case of a sudden change or step function), and the point of time or space at which the nth HV, H_n, assumes its mth value, V_m. This difference may be positive – when the OV is the cause and thus precedes the HV, the effect – or negative in the opposite case. The term 'lag' is used for T_{jm}, whether it refers to a timelag or distance. Q_r is the credibility level of the rth rule. It lies between 0 and 1, and depends on two factors:

- how well the morph fits the datapoints over its domain, and
- how many and how similar the rules were that have been pooled to form the rule at hand.

When an estimate of a HV value is desired at a certain value of the lag variable, the user has to provide in its vicinity a sequence of values of all available OVs that are assumed to be causally related to the HV. These sequences are then submitted to the morph-fitting program (MFP). The system then looks in the knowledge base for the *N* best estimates (*N* specified by the user) coming from rules that

- connect the HV sought and the available OVs;
- refer to the same type of morph as the newly fitted one;
- involve morph parameters and lag values that are 'similar enough' to those in the query, i.e. that are within the user-specified range of pooling rules.

The so-called *confidence level* of the estimate, C_e, depends on the credibility level of the rule used as well as how well the new morph fits its datapoints and how close its parameters are to those of the morph matched in the knowledge base.

Let us now assume that the estimation is performed and up to *N* values of the HV are returned for each lag value that yields such a possibility. The system will calculate the average of the *N* estimates weighted by their confidence levels. This process thus provides datapoints, each specifying weighted average HV vs. lag value, over the whole range of interest. The system then finally invokes the MFP to produce the functional form desired. Its validity is based on the assumption that the OVs, whose morphs were used for the estimation, obeyed the same laws when the observations were made for the knowledge base as when they were measured for the estimation. Furthermore, the relations between and within the groups of OVs and HVs do not, statistically speaking, vary over time.

The system employs the following modules.

(i) The *GPR-1* fits a minimal set of basic patterns, morphs, to a sequence of open variable datapoints.
(ii) The *GPR-2* establishes rules between sets of parametric values of morphs describing open variable behaviour and individual values of hidden variables.
(iii) The *GPR-3* pools rules that connect the same open variable and hidden variable and satisfy certain statistical and rule-generation criteria. The number and credibility of rules increase with experience.
(iv) The *GPR-4* estimates the values of hidden variables at desired time points.
(v) The *GPR-5* extends the system to distributed processing and intelligence. It merges source files and knowledge bases, established by satellite computers at different observation points, if certain statistical and file-generation criteria are satisfied – as verified by the system automatically.
(vi) The *GPR-6* extends the system's capabilities to estimating the *functional form* of hidden variable distributions rather than estimating only individual values of hidden variables.

ACKNOWLEDGEMENTS

It is impossible to list every past member of the now extinct 'Poker Group'. We estimate that more than 40 people have, at one time or another, contributed to its efforts and we are grateful for their ideas, programming and critical comments. NSF Grants GJ-658, GJ-658/A*1, and MCS76-2478 provided partial support to these studies.

The experience gained in the work on Draw Poker is utilised in our current activity on automatic analysis and synthesis of strategies. We are indebted to the other members of our Group for Computer Studies of Strategies: (in random order) Shinji Moriya, Ron Lo, Neal Mazur, Bill Chang, Robert Cromp, Paul Duerig, Paul Ehrler, Michael Belofsky, Richard Wozniak, Gerald Donlon, Nancy Strohmeier and Kulbir Arora. The efforts of this group, as well as the writing of this paper, have been supported by the AFOSR Grant 81-0220.

Finally, we acknowledge the permission of the Association for Computing Machinery, Inc. to reprint excerpts and one of the figures from our prior publication (Findler (1977)).

APPENDIX

Outline of the Rules of Draw Poker as Played by the SUNY-Buffalo Poker System

A standard 52-card pack is used. After each game, the turn to deal passes to the left. Before each deal, every player pays a fixed number of chips (the *ante*) into a pool (the *pot*) which will ultimately be awarded to the player with the best hand.

The dealer deals five cards face down to every player. The game then passes through six States:

1. *Pre-draw opening state.* Starting with the player at the dealer's left, each player either *opens* by announcing a bet and paying the stated amount into the pot, or *checks* (i.e. passes) by betting nothing. As soon as some player opens, the game enters State 2. If no player opens, the same player shuffles the cards and deals again.
2. *Pre-draw betting state.* Every player in turn may *fold* (i.e. drop) by paying nothing and withdrawing from the game, *call* by paying enough to make his total contribution equal to the current bet, or *raise* by increasing the bet and paying enough to make his total contribution equal to the new bet. State 2 ends when each player has either met the current bet (i.e. stayed *alive*) or folded.
3. *Drawing state.* Each active player in turn may discard some of his cards face down. (In real games of Poker, it is customary to limit the exchange to three cards.) The dealer gives him the same number of new cards face down from the undealt portion of the pack.

4. *Post-draw opening state.* This state is just like State 1 except that players who have folded do not take part and if no player opens, the game proceeds to State 6.
5. *Post-draw betting state.* This state is just like State 2.
6. *Showdown state.* The players who have not folded reveal their hands in unison. The player with the highest-ranking hand wins the pot. In a tie, the winners share the pot equally.

In descending order of strength (and rarity), the nine types of Poker hands are:

1. *Straight flush* five cards of the same suit and in sequence, e.g. H9-H8-H7-H6-H5.
2. *Four of a kind* four cards of the same rank, e.g. SK-HK-DK-CK-H6.
3. *Full house* three cards of one rank and two cards of another, e.g. S2-D2-C2-HJ-CJ.
4. *Flush* five cards of the same suit, e.g. DA-D10-D8-D5-D3.
5. *Straight* five cards in sequence, regardless of suit, e.g. H5-C4-C3-S2-HA.
6. *Three of a kind* three cards of the same rank, e.g. H10-D10-C10-DA-C4.
7. *Two Pair* two cards of one rank and two of another, e.g. S9-C9-H5-C5-H8.
8. *Pair* two cards of the same rank, e.g. D6-C6-S10-C5-H2.
9. *High-card* a hand belonging to none of the above types, e.g. SA-CQ-H9-S8-S4.

The cards rank Ace(highest)-King-Queen-Jack-10-9-8-7-6-5-4-3-2(lowest), except that in straights and straight flushes the Ace may rank high (A-K-Q-J-10) or low (5-4-3-2-A). Hands of the same type are adjudged by the ranks of their cards; for example, K-K-3-3-6 ('kings up') beats Q-Q-J-J-A ('Queens up'), and 9-9-9-3-3 ('nines full') beats 8-8-8-K-K ('eights full').

REFERENCES AND BIBLIOGRAPHY

Crawford, J. R. (1961), *How to be a consistent winner in the most popular card games.* Garden City, New York: Dolphin Books.

Findler, N. V. (1973), Computer experiments on forming and optimising heuristic rules, in *Artificial and Human Thinking,* Elithorn, A. and Jones D. (eds.), Amsterdam: Elsevier, 177–188.

Findler, N. V. (1977), Studies in machine cognition using the game of Poker, *Comm. ACM,* **20**, 230–245.

Findler, N. V. (1979), Computer Poker, *Scientific American,* 144–151.

Findler, N. V. (1980a), Aspects of computer learning, *Cybernetics and Systems,* **11**, 65–84. (Also reprinted in Findler, N. V., Horn, W. and Trappl, R. (eds), *Progress in Cybernetics and Systems Research,* **11**, Washington DC: Hemisphere Publishing, 1982.)

Findler, N. V. (1980b), Pattern recognition and generalised production systems in strategy formation, Proc. Fifth Internat. Conf. on Pattern Recognition, Miami, Florida.

Findler, N. V. (1982a), A multi-level learning technique using production system, *Cybernetics and Systems,* **13**, 25–30.

Findler, N. V. (1982b), An overview of the quasi-optimiser system (submitted for publication).

Findler, N. V. (1982c), On a system that dynamically generates its own experimental design (submitted for publication).

Findler, N.V. (1983a), An expert subsystem based on generalised production rules, *Proc. Sixteenth Hawaii Internat. Conf. on System Sciences, Vol. 1,* 401–405.

Findler, N. V. (1983b), Automatic analysis and synthesis of strategies: a new branch of Artificial Intelligence, *Proc. IEEE Phoenix Conf. on Computers and Communication,* 239–245.

Findler, N. V. (1983c), On a computer-based theory of strategies, Kybernetes, **12**, 89–97.

Findler, N. V., Brown, J. E., Lo, R. and You, H. Y. (1982), A module to estimate numerical values of hidden variables for expert systems (forthcoming in International Journal of Man-Machine Studies).

Findler, N. V., Klein, H., Gould, W., Kowal, A. and Menig, J. (1972), Studies on decision making using the game of Poker, *Proc. IFIP Congress 71,* Amsterdam: North-Holland, 1448–1459.

Findler, N. V., Klein, H., Johnson, R. C., Kowal, A., Levine, Z. and Menig, J. (1974), Heuristic programmers and their gambling machines, *Proc. ACM National Conf., San Diego, CA,* 28–37.

Findler, N. V., Klein, H. and Levine, Z. (1973), Experiments with inductive discovery processes leading to heuristics in a Poker program, in *Cognitive Processes and Systems*, Beckmann, M., Goos, G. and Künzi, H. P. (eds.), Berlin: Springer, 257–266.

Findler, N. V. and Martins, J. P. (1980), On automating computer model construction, the second step toward a Quasi-Optimizer system, *Journal of Computer and Optimization Sciences,* **2**, 119–136.

Findler, N. V., Mazur, N. and McCall, B. (1982), A note on computing the asymptotic form of a limited sequence of decision trees (forthcoming in *Information Sciences*).

Findler, N. V. and Morgado, E. (1982), Morph-fitting: an effective technique of approximation, *IEEE Trans. on Pattern Analysis and Machine Intelligence* (forthcoming).

Findler, N. V., Sicherman, G. and Feuerstein, S. (1979), Teaching strategies to an Advice Taker/Inquirer system, *Proc. Euro. IFIP 79 Conf., London, England,* 457–465.

Findler, N. V. and van Leeuwen, J. (1979), The complexity of decision trees, the Quasi-Optimizer, and the power of heuristic rules, *Information and Control,* **40**, 1–19.

Jacoby, O. (1947), *Oswald Jacoby on Poker.* Garden City: New York, Doubleday.

Morehead, A. H. (ed.) (1964), *Official Rules of Card Games* New York: Crest Books.

Morehead, A. H., Frey, R. and Mott-Smith, G. (1964), *The New Complete Hoyle* Garden City, New York: Garden City Books.

Pearson, C. E. (1981), The Zadeh Poker Strategy and How I Approximate it. Unpublished Master's Project, Department of Computer Science, State University of New York at Buffalo.

Roy, T. L. (1976), The statistically Fair Poker Player. Unpublished Master's Project, Department of Computer Science, State University of New York at Buffalo.

Sicherman, G. L. (1979), Implementing Zadeh's Bluffing Strategy, *Poker Group Internal Memo No. 234.*

Wallace, F. R. (1968), Advanced Concepts of Poker. Wilmington, Delaware: I and O Publishing Co..

Yardley, H. O. (1961), The Education of a Poker Player. New York: Pocket Books.

Zadeh, N. (1974), Winning Poker Systems. Englewood Cliffs, New Jersey: Prentice-Hall.

18

A set of functions to play New Eleusis

Michael J. A. Berry
I. P. Sharp Associates, 148 State Street, Suite 415, Boston, Massachusetts 02109, USA

ABSTRACT

New Eleusis is a game used to study problem solving. The author has written a set of APL programs which employ hypothetico-deductive reasoning to play this game.

THE GAME

New Eleusis is a card game, invented by Robert Abbott, which has been used to simulate an aspect of scientific problem solving. Gardner (1977) calls it a model of 'the search for truth (scientific, mathematical, or metaphysical)'. (See also Romesburg (1978).) The set of APL functions to play New Eleusis which are described here constitutes an attempt to simulate the type of intelligent problem solving through experimentation commonly known as the 'scientific method'.

Players of Eleusis use inductive or hypothetico-deductive reasoning to determine the 'laws of nature' which the dealer, referred to as God, has laid out. God makes up a rule governing the order in which cards from an ordinary deck may succeed one another. The rule may take any form, but it must be determined by the cards themselves rather than external factors. Examples of rules are: every prime numbered card must be followed by a red card; no two cards of the same suit may be played successively; every club must be followed by an even card; etc. The players experiment by playing cards which are then either accepted or rejected by God. The accepted cards are placed on the 'main-line' and rejected cards join 'sidelines' so that the entire history of the game is visible. As a pattern of cards emerges on the table, players develop hypotheses about the rule governing play which they can test by playing additional strings of cards. See Abbott (1977) for a detailed description of the rules of Eleusis.

Eleusis is of interest to both psychologists and computer scientists (see, for example, Dietterich (1980) and Gorman (1981)) because it models a logical process which is generally thought of as being peculiar to intelligent beings. The task which faces an Eleusis player may be broken into several steps. First the player must notice patterns in the layout and come up with hypotheses to explain them. The player must then construct experiments which will confirm or disconfirm the hypotheses. If several rules seem to describe the observed patterns, the player must decide which rules are more likely to be correct. When a player thinks that he has discovered God's rule, he becomes a prophet and takes over God's role of passing judgement on the plays of other players. Naturally, the prophet must be capable of explaining the rule to the other players. The program discussed here describes rules in fully grammatical English sentences. These activities would seem to require a fair amount of intelligence so it is perhaps surprising that a relatively simple collection of APL functions can perform as well as most human players on a stylised version of this 'search for truth'.

It is convenient to refer to the Eleusis 'program', but it actually consists of over fifty function modules, most of which are written in direct definition.

Direct definition is a new form of representing functions in APL introduced by Dr. K. E. Iverson, inventor of the language. It consists simply of the name of the function followed by an expression in terms of the left and right arguments. Any variables assigned are strictly local to the function. There is no branching and so none of the headaches associated with flow of control. A conditional form exists which allows either of two statements to be executed depending on the value of a boolean expression which separates them. The existence of the conditional implies the possibility of recursion since any APL function may call any other including itself.

A direct definition function is a self-contained module which can be changed or replaced without affecting the rest of the system. The Eleusis program can be made to play new strategies or take different information into account by replacing modules such as one might replace circuit boards in an electronic device.

To find rules the program applies various 'screen functions' or filters to the data. Other functions are applied to the resulting boolean vectors (prime/not prime), (red/black), etc. to search for patterns. Different functions look for different patterns. The most common types are repeating periodic patterns and precedence relationships. These types may be joined by expressions using the words 'and', 'or' and 'following'.

The list of screen functions is simply a character array, each row of which is the APL expression for the screen. The rules are encoded as vectors of number pairs. The first number in each pair is an index to the list of functions. The second number is the result which would be returned by that function if the proposition were true. A translation function uses these pairs to build up the English phrases describing a rule.

The list of screen functions can be easily updated. For example, if the program were to play against mathematicians instead of psychologists, more numerically oriented screens might be added. Functions to look for new types of patterns may be added just as easily although their definitions are usually more complicated. (See accompanying program description for details.)

ORGANISING THE DATA

One of APL's great strengths has always been its ability to deal with rectangular arrays as easily as with scalars. Unfortunately, not all data are rectangular. Until recently, dealing with 'ragged' data presented some difficulty.

To get around this problem while retaining the power and generality of APL's array operations, several implementations now include nested arrays. Any APL object may be 'enclosed' and treated like a scalar. This allows it, in itself, to be an element of another array.

One of the greatest difficulties in a problem solving exercise such as Eleusis is keeping track of the pertinent information. The program uses nested arrays for this purpose to great advantage.

The program maintains a 'prediction matrix' to help it quickly choose cards which will yield the maximum amount of information when played. It consists of a row for each rule under consideration and a column for each past and future turn. Each element of the matrix is an enclosed vector of cards allowed by rule i at turn j. Various functions such as intersection and union can be applied along either the rows or the columns of the array to answer many questions about the rules. The program also uses this array to tell when one rule implies the same plays as another so that the syntactically more complex rule may be thrown out.

Regular non-nested arrays also play a large role in the pattern recognition functions. A boolean connectivity matrix is maintained to keep track of which rules might reasonably be joined with an 'or'. Through matrix operations on this matrix and an array representing patterns in each of the screens, all the reasonable 'or' rules can be generated at one time for testing.

CONCLUSION

I hope that this work has shown that the great power of APL can profitably be brought to bear on problems in artificial intelligence. Indeed, the richness and generality of APL's set of primitives and the way in which the language lends itself to a style of writing which emphasises small modules which can be changed or updated without affecting the rest of the system makes it an ideal language in which to write any complex or experimental system. The Eleusis example used in this paper is non-trivial. Several teams have set out to write Eleusis-playing programs in the traditional languages of AI and given up (Robert Abbott, 1980 and 1981 – personal communications). The only other working Eleusis program of which the author is aware is that of Dietterich (1980), which required 9,000 lines of Pascal.

REFERENCES

Abbott, Robert (1977), *The New Eleusis,* Box 1175 GPO, New York, NY 10001, USA.

Dietterich, Thomas G. (1980), The Methodology of Knowledge Layers for Inducing Descriptions of Sequentially Ordered Events, University of Illinois Thesis, #UIUCDCS-R-80-1-24.

Gardner, Martin (1977), On Playing New Eleusis, the Game that Simulates the Search for Truth, *Scientific American,* October, 18–25.

Gorman, Michael E. (1981), How Communication and Confirmatory Strategies Affect the 'Search for Truth', Doctoral Dissertation, University of New Hampshire.

Romesburg, Charles H. (1978), Simulating scientific inquiry with the card game Eleusis, *Science Education,* **63**(5), 599–608.

APPENDIX – ELEUSIS PROGRAM DESCRIPTION

The program acts as a player of the game New Eleusis which was designed to model the hypothetico-deductive reasoning which is at the heart of the scientific method.

The program is written in an experimental version of Sharp-APL which includes nested arrays. The functions used are largely in direct definition so the system is highly modular.

The program will play 'Solitaire' or as one of a group of players vying to discover a secret rule.

Examples of the screen functions used to isolate a single aspect of a string of cards.

```
SUIT: ⌊ω÷100
COLOR: ω>300
NUMERIC: 100|ω
FACE: (100|ω)∊11 12 13
PRIME: (NUMERIC ω)∊1 2 3 5 7 11 13
```

Examples of several direct definition functions which together perform a complex task. (In this case, searching for rules of the form 'Every Nth card starting with the Ith meets condition A or condition B').

```
ORRULES: MATCHORαOUTALT ORFNS OROPω
MATCHOR:ENCODE ⍉ALTS, (0≠ω)+̸ω, (,CM) +̸PAIRGEN ORFNS
OUTALT: (ALTGENα)+.×<+⃥∧/[2] (αTWISTαALTMASKω)∧.≤⍉ω
      ⍝ω IS MATRIX OF OR RULE HITS.
        α IS NUMBER OF ALTERNATIONS TO LOOK FOR
PAIRGEN: ((1↑ρω)+̸ω, (ρω)ρOR, 0), ((ρω)* 2 1)ρω
```

```
ALTGEN: 5⊥ (Z[ ↓ ((⍳⍺)/ ⍉⍳⍺), [1.5] Z←PIOTA⍺]), [.5] (⍳⍺)/⍳⍺ ⍝CALLED
      BY OUTALT
TWIST: (0 0,−⍺) ↓ ((2 ↑ RHO) ⍴ (RHO[1] ⍴ (RHO ← ⍴⍵) [2])/¯1 + PIOTA⍺)
      ⍉ ⍵ ⍝CALLED BY OUTALT. LINES UP MASK.
ALTMASK: (⍳⍺)/[1] 0 = (⍳⍺)∘.|((0, ⍺) + ⍴⍵) ⍴⍳⍺ + ¯1 ↑ ⍴⍵
      ⍝ CALLED BY OUTALT
PIOTA: (, (⍳⍵)∘.≥⍳⍵)/(⍵*2) ⍴⍳⍵
```

A Sample Game

One human player versus the program. God's secret rule is that each card must differ from the one before it by 1, 2 or 3.

```
      PLAY
SEED CARD: 7C
PLAY: 9H
ACCEPTED? YES
PLAY: M
MY PLAY IS QC
OK? YES
PLAY: 3D
ACCEPTED? NO
PLAY: M
MY PLAY IS KH
OK? YES
PLAY: AC
ACCEPTED? NO
PLAY: M
MY PLAY IS 2S
OK? NO
PLAY: 7H
ACCEPTED? NO
PLAY: M
MY PLAY IS 2H
OK? NO
PLAY: AH
ACCEPTED? NO
PLAY: M
MY PLAY IS AS
OK? NO
PLAY: 4H
ACCEPTED? NO
PLAY: M
MY PLAY IS KC
```

OK? NO
PLAY: 10H
ACCEPTED? YES
PLAY: M
MY PLAY IS 6S
OK? NO
PLAY: 6C
ACCEPTED? NO
PLAY: M
MY PLAY IS AS
OK? NO
PLAY: 7C
ACCEPTED? YES
PLAY: M
MY PLAY IS 6H
OK? YES
PLAY: 9C
ACCEPTED? YES
PLAY: M
MY PLAY IS 4C
OK? NO
PLAY: JC
ACCEPTED? YES
PLAY: M
MY PLAY IS AD
OK? NO
PLAY: 7D
ACCEPTED? NO
PLAY: M
MY PLAY IS JD
OK? NO
PLAY: 10D
ACCEPTED? YES
PLAY: M
MY PLAY IS 8S 7C 5C 7S 8S
OK YES
I DECLARE MYSELF TO BE A PROPHET.
PLAY: →
AT THE END OF THE GAME, THE PATTERN LOOKED
LIKE THIS:
15 ON THE MAINLINE, AND 16 ON SIDE LINES
MAIN SIDE

7C |
9H |
QC | 3*D*
KH | *AC* 2*S* 7*H* 2*H* *AH* *AS* 4*H* *KC*
10*H* | 6*S* 6*C* *AS*
7C |
6H |
9C | 4*C*
JC | *AD* 7*D* *JD*
10*D* |
8*S* |
7*C* |
5*C* |
7*S* |
8*S* |

THERE IS ALWAYS A CHANGE OF NUMERIC VALUE
NO CARD DIFFERS FROM ITS PREDECESSOR BY MORE THAN 3

19

The three-cushion billiard game

H. de Swaan Arons
Delft University of Technology, Department of Mathematics
Julianalaan 132, 2628 BL Delft, The Netherlands

ABSTRACT

Three-cushion billiards is a popular billiard game in many West European and South American countries and in Japan. Playing three-cushion billiards requires a good technique for accurate shooting but this is not sufficient. The stroke indicates the end of a decision process during which a player confronted with the given positions of the three balls on the table surface has to find a potentially successful shot. This under the restriction that the cue ball must touch the cushions at least three times before striking the second object ball. For this purpose a player has to recognise position characteristics and has to make a sequence of decisions based on more or less vague grounds.

In the paper a computer program is presented that has been developed to be indiscernible from human playing. For that reason it has interesting connections with artificial intelligence.

INTRODUCTION

Three-cushion billiards is an attractive billiard game and is popular in Western Europe (particularly in Belgium, the Netherlands, France, Austria, West Germany and Denmark), Japan and South America. Its popularity is increasing in the United States but there the 'pocket' billiard games are still more popular.

In three-cushion billiards a *carambole* is made when a player with his cue ball hits the other two (object) balls under the restriction that the cue ball must touch the cushions at least three times before striking the second object ball. Any order is permissible: the cue ball may strike three cushions before coming in contact with the two object balls; two cushions, object ball, another cushion or more and then the other object ball etc. More often the method is the cue ball against an object ball, then three or more cushions and the other object ball. See Fig. 1.

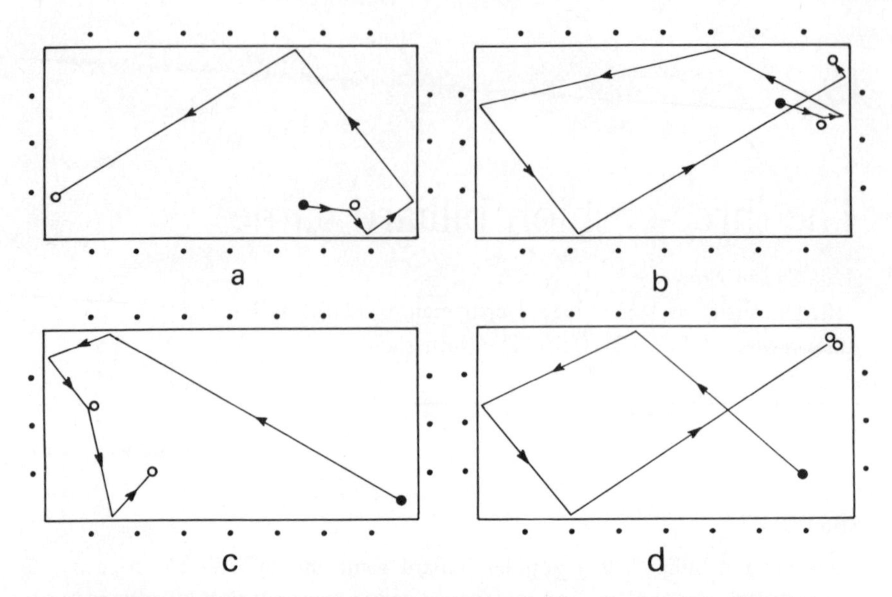

Fig. 1 – Examples of valid three-cushion shots. (a) a three-cushion shot, (b) a five-cushion shot, (c) a three-cushion shot with the cue ball first striking two cushions, and (d) a bank shot via three cushions.

Each successful shot results in a point score for the player and entitles him to another shot. The game is played on a billiard-table twice as long as it is wide, 2.84×1.42 m^2. The balls have a radius of 0.0305 m.

It is considered a rather difficult game. A player's ability is given by the average of points made per turn, for instance throughout a tournament. A top international player needs about 50 turns for 60 points (average of 1.200). It also means that on the average he has missed 49 times.

There are many important aspects of the game, but here we confine ourselves to mentioning only a few of them. First, an attempt to score a point often appears to be crossed by an accidental contact of the cue ball with the first object ball, and the question is how to avoid this so-called *kiss.* Another point of interest is the use of the widely publicised and much sought-after *diamond systems* (e.g. Ceulemans (1980), Marty (1967) and Conti (1961)). Diamonds are spots on the wooden rails of the table, seven on each long rail and three on each short rail; they can be and are used to estimate the trajectories of the balls (particularly the cue ball) on the relatively large table surface and using the diamonds could improve the three-cushion play. Further, it proves possible to make a carambole in such a way that the positions in which the balls rest after the shot is completed make it most probable that the next shot can be easily made. Playing in this way enhances the chances of building up a run (a number of consecutive scores).

After this short introduction to three-cushion billiards we devote our attention to the player. From the first moment of observing the three balls, the player successively has to recognise position characteristics, to make a sequence of decisions and finally to shoot. This process in some way involves recognition, which is of great importance in making the right decisions, ultimately leading to a potentially successful shot. Modelling this process has been the aim of our efforts. It requires insight into a player's thinking and decision making, and modelling these human activities has many connections with artificial intelligence. Neither the technique of shooting (the stroke) nor the mechanics of the shot (the motion of the balls, the balls hitting each other or the cushions) are considered here. However it is obvious that for the purpose mentioned above a computer model of the shot itself is indispensible to decide whether or not a shot could be successful. For a continuous-time model of the shot the reader is referred to Kooiman (1977) and Kooiman and de Swaan Arons (1977). A discrete-event version is given by de Swaan Arons (1981).

THE THREE-CUSHION BILLIARD GAME

A player is confronted by the positions of the three balls, one of which is the cue ball. In one way or another, he has to find a successful shot and to shoot accordingly. Now we are concerned with the player's considerations influencing his decisions and ultimately leading to a possibly successful three-cushion shot. For the time being, strategies (for instance shots deliberately taken to try to leave the balls safe for the opponent after they stop moving, with no real intention to make a point on the shot), nerves and other psychological factors are not considered.

A player's considerations are the result of a conscious or unconscious learning process. The considerations themselves are often unconscious, too, since practically all players appear not to be aware how they make up their minds, what they consider and in what order. Being unable to do so, they cannot supply a clear insight into their own thinking. So, in fact, the question is: what does a player think and decide in order to find a successful shot. These questions and their possible answers are of more general interest. For a long time man has been intrigued by his own thinking processes. Some knowledge of a player's thinking could help give more insight into human thinking in general. Some of a player's considerations are roughly known. For instance, one of the first things a player approaching the table will immediately notice are two object balls lying close together, enabling him to consider a so-called *bank shot.* Such a shot, where the cue ball strikes three or more cushions before hitting the two object balls, is generally judged easier to make. Further, quite often the choice of which of the two object balls is the first object ball is important. The relatively large table surface requires accurate cueing. So if a three-cushion shot has a good chance to be successful when played via the nearest object ball, a player will decide to consider such a shot first because the corresponding stroke can be performed more accurately. Also another decision could have been made, for instance in the case that one of the object balls is positioned near one of the corners. For more than one reason such a ball is preferred to be the second object ball. Many others of these ad hoc decisions can be mentioned. However, their (relative) importance can not easily be estimated and quite often one has to deal with conflicting choices. So, for the time being, only a few of such position characteristics, which are easily recognised by most players, are considered.

Another, even more important problem is the following. When the decision has been made concerning the choice of the first object ball, how does a player select a first serious attempt? One can safely assume that a player makes use of his experience, that is, he compares the positions of the balls (or some corresponding characteristics) with those saved in his memory in order to find a solution. However, we confine ourselves by only mentioning this rather difficult and unknown process.

Having thought of a possible shot, a player has to make many decisions. For instance, he has to decide whether or not the shot must be rejected because it is too risky. This is the case when it requires a stroke in which the cue tip hits the cue ball too far outside the centre, when it is not certain that the cushions are struck in the desired order or when the shot requires the cue ball to hit the first ball very thin, over too great a distance, etc.

Next, if the shot looks promising enough to him, he will try and refine the shot (in his thoughts). Again this involves a sequence of decisions concerning the velocity and precisely where the cue ball has to be struck and in what direction. If a possible shot is rejected, another one will be searched for. Finally, as a result of the thinking the player strikes the cue ball.

It is clear that the above describes a player's thinking only in global terms, but it is enough to create a rough conceptual model that can be put into mathematical terms. Once having available a working computer program some indications can be given about its validity.

A COMPUTER MODEL OF THREE-CUSHION BILLIARDS

In the previous section an attempt was made to put a player's thinking into words, to find out what decisions he has to make. Based on these first explorations a global model can be created as a next step to a computer model of three-cushion billiards. In this section a detailed description of such a model is given. It will be discussed in terms of the various blocks of the flow diagram in Fig. 2, which presents a global model of three-cushion billiards.

Immediately after having recognised the positions of the balls, a player is assumed to make a distinction between bank shots where no 'first' object ball has necessarily to be established and 'ordinary' shots. Although a player generally considers bank shots first, they will be looked at later on.

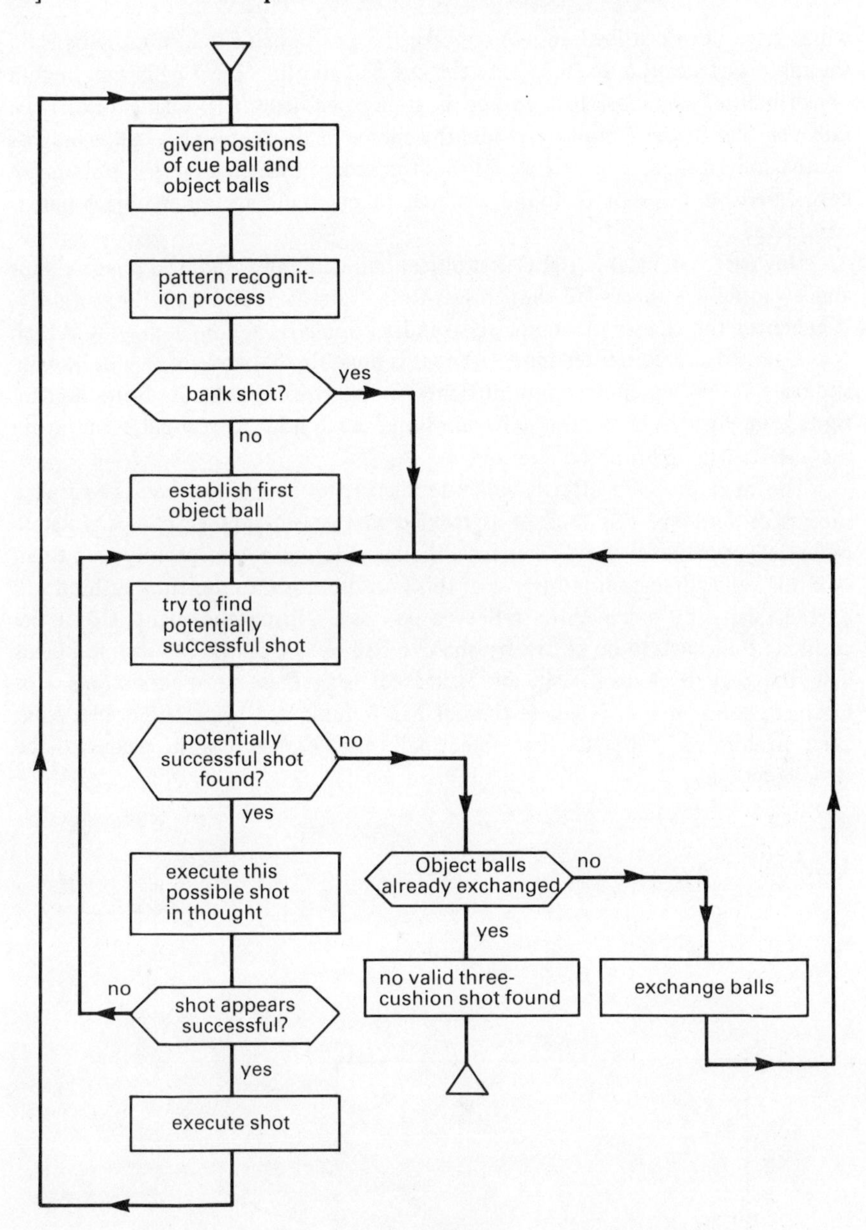

Fig. 2 – Flow diagram of a global model of three-cushion billiards.

In the case of the ordinary shots, the next thing to be done is to establish the first object ball. To be able to do so, criteria have to be developed which must be observed in some pattern recognition process. All criteria (some of which have been outlined above) concern the positions of one or more balls on the table surface: the distance between cue ball and the object balls, whether an object ball is lying close to a corner, in some specified areas, against one of the rails etc. Yet in the computer model the choice of the first object ball is only of relative importance. It merely establishes the order in which all possible shots are considered: if no shot is found via one object ball, the other object ball is considered.

However, taking the 'right' first object ball facilitates finding a possible shot and eventually a successful shot in less time. Moreover, and more importantly, it enhances the chance of finding shots indiscernible from human playing, which is the aim of the computer model. Yet it is possible that unwanted 'not human' shots are found which are quite difficult to discern automatically from 'human' shots, due to a lack of clear criteria. Some ideas how to recognise and avoid these shots will be proposed later on.

The next problem after having established the first object ball is to find a successful shot via this ball. It is tackled in two subsequent phases. First, a potentially successful shot is sought, although this will not necessarily lead to an eventual valid three-cushion shot. For this purpose, for the moment a cushion will unrealistically be assumed to reflect a ball as a mirror does light. Given the cushions that have to be struck by the cue ball before it hits the second object ball, the way back can easily be estimated using these ideal reflections. For instance, consider Fig. 3, where the cue ball is numbered 1 and object ball 2 has been established to be the first object ball (e.g. because it is the nearer of the two object balls).

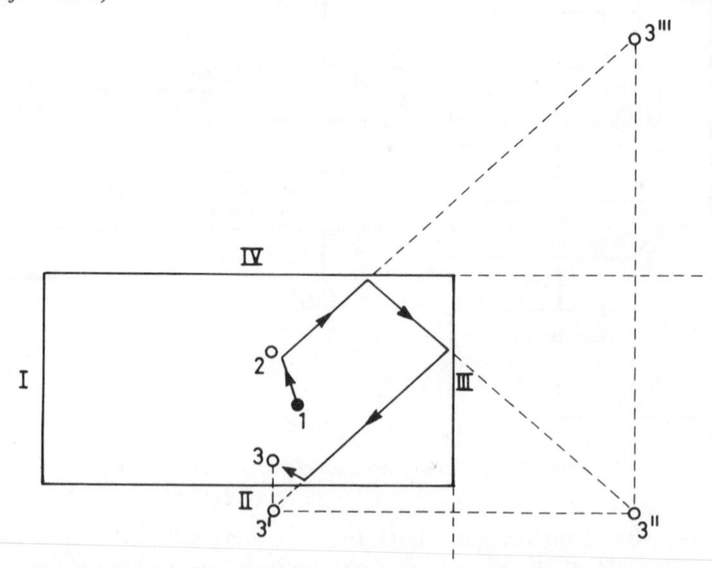

Fig. 3 – Ideal reflections applied to find a potentially successful shot.

When the cue ball has to strike cushions II, III and IV respectively, as is suggested in the figure, before hitting ball 3, the reflection principle mentioned above subsequently generates the images $3'$, $3''$ and $3'''$. In this way a three cushion shot has been reduced to a fictitious plain shot (1-2-$3'''$) i.e. a shot where the cue ball strikes both object balls before striking one of the cushions.

Generally, these shots are quite easy, provided that the angle cue ball – first object ball – second object ball lies within some range. In the figure the angle 1–2–$3'''$ (the fictitious plain shot) is obtuse, say 135 degrees and the corresponding plain shot can easily be made. If the angle 1–2–$3'''$ were larger, e.g. 170 degrees, the plain shot could only be made by a follow shot: the cue ball after striking the first object ball keeps rolling due to angular velocities as a result of cueing the cue ball high. Such a shot is less easy, which is also the case when the angle 1–2–$3'''$ is much less obtuse or even acute. Then a difficult draw shot has to be made by cueing the cue ball below the centre. So, when the angle lies outside some given range, a given possibility will not be further considered.

A sequence of cushions also has to be rejected when the corresponding shot appears to be impossible. For instance, when the cue ball and the first object ball in the figure are shifted sufficiently to the right over the same distance, the given sequence of cushions (II, III, IV) will appear to be impossible. In such cases or when a shot has been decided to be too risky, another sequence of cushions is investigated. For instance, the sequence II, I, IV also seems to offer a sound possibility.

In general, many sequences are possible and the problem is in what order they should be investigated. Obviously, in this case it is also profitable to take a player's experience into account as much as possible. Therefore shots via three subsequent cushions are considered first, then four subsequent cushions. If still no success has been achieved, a series of miscellaneous, more difficult shots are considered. When a sequence has been accepted (in thought) a series of shots are tried, all of them being variations on the fictitious plain shot, bearing in mind that the estimated trajectory of the ball will generally be close to a successful shot. The variations are obtained by slightly disturbing the initial values of the discrete-event model, for instance by making slight changes in the direction and in the *spin* (discussed later on) that should be put on the ball. If none of the attempts has achieved success, another sequence of cushions is tried. If a successful shot has been found only some refinements (e.g. adjustment of the velocity) are applied.

Now we return to the bank shots. These are treated similarly; the only difference is that now the images of both object balls are computed. Whether a bank shot could be accepted also depends on the positions of both these images with respect to the position of the cue ball: the plain shot thus obtained has to be an easy one.

The model described thus far has been created to be comparable with the process of trial and error taking place in a player's mind. Once a certain shot has been established (corresponding to a given sequence of the cushions) a player is (in his mind) trying to execute corresponding shots to change direction, spin etc. and is always being aware of his own technical limitations and of a failure, e.g. due to the cue ball unwantedly striking a wrong cushion, a process eventually leading to the actual shot.

It no solution can be found, even after having interchanged the 'first' and 'second' object balls, it appears that the computer model is not able, given the positions of the balls, to find a three-cushion shot.

It has not yet been mentioned what translational and angular velocities should initially be given when an accepted sequence of cushions has been found and a shot has to be prepared. First, an estimate of the initial velocity is found, dependent on the length of the trajectory that the cue ball has to cover and the number of cushions that will be struck. When a successful shot has been found the velocity is gradually reduced until a three-cushion shot can no longer be successfully achieved.

Another point that still has to be established is where to cue the cue ball. Depending on the angle between cue ball, first object ball and the image of the second object ball, the cue ball is struck above (sometimes for a follow shot), below (draw shots) or in the centre. The side spin is mainly established by the order of the cushions that will be struck. When the cue ball has to go clockwise around the table (e.g. I, II, III, or II, III, IV) right side spin is put on and left side spin when the cue ball goes counter-clockwise.

A last important point is selecting the spot on the first object ball which a player should aim at. In most cases, a plain shot can be dealt with in various ways. For the time being, the model uses only one type of plain shot.

So far, attention has been focused on finding a three-cushion shot. No restrictions whatsoever have been made on the way a successful shot has come about. So, lucky shots or shots which are excessively sensitive to small disturbances of the stroke etc. all count, although these kinds of shot cannot be considered as 'human' shots. These aspects will receive special attention when the validity of the computer model is discussed below.

THE VALIDITY OF THE COMPUTER MODEL

The continuous-time model of carambole billiards (performing all computations of the actual shot) has been validated and is a truthful copy of the real billiard game. The discrete-event model, derived from the continuous-time model and used in the model of three-cushion billiards, behaves the same. So, of the three-cushions computer model only the 'thinking' part has to be validated.

This validation process is hindered by the fact that, instead of a player's thinking, only the results (i.e. the shots) can be observed. However, a player's shot contains a lot of information about his thinking and thus the quality of the computer model can be improved by observing and interpreting these shots.

If all real and corresponding computer shots were equal, the computer model would be an excellent description of a player's thinking. Unfortunately, this is not the case. So the question is: given the same positions of the balls and a computer shot which is not equal to a player's shot what can be concluded with respect to the validity of the computer model? Here a few remarks must be made.

First, what exactly is meant by a player's shot? Of course, it is a shot by *a* player, not necessarily by *the* player. In many cases a great majority of players will choose the same shot, but in many other cases they will not. So, a computer shot can differ from one and be equal to another player's shot. Therefore, when a computer shot is equal to a player's shot it may safely be considered as human. However, if it does not, it may not be concluded that the computer model is invalid. Yet in the computer model some shortcomings can be mentioned as being very difficult to trace. This can be illustrated by some examples. One of the main difficulties in three-cushion billiards is to avoid the accidental contact of the cue ball with the first object ball, because a miss will follow. Better players are very well able to avoid the kiss. However, sometimes they fail and then a miss occurs. When the computer model, trying to find a shot, meets a miss caused by a kiss, it will search for another shot, because it has been programmed to find successful shots. Consequently, human misses are not simulated adequately. Rather rarely it happens that, after a kiss, a lucky three-cushion shot is made. Such shots can be rejected, but in the model they are not. In practice lucky shots occur, so they should also occur in the computer model, though approximately at the same rate as in reality, which is not exactly the case.

Another example concerns the computer shots being seldom played in reality. A player's striking accuracy has its limitations. There are shots which are too risky because they require too accurate striking: only a slight disturbance from the stroke would cause a miss. For this reason a player will look away from trying these shots. However, a digital computer is not bothered by such inaccuracies and strikes exactly as it has planned: it does not recognise risky shots. This sensitivity property (a player does not consider risky shots because these are too sensitive in the stroke) can easily be expressed in numerical terms. Given the initial angular and translational velocities successfully leading to a three-cushion shot, the fraction α of successful shots of N variations on the original shot could be taken as a measure of the sensitivity of the shot. This method will certainly need further consideration. For instance, the minimal number of variations and particularly the minimal fraction α_{min} will have to be experimentally established in order to get a reliable norm for rejecting a successful shot. If $\alpha < \alpha_{min}$, a successful shot is considered too sensitive, and although a valid three-cushion shot it will be rejected. This approach prevents highly improbable shots being accepted as ordinary shots. On the other hand, it is to be hoped that shots having a large α will generally be considered as easy shots.

The computer model plays an average score of about 6.000, so it is about four times better than the best human players. For instance, the Belgian world champion Raymond Ceulemans plays about 1.600–1.700 and the Japanese Nabuaki Kobayashi a little less, 1.300–1.400. In this respect the three-cushion computer is better than the chess computer that is still not able to defeat a moderate international master. However, although playing a very high average score, too often the three-cushion model produces non-human shots.

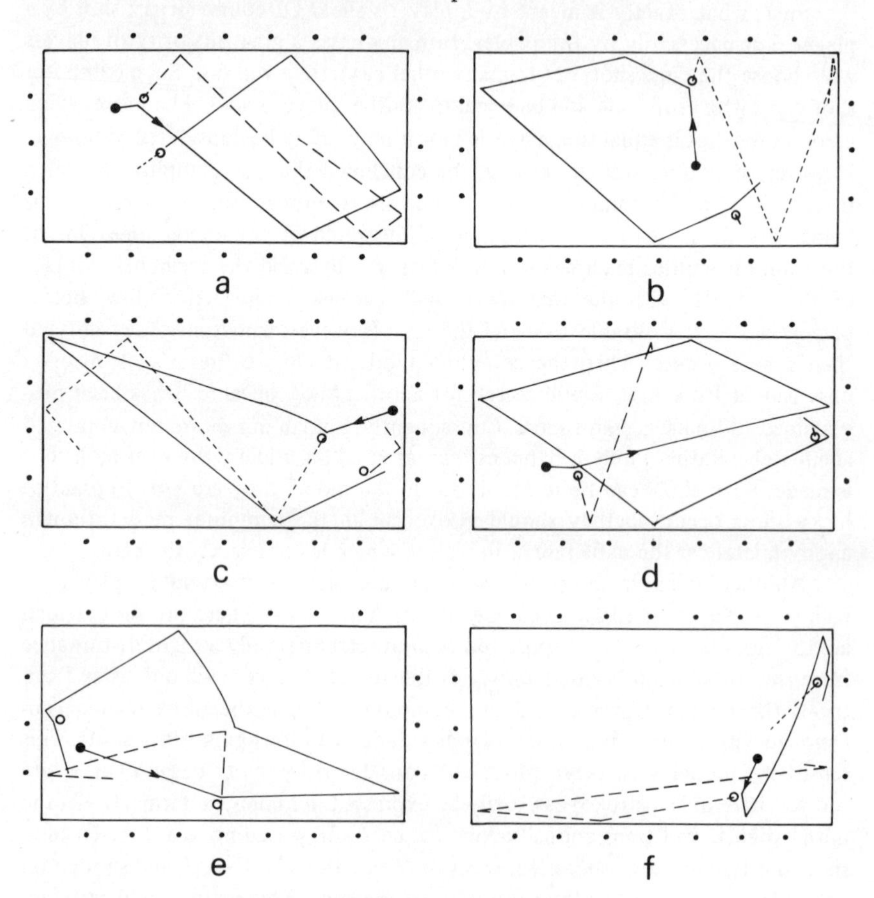

Fig. 4 – Some examples of computer shots.

In Figure 4, a few computer shots are presented. The black ball is the cue ball. Shots (a) and (b) are typical examples of rather safe shots and will certainly be considered as human shots. Risky shots are (c) (cue ball must reach long rail just before the corner) and (d) (too sensitive to disturbances from the necessary direction). More or less lucky shots are (e) (a point is scored despite a kiss) and (f) (where the cue ball has to pass the second object ball first) and therefore these cannot be considered as human shots.

PROPOSED IMPROVEMENTS AND FURTHER REMARKS

From the previous sections we may conclude that the present computer model behaves satisfactorily, as far as its average score is concerned. However, this has also appeared to be its main weakness, a situation that is completely different from the computer chess case for example.

The method proposed above to prevent non-human shots should be looked at more closely, not only because it will probably improve the quality of the model but also because it formulates human decisions in numerical terms.

Other improvements will also have to be considered. Much more attention will have to be devoted to the pattern recognition part, i.e. what useful indications can be derived from the positions of the balls, in order to make as little as possible of so-called brute force techniques. Until now only simple characteristics have been considered but there are many others and using them will certainly improve the quality of the game and decrease computing times. The same holds for the initial velocity (the stroke) for which a rough estimate has been used, and only with much effort (computing time) could an appropriate initial velocity have been found. Using a better estimate of the initial velocity would facilitate finding a shot within a reasonable amount of time. Another important improvement would be the following. In the model for plain shots, only one way of aiming at the first object ball has been available. Many other possibilities exist (more or less thin) but consequently the height of the striking point at the cue ball has to vary accordingly. Such extension of stroke possibilities looks very profitable for the model's performance.

ACKNOWLEDGEMENTS

The author wishes to thank Olaf Corljé and Tom Schiethart for their valuable contributions to this paper.

REFERENCES

Ceulemans, R. (1980), *Mister Honderd* (in English, French, Dutch, German, Spanish and Japanese), De Tor, Amsterdam.

Conti, R. (1961), *Billard für jedermann,* Geselschaft für Druck und Verlag, Vierzen.

Kooiman, A. (1977), A hybrid computer simulation of billiards, M.Sc. thesis, Delft University of Technology, Dept. of Mathematics.

Kooiman, A., de Swaan Arons, H. (1977), A hybrid simulation of billiards, in particular three-cushion billiards, *Proc. of the international symposium 'Simulation '77',* Acta Press Montreux.

Marty, J. (1967), *Le Billard par l'image,* Desseaux et Fils, Coulombe.

de Swaan Arons, H. (1981), Three-cushion billiards: mathematics and modelling, *Proc. AMS 81 conference Lyon.*

PART V – SEARCH THEORY

INTRODUCTION

Search theory is fundamental to a study of virtually all games, particularly two-person zero-sum games of perfect information such as Chess, Checkers, Othello and Go.

To take Chess as a specific example, in considering which move to play it is vitally important to analyse ahead through the opponent's possible replies, one's own response to those replies and so on.

Previous papers in this volume demonstrate that there is far more to game-playing than search alone, but the fact remains that search in one form or another is the basic mechanism underlying virtually all successful game-playing programs, now and in the foreseeable future.

Most of the theory of searching game-trees was worked out in detail over a decade ago. A good account is given by Nilsson (1980).

It is tantalising to realise that there is a straightforward algorithm known as the minimax algorithm, which enables the best move in any position in Chess (or Go, Othello etc.) to be found, at least in principle.

Assuming that a tree could be constructed of every possible different variation to the end of the game (and making a few simplifications to the rules to guarantee that the game must always terminate in a finite number of moves), it is only necessary to work backwards from the terminal positions for which the value (win, loss or draw) is obviously easily determined. It can then be assumed, for example, that a player with a choice of moving to a position which is a terminal win or two others which are terminal losses will choose the former and hence the position from which he is moving can be classified as a theoretical win in one move.

Working backwards in this way, every position which can be won in at most 1, 2, 3, . . . moves by either side can be determined until eventually the standard starting position or any other position of interest is reached. Any position not known to be a win for either side at the end of this process is considered to be a theoretical draw.

Needless to say, the flaw is that the total number of positions to classify in this way is astronomically huge. The first simplification is thus to examine positions only a fixed number of moves ahead and to replace the simple three-valued evaluation, win, loss or draw, with an approximate numerical one, indicating the value of a position on some imaginary scale between won and lost.

Even making this simplification, the method is not a practical possibility if the lookahead is more than a few moves deep. For Chess there are frequently at least 30 moves in every position so looking even 4 ply (i.e. 4 'half-moves' of White and Black alternately) ahead gives almost a million cases to consider. For Go, with far more moves at each turn, the position is much worse.

Fortunately, there is quite a straightforward algorithm known as the alpha-beta algorithm which enables the number of positions which need to be examined to be reduced to approximately twice the square root of its previous value, without any loss of reliability in the result.

Although the alpha-beta algorithm is 'risk free', other methods of extending the depth of search possible for a given amount of computation generally are heuristic, for example 'choose only six moves at each stage to analyse further'.

Extending the theory of searching game trees beyond the point it has already reached is a difficult task involving mathematical analysis of a sophisticated nature.

This section comprises three papers on different aspects of search theory each focusing on the alpha-beta algorithm and possible improvements and embellishments to it. The first paper sets out basic definitions and theoretical results and examines the alpha-beta algorithm in comparison with another algorithm known as SSS*. The second paper provides an empirical analysis of the alpha-beta algorithm. In the final paper alpha-beta is compared with another algorithm known as Scout, both in their standard sequential and their parallel searching versions.

REFERENCE

Nilsson, N. (1980), *Principles of Artificial Intelligence.* Tioga, Palo Alto, California.

20

Game-searching theory: survey of recent results†

Judea Pearl
Cognitive Systems Laboratory, School of Engineering and Applied Science, University of California, Los Angeles, California 90024, USA

ABSTRACT

This paper summarises recent analytical investigations of the performance of common game-searching techniques. The results are reported without proofs, together with discussions of motivations and interpretations.

The highlights include the following: determination of the branching factors of the alpha-beta and SSS* algorithms, the effect of successor orderings on the complexity of alpha-beta and the effect of search depth on the quality of decisions.

INTRODUCTION

Game searching differs from shortest-path search in two essential ways. First, the solution desired is not a simple sequence of moves (i.e. a path) but rather a strategy (i.e. a subtree) which specifies the player's best response to every conceivable move of the opponent. Second, the quality of a given strategy is determined solely on the basis of the terminal nodes it contains but is not a function of the structure (e.g. number of branches, branch cost, solution depth, etc.) leading to these nodes.

The theoretical results reported in this paper concern three main issues: establishing absolute limits on the complexity of game searching procedures, comparing performances of known procedures under various conditions, and evaluating the quality of decisions as a function of the search effort.

The model most frequently used for evaluating the performance of game-searching methods consists of a uniform tree of depth d (d even) and degree n,

†This work was supported in part by National Science Foundation grants MCS 78-07468 and MCS 78-18924.

where the terminal positions are assigned random values independently drawn from a common distribution F. We shall refer to such a tree as a (d, n, F)-tree. The expected number of terminal nodes examined during the search and its branching factor have become standard criteria for the complexity of the search method.

DEFINITION

Let A be a deterministic algorithm which searches the (d, n, F)-game and let $I_A\,(d, n, F)$ denote the expected number of terminal positions examined by A. The quantity:

$$R_A(n, F) = \lim_{d \to \infty} \, [I_A\,(d, n, F)]^{1/d}$$

is called the *branching factor* corresponding to the algorithm A.

The results reported in this paper are direct consequences of a somewhat surprising convergence property of minimax trees (Pearl, 1980a).

THEOREM 1

(a) The root value of a (d, n, F)-tree with continuous strictly increasing terminal distribution F converges, as $d \to \infty$ (in probability) to the $(1 - \xi_n)$-fractile of F, where ξ_n is the solution of $x^n + x - 1 = 0$.

(b) If the terminal values are discrete, $v_1 < v_2 < \ldots < v_M$, then the root value converges to a definite limit iff $1 - \xi_n \neq F(v_i)$ for all i, in which case the limit is the smallest v_i satisfying $1 - \xi_n < F\,(v_i)$.

(c) If one of the discrete values, say v_i, satisfies $F(v_i) = 1 - \xi_n$, the root value converges to a bivalued random variable attaining the values v_i and v_{i+1} with probabilities $1 - \xi_n$ and ξ_n, respectively.

THE BRANCHING FACTOR OF ALPHA-BETA

The alpha-beta (α-β) pruning algorithm is the most commonly used procedure in game-playing applications. Yet although the exponential growth of game-tree searching is slowed significantly by that algorithm, quantitative analyses of its effectiveness have been frustrated for over a decade. One concern has been to determine whether the α-β algorithm is optimal over other game-searching procedures.

Slagle and Dixon (1969) showed that the number of terminal nodes examined by α-β must be at least $n^{\lfloor d/2 \rfloor} + n^{\lceil d/2 \rceil} - 1$ but may, in the worst case, reach the entire set of n^d terminal nodes. The analysis of expected performance using uniform trees with random terminal values had begun with Fuller, Gaschnig and Gillogly (1973) who obtained formulas by which the average number of terminal examinations, $N_{n,d}$, can be computed. Unfortunately, the formula would not facilitate asymptotic analysis; simulation studies led to estimates $R_{\alpha\text{-}\beta} \approx (n)^{0.72}$.

Knuth and Moore (1975) analysed a less powerful but simpler version of the α-β procedure by ignoring deep cutoffs. They showed that the branching factor of this simplified model is $0(n/\log n)$ and speculated that the inclusion of deep cutoffs would not alter this behaviour substantially. A more recent study by Baudet (1978) confirmed this conjecture by deriving an integral formula for $N_{n,d}$ (deep cutoffs included) from which the branching factor can be estimated. In particular, Baudet shows that $R_{\alpha\text{-}\beta}$ is bounded by $\xi_n/1 - \xi_n \leqslant R_{\alpha\text{-}\beta} \leqslant M_n^{1/2}$ where ξ_n is the positive root of $x^n + x - 1 = 0$ and M_n is the maximal value of the polynomial

$$P(x) = \frac{1 - x^n}{1 - x} \cdot \frac{1 - [1 - x^n]^n}{x^n}$$

in the range $0 \leqslant x \leqslant 1$. Pearl (1980a) has shown both that $\xi_n/1 - \xi_n$ lower bounds the branching factor of every directional game-searching algorithm and that an algorithm exists (called SCOUT) which actually achieves this bound. Thus, the enigma of whether α-β is optimal remained contingent upon determining the exact magnitude of $R_{\alpha\text{-}\beta}$ within the range delineated by Baudet.

This enigma has been resolved (Pearl, 1980b) with the aid of Theorem 1 and the fact that if the terminal values of a (d, n, F)-tree are drawn from a characteristic distribution $\phi(X)$, then the distribution of every node in the tree would be identical in shape to $\phi(X)$ save for a scale factor depending on the node's level (Pearl, 1980c). The result is summarised by the following theorem (Pearl, 1980b).

THEOREM 2

The branching factor of the α-β procedure for a continuous-valued uniform tree of degree n is given by:

$$R_{\alpha\text{-}\beta} = \frac{\xi_n}{1 - \xi_n} \qquad (1)$$

where ξ_n is the positive root of the equation $x^n + x - 1 = 0$.

Corollary

The α-β procedure is asymptotically optimal over the class of directional game-searching algorithms.

The corollary follows from (1) and the fact that $\xi_n/1 - \xi_n$ lower bounds the branching factor of any directional algorithm (Pearl, 1980a). The asymptotic behaviour of $R_{\alpha\text{-}\beta}$ is $0(n/\log n)$, as predicted by Knuth and Moore (1975). However, for moderate values of $n (n \leqslant 1000)$, $\xi_n/1 - \xi_n$ is fitted much better by the formula $(0.925) n^{.747}$ (see Fig. 4 of Pearl (1980a) which vindicates the simulation results of Fuller, Gaschnig and Gillogly (1973)). This approximation offers a more meaningful appreciation of the pruning power of the α-β algorithm.

Roughly speaking, a fraction of only $(0.925)n^{0.747}/n \approx n^{-1/4}$ of the legal moves will be explored by α-β. Alternatively, for a given search time allotment, the α-β pruning allows the search depth to be increased by a factor $\log n/\log R_{\alpha\text{-}\beta} \approx 4/3$ over that of an exhaustive minimax search.

The establishment of the precise value of $R_{\alpha\text{-}\beta}$ for continuous-valued trees, together with a previous result that $R_{\alpha\text{-}\beta} = n^{1/2}$ for almost all discrete-valued trees (Pearl, 1980a), resolve two major uncertainties regarding the asymptotic behaviour of α-β. However, until very recently the global optimality of α-β has been an unresolved issue. Naturally, the focus of attention turns to non-directional algorithms, raising the question whether any such algorithm exists which exhibits a branching factor lower than $\xi_n/1-\xi_n$.

A MINIMAX ALGORITHM BETTER THAN ALPHA-BETA? YES AND NO

Recently, Stockman (1979) has introduced a non-directional algorithm called SSS* which examines strictly fewer nodes than α-β. The exact magnitude of this improvement has not been evaluated yet, and hopes were raised that the superiority of Stockman's algorithm reflects a reduced branching factor thus rendering α-β asymptotically suboptimal.

A simple heuristic argument exists which refutes these hopes and indicates that SSS* and α-β possess identical branching factors. It is based on the fact that when the terminal nodes are assigned only two values (say 1 and 0), the performance of SSS* becomes identical to that of α-β.

Let $R_A(n, p)$ stand for the branching factor of algorithm A under the condition that each terminal value may be 1 or 0 with probability P and $1-P$ respectively. Since the search of continuous games is harder than bivalued games, we should assert:

$$R_{SSS*}(n, P) \leqslant R_{SSS*}(n, F) \text{ for all } 0 \leqslant P \leqslant 1$$

In particular, for $P = \xi_n$, we obtain:

$$R_{SSS*}(n, F) \geqslant R_{SSS*}(n, \xi_n) = R_{\alpha\text{-}\beta}(n, \xi_n) = \frac{\xi_n}{1-\xi_n}$$

which together with:

$$R_{SSS*} \leqslant R_{\alpha\text{-}\beta} = \frac{\xi_n}{1-\xi_n}$$

gives:

$$R_{SSS*} = R_{\alpha\text{-}\beta}$$

The weakness of this argument lies in the possibility that SSS* belongs to the rare class of algorithms whose performances improve with randomisation, thus violating the assertion $R_{SSS^*}(n, P) \leqslant R_{SSS^*}(n, F)$. This weakness has motivated the evaluation of R_{SSS^*} by direct methods using techniques similar to those of Baudet (1978) and Pearl (1980b). The evaluation has been completed recently (Roizen and Pearl (in preparation)) with a definite confirmation of the relation:

$$R_{SSS^*} = R_{\alpha\text{-}\beta} = \frac{\xi_n}{1-\xi_n}$$

Thus, the superiority of SSS* over α-β is not reflected in their growth rates; the two algorithms can, therefore, be regarded as asymptotically equivalent.

Notably, the problem of determining the existence of an algorithm superior to α-β can be reduced to the simpler problem of finding a superior algorithm for searching a standard bi-valued tree, i.e. a tree for which the terminal nodes are assigned the values 1 and 0 with probability ξ_n and $1 - \xi_n$, respectively (Pearl, 1980a). Tarsi (paper in preparation) has demonstrated that no algorithm can search this standard tree without inspecting an average of at least $[\xi_n/1-\xi_n]^d$ terminal nodes. This result renders α-β asymptotically optimal of all search algorithms.

WHEN IS SUCCESSOR ORDERING BENEFICIAL?

The analyses presented in the preceding two sections assumed that the order in which α-β selects nodes for expansion is completely arbitrary, say from left to right. In practice, the successors of each expanded node are first ordered according to their static evaluation function. Successors of MAX nodes are then expanded in descending order of their evaluation function (i.e. highest first) and those of MIN nodes in ascending order (i.e. lowest first). It is normally assumed that such preordering increases substantially the number of cutoffs induced and results in a lower branching factor.

Clearly, when the static evaluation function is well informed (i.e. closely correlates with the actual node value), such ordering will induce all possible cutoffs yielding $R = n^{1/2}$. On the other hand, when the static evaluation is uninformed the ordering is superfluous and yields

$$R = \frac{\xi_n}{1-\xi_n}$$

like random ordering. The analysis of this section attempts to quantify the relation between the informedness of the static evaluation function and the branching factor induced by successor ordering.

For simplicity we treat bivalued n-ary trees with probability $P = \xi_n$ that a terminal node obtains the value 1. The information quality of the static evaluation function V can be characterised by two distribution functions:

$$\begin{cases} F_W(x) = P\ [V \leqslant x \text{ given that a node is actually a WIN}] \\ F_L(x) = P\ [V \leqslant x \text{ given that a node is actually a LOSS}] \end{cases} \tag{2}$$

If we treat x as a variable parameter, F_W can be regarded as a function of F_L, i.e. $F_W = g[F_L]$. $g(z)$ is a monotonic weakly increasing function of z between the points (0, 0) and (1, 1). Totally uninformed V will be represented by $g(z) = z$ while 'noiseless' V would be characterised by

$$g(z) = \begin{cases} 0 & z < 1 \\ 1 & z = 1 \end{cases} .$$

The parameter which directly controls the branching factor is given by the integral:

$$S = \frac{1 - \xi_n}{\xi_n}\, n \int_{z=0}^{1} [\xi_n - g(z)\,(1 - \xi_n)]^{n-1}\, dz$$

THEOREM 3

The branching factor of α-β with successor ordering over a (d, n, ξ_n) – game tree is given by:

$$R(S) = [n + \frac{A(S)}{2}\ (1 + \sqrt{1 + 4n/A^2(S)}\,)]^{1/2}$$

where:

$$A(S) = \frac{\xi_n^4}{1 - \xi_n}\, S - \frac{1 - \xi_n}{\xi_n}\, n\ .$$

Numerical computations of $R(S)$ show that, for all n, $R(S)$ is almost linear with S, gradually increasing from its minimal value $R = n^{1/2}$ to its maximal value

$$R(S = 1) = \frac{\xi_n}{1 - \xi_n}\ .$$

WHEN IS LOOKAHEAD BENEFICIAL?

The basic rationale behind all game-searching methodologies is the belief that lookahead followed by minimaxing improves the quality of decisions or, in other words, that the 'back-up' evaluation function has a greater discrimination power to distinguish between good and bad moves. Although no theoretical model has supported this belief, it has become entrenched in the practice of game-playing and its foundation rarely challenged.

Two heuristic arguments are usually advanced in support of lookahead. The first invokes the notion of *visibility*, claiming that since the fate of the game is more apparent near its end, nodes at deeper levels of the game-tree will be more accurately evaluated and choices based on such evaluation should be more reliable. The second alludes to the fact that whereas the static evaluation is computed on the basis of the properties of one single node, the back-up value integrates the features of all the nodes lying on the search frontier, and so should be more informed. This latter argument essentially takes after the model of *filtering;* the more samples, the lower the noise.

A recent work of Nau (1980) demonstrated that the filtering argument is utterly fallacious. In a large class of game trees, reaching deeper consistently degrades the quality of a decision. This phenomenon, which Nau termed *pathological,* is not confined to the special game-trees considered by Nau but can be shown to be a common occurrence in the ensemble of games defined by the standard probabilistic model of (h, n, P)-trees.

Assume that the evaluation function V computed at each terminal node of a (h, n, P)-tree reflects the likelihood of that node being a WIN position. The quality of such an estimate can be characterised by the pair of distribution functions defined in (2). Given the pair $F_W(x)$ and $F_L(x)$, one can compute the two conditional distributions of V_d, the minimax value of the root node:

$$F_{\mathrm{W}}^{d}(x) = P[V_d \leqslant x \text{ given that the root is WIN}]$$

$$F_{\mathrm{L}}^{d}(x) = P[V_d \leqslant x \text{ given that the root is LOSS}]$$

The analysis shows that , regardless of the leaf-pair (F_W, F_L), the back-up pair

$$(F_{\mathrm{W}}^{d}, F_{\mathrm{L}}^{d})$$

satisfies

$$\lim_{d\to\infty} (F_{\mathrm{W}}^{d} - F_{\mathrm{L}}^{d}) = 0$$

This implies that as the search depth increases, the minimax value of the root node possesses the same statistics regardless of whether the root is in fact a WIN or a LOSS. Thus, the ability to discriminate between a WIN and a LOSS situation deteriorates by the minimax back-up procedure.

To understand why the filtering argument fails in the case of game trees, consider the task of estimating the value of an arbitrary function $y(x_1, x_2, \ldots,$

x_n) on the basis of the estimates $\hat{x}_1, \hat{x}_2, \ldots \hat{x}_n$ of its arguments. Knowing $\hat{x}_1 \ldots \hat{x}_n$ can improve the estimation of y if we integrate them according to strict statistical rules, e.g. form the conditional expectation of y given $\hat{x}_1 \ldots \hat{x}_n$. Instead, the minimax procedure amounts to taking $y(\hat{x}_1, \hat{x}_2, \ldots \hat{x}_n)$ as an estimate for y; it computes the minimax value of the estimators rather than an estimate of the minimax.

This point can be further illustrated by the following game-tree. Assuming

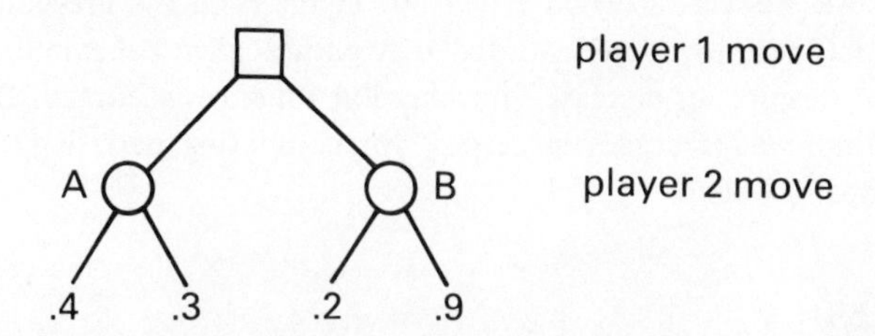

that the terminal values signify the probability that player 1 can force a WIN from these positions. Which move should be selected, toward A or toward B? The minimax evaluation procedure would assign to node A the value .3, to node B the value .2, and so would lead player 1 to prefer A over B. On the other hand, if one computes the probabilities that nodes A or B are WIN (for player 1) one obtains:

$$P(\text{A is WIN}) = P(\text{all A's successors are WIN}) = .3 \times .4 = .12$$

$$P(\text{B is WIN}) = P(\text{all B's successors are WIN}) = .9 \times .2 = .18$$

and so, B is to be preferred. It is clear from this example that if one wants to maximise the chances of choosing WIN positions, the minimax rule is inadequate and should be replaced by product propagation rules: $\prod_i P_i$ for MIN nodes and $1 - \prod_i (1 - P_i)$ for MAX nodes. If these propagation rules are used, the phenomenon of pathology should be reduced if not eliminated.

However, the example also facilitates a line of defence in favour of the minimax rule. In practical game playing, one is not concerned with maintaining a WINNING position (i.e. winning regardless of what the opponent does) but simply with beating a given fallible opponent. Such an opponent, if he shares our assessment of the terminal values, can be *predicted* to choose the left move from position B and the right move from position A. Therefore, on the basis of such a prediction, we have:

$$P(\text{player 1 wins from A}) = .3$$

$$P(\text{player 1 wins from B}) = .2$$

which agrees with the minimax calculation. In summary, although the minimax rule is inadequate when playing against an omnipotent opponent, it tacitly contains a realistic model of a fallible opponent who shares the knowledge and limitations of player 1, and therefore should be effective against such opponents. This, perhaps, may account for the fact that pathology is not observed in practical game-playing programs; the quality of play usually improves with search depth.

Another reason for the absence of pathology in practical game playing could be that the evaluation functions become more accurate toward the end of the game (i.e. increased visibility) an effect not included in the preceding analysis. Nau (1981) has recently demonstrated that pathological behaviour occurs in a specific game despite an increase in evaluation function accuracy. Determining the rate of improved accuracy necessary for combating pathology remains an open theoretical problem.

REFERENCES

Baudet, G. M. (1978), On the branching factor of the alpha-beta pruning algorithm, *Artificial Intelligence,* **10**, 173–199.

Fuller, S. H., Gaschnig, J. G. and Gillogly, J. J. (1973), An analysis of the alpha-beta pruning algorithm. Department of Computer Science Report, Carnegie-Mellon University.

Knuth, D. E. and Moore, R. N. (1975), An analysis of alpha-beta pruning, *Artificial Intelligence,* **6**, 293–326.

Nau, D. S. (1980), Pathology on game trees: A summary of results. *Proceedings of the First National Conference on Artificial Intelligence,* 102–104.

Nau, D. S. (1981), Pearl's game is pathological. *Technical Report TR-999,* Computer Science Department, University of Maryland.

Pearl, J. (1980a), Asymptotic properties of minimax trees and game-searching procedures, *Artificial Intelligence,* **14**(2), 113–138.

Pearl, J. (1980b), The solution for the branching factor of the alpha-beta pruning algorithm. UCLA-ENG-CSL-8019, Cognitive Systems Laboratory, University of California, Los Angeles.

Pearl, J. (1980c), A space-efficient on-line method of computing quantile estimates, UCLA-ENG-CSL-8018, Cognitive Systems Laboratory, University of California, Los Angeles. To be published in *Journal of Algorithms.*

Roizen, I. and Pearl, J. A. Minimax algorithm better than alpha-beta?: Yes and no. In preparation.

Slagle, J. R. and Dixon, J. K. (1969), Experiments with some programs that search game trees, *Journal of the ACM,* **2**, 189–207.

Stockman, G. (1979), A minimax algorithm better than alpha-beta? *Artificial Intelligence,* **12**, 179–196.

Tarsi, M. Optimal searches of game trees. In preparation.

21

The α-β algorithm: incremental updating, well-behaved evaluation functions, and non-speculative forward pruning

Peter W. Frey
Northwestern University, Evanston, IL 60201, USA

The last decade has produced a major increase in our understanding of the α-β algorithm. This report provides an empirical analysis of α-β with and without refinements, compares these results with theoretical predictions, and introduces a novel procedure for enhancing the efficiency of the algorithm.

Early efforts to increase the effectiveness of α-β pruning focused primarily on procedures for ordering descendants at each non-terminal node in the game tree (see, for example, Slagle and Dixon, 1969). The competitive chess programs created in the late sixties and early seventies relied heavily on these ordering procedures and also employed speculative forward pruning of the least-promising alternatives. Current chess programs have replaced these ordering procedures with other techniques which require considerably less processing at each node and produce more α-β cutoffs (e.g. Slate and Atkin, 1977). Ordering at each node requires that all descendants be generated and processed in some detail. This strategy is very inefficient in comparison to others which can produce an early cutoff without generating and processing all the descendants. In fact, theoretical analysis indicates that nearly half of the time spent ordering successor moves will be wasted (Knuth and Moore, 1975) because the order of move consideration at certain types of node is irrelevant to the efficiency of the α-β algorithm.

Chess programming efforts in the seventies demonstrated the power of several clever techniques. The 'killer' heuristic in particular has proved to be extremely valuable. It requires very little additional processing and greatly reduces the size of the search space. The killer procedure remembers the move which is currently considered best at each level of the tree and tries this move first at each new node before any descendants are generated. This procedure dates back at least to the late sixties (Greenblatt, Eastlake and Crocker, 1967).

A second useful innovation is the iterative α-β search. This technique conducts the search in stages, starting with shallow searches and gradually increasing the depth of search until time or space runs short. This procedure has two major advantages. It makes search termination possible at any time since the machine can play the move selected by the most recent complete iteration. This is very helpful for time control under tournament conditions. The iterative procedure also supplements the local ordering information produced by the killer heuristic by providing a breadth first component to the search. The principal variation of the most recently completed iteration is used to construct the initial limb of each succeeding search tree. Even when nodes are counted for all iterations combined, the total is still less than that observed with a single search equal in depth to that of the last iteration. An excellent description of this approach appears elsewhere (Slate and Atkin, 1977).

In early applications of the α-β algorithm, it was commonplace to construct and store a board representation at each level of the game tree. Current programs store only the position currently being processed and remember which changes are required to move down to the base of the tree. This procedure is called incremental updating and downdating. It requires less memory than the conventional approach, somewhat less processing, and usualy more complex coding. One aspect of this approach is to maintain tables of information which are needed by the evaluation function and to update and downdate these incrementally as the search process explores the game tree. This reduces the amount of redundant processing which is required at terminal nodes (Slate and Atkin, 1977).

When evaluation information is developed cumulatively as the search process approaches the tip nodes, it becomes feasible to construct a modified α-β window to determine if the current position, given any variety of successors, could possibly alter the current game value. If the evaluation function is well-behaved (i.e. limits can be established on the maximum perturbation that can be produced by any single move, this technique permits forward pruning without affecting the final move chosen or the final game value. The idea is quite simple. It is not necessary to pursue a sequence of moves to the terminal depth if the current value indicates that no combination of moves at a deeper level could possibly alter the game value. This technique can be referred to as non-speculative forward pruning (NSFP).

To demonstrate the power of these refinements, the author has analysed a strategy game, Treasure Search, which is well-suited for comparing different versions of the minimax procedure. Treasure Search is played on an 8×8 grid and is useful for computer analysis because move generation, board updating, and position evaluation are very straightforward. The version examined in this paper involves a branching factor slightly less than 8 and therefore leads to reasonably complex trees of non-trivial depth. In this respect, Treasure Search is similar to many of the less complex strategy games such as Connect Four,

Checkers, or Othello. Details for this game including the rules, general strategy, and a program listing appear elsewhere (Frey, 1980).

The effectiveness of five different search algorithms was analysed by examining 3 representative game positions with a 7-ply search. Computations based on the number of terminal positions encountered with a full minimax search indicate that the game approximates a uniform search tree with a branching factor of 7.56. Recent reports by Fuller, Gaschnig and Gillogly (1973), Knuth and Moore (1975), and Newborn, Ziv and Neumann (1975) have used theoretical models of the game tree to estimate the effectiveness of α-β for uniform game trees of various dimensions. It is of interest to compare these estimates with empirical data.

The results of the author's analysis are summarised in Table 1. The full minimax procedure encountered 1.6 million nodes during the search process including 1.4 million bottom positions.

Table 1

Average number of nodes examined in a 7-ply analysis of three representative game positions from Treasure Search.

Algorithm	Total number of nodes generated during search	Number of nodes examined at maximum depth
Minimax	1,628,692	1,411,345
α-β	45,963	34,010
α-β w/killer	9,665	6,403
iterative α-β w/killer	6,278	4,416
iterative α-β w/killer & NSFP	2,063	689

The formula developed by Fuller, Gaschnig and Gillogly (1973) estimates that a uniform game tree of these dimensions should produce 78,310 bottom positions when α-β is applied. The data in Table 1 indicate that this is an overestimate by more than a factor of 2. For this game, an average of 34,010 bottom positions were produced by the α-β algorithm. The theoretical model assumed by Fuller *et al.* assumes that the values assigned to tip nodes are chosen from a continuous distribution and are independent. Knuth and Moore (1975) point out that these assumptions are not characteristic of a typical game tree and therefore the theoretical calculations probably overestimate the number of tip nodes for α-β. The author's results clearly support that expectation (i.e. 34 thousand is considerably less than 78 thousand).

When several of the common refinements are added to α-β, the number of tip nodes encountered by the search process is decreased very substantially. The killer heuristic reduces the number of tip nodes from 34 thousand to 6.4 thousand. Adding the iterative procedure reduces this number to 4.4 thousand even with the number of tip nodes being added for all iterations. The power of these relatively straightforward refinements is considerable. Using α-β with perfect ordering would produce 3699 tip nodes. The enhanced algorithm comes very close to perfect ordering. The killer heuristic and iterative procedure are general in nature and can be easily and effectively applied to almost all implementations of the α-β algorithm. Because of this general applicability, theoretical estimates of α-β's unrefined power are of academic interest only. The results in Table 1 indicate a difference of more than 20 to 1 between the estimate of Fuller *et al.* and the empirical result with the refined algorithm.

For strategy games which employ well-behaved evaluation functions, programs which incrementally update and downdate evaluation tables can also take advantage of non-speculative forward pruning (NSFP). If the maximum change in the game value which can be produced by any one move can be bounded within reasonable limits, it is possible to project an expanded cutoff window to preterminal nodes. In Treasure Search the score changes by no more than 9 and no less than 0 on any one move. In this environment, the NSFP procedure produces very impressive results. Table 1 indicates that this refinement reduces the number of nodes in the game tree by an additional factor of 3. A search space which contains over 1.6 million game positions can be effectively searched by examining slightly more than 2 thousand nodes. The NSFP technique is not very useful for games like Chess or Checkers where piece exchanges can produce major perturbations in the game value in one or two moves. For other games, however, such as Go, Othello, or Konane, the NSFP technique can be a valuable tool.

REFERENCES

Frey, P. W. (1980), Machine problem solving, Part 3; The alpha-beta procedure, *Byte,* 244–264.

Fuller, S. H., Gaschnig, J. G. and Gillogly, J. J. (1973), Analysis of the alpha-beta pruning algorithm. Technical Report, Dept. of Computer Science, Carnegie-Mellon University, Pittsburgh, PA 15213.

Greenblatt, R. D., Eastlake III, D. E. and Crocker, S. D. (1967), The Greenblatt Chess Program. *Proc. AFIPS Fall Joint Computer Conference,* **31**, 801–810.

Knuth, D. E. and Moore, R. (1975), An analysis of alpha-beta pruning, *Artificial Intelligence,* **6**, 293–326.

Newborn, M., Ziv, A. and Neumann, M. (1975), An analysis of the alpha-beta algorithm for trees of depth two. Technical Report, Dept. of Computer Science, Israel Institute of Technology, Haifa, Israel.

Slagle, J. and Dixon, J. (1969), Experiments with some programs which search game trees, *Journal of the Association for Computing Machinery*, **16**, 189–207.

Slate, D. J. and Atkin, L. R. (1977), Chess 4.5 – The Northwestern University chess program, in Frey, P. W. (ed.), *Chess Skill in Man and Machine*, New York: Springer-Verlag, 82–118.

22

A comparison of parallel implementations of the alpha-beta and Scout tree search algorithms using the game of checkers†

Selim G. Akl and Ralph J. Doran
Department of Computing and Information Science,
Queen's University, Kingston, Ontario, Canada

ABSTRACT

A parallel version of Pearl's Scout algorithm for searching game trees is empirically compared with the authors' parallel implementation of the alpha-beta algorithm, using a simulated parallel model of computation. A checkers-playing program is selected as the medium for the comparison. Two versions of the program were written using either alpha-beta or Scout to search the game trees they generated. In evaluating each program three criteria were used: the running time, the total number of nodes examined and the number of terminal nodes scored.

These experiments indicate that for opening positions parallel Scout outperforms parallel alpha-beta. For midgame as well as ending positions, however, parallel alpha-beta is distinctly superior in performance. These results seem to confirm similar findings obtained in a comparison of the sequential versions of the two algorithms using the game of Kalah.

INTRODUCTION

The increasing feasibility of concurrent processing technology in the last few years has prompted several AI researchers to propose various algorithms and hardware organisations for searching game trees in parallel (see, for example, Akl, Barnard and Doran (1979, 1980a and 1980b), Baudet (1978), Coraor and Roinson (1976), Fishburn, Finkel and Lawless (1980a and 1980b), Marsland, Campbell and Rivera (1980), Stockman (1979)).

†This work was supported by the Natural Sciences and Engineering Research Council of Canada under grant NSERC-A3336.

An overview and critical assessment of this work is presented by Marsland and Campbell (1981). Recently, a new (sequential) tree search algorithm, dubbed Scout, was developed by J. Pearl (Pearl, 1980a and 1980b).

The algorithm meets a number of asymptotic optimality conditions and appears to have some inherent concurrency that could be exploited on a parallel computer.

The purpose of this paper is twofold. First, a parallel version of Scout is described which uses an approach similar to the authors' parallel implementation of the alpha-beta algorithm (Akl, Barnard and Doran (1979, 1980a and 1980b)). Parallel Scout and Parallel alpha-beta are then empirically compared. Parallelism is simulated on a conventional serial computer. The simulated parallel model of computation is a Multiple Instruction stream Multiple Data stream (MIMD) computer (Flynn, 1966). In this model a fixed number of asynchronous (hardware) processors work independently on different parts of the problem to be solved, exchanging messages when necessary through a common memory or via communication lines. The number of these processors is a parameter of the simulation program. The simulated environment also provides multiple (software) processes: a process is created for each node that is to be examined and runs on a processor if (or when) one is available. A checkers-playing program is selected as the medium for the comparison. Two versions of the program were written using either Parallel Scout or Parallel Alpha-Beta to search the game trees they generated. In evaluating each program three criteria were used: the running time, the total number of nodes examined and the number of terminal nodes evaluated.

The reader not familiar with parallel processing may find it helpful to consult Baer (1980) or Stone (1980) which provide a reasonable introduction to the subject.

THE SEQUENTIAL SCOUT ALGORITHM

Before describing the parallel version of Scout, a detailed study of the sequential algorithm is given. A full description and analysis are provided in the original papers (Pearl, 1980a and 1980b).

Scout is an algorithm for searching minimax trees arising in two-person games of perfect information. In evaluating the worth of a position S for one of the two players, say MAX, the algorithm first computes $V(S_1)$, the minimax value of the leftmost son of S, then 'scouts' the remaining sons $S_2, \ldots, S_n$ to determine if any may have a higher value. If this is the case for position S_i say, then the exact minimax value (S_i) of this position is computed and used in subsequent scouting tests. Otherwise, S_i is discarded from further consideration. When all the sons of S have either been evaluated or discarded, the most recently computed minimax value $V(S_k)$ is returned as $V(S)$. A similar idea is applied in the evaluation of a MIN position. In *testing* a position each of its sons is tested in turn until either one son exempts it from evaluation or all the sons have been tested. Scout thus uses two recursive procedures EVAL (to evaluate a position) and TEST (to perform the scouting checks). Algorithmic descriptions of these procedures are given in Figs 1 and 2.

```
procedure EVAL(S)
    /* Return V(S) the minimax value of position S */
If S is terminal then v = terminal value of S else V = EVAL(S_1)
    /* S_1, S_2, . . . S_n are the sons of S */
    for i = 2 to n do /* Scout the remaining sons */
      if S is MAX then /* V(S_i) > v ? */
          if TEST(S_i,v, >) = TRUE then v = EVAL(S_i)
      else if TEST (S_i, v, <) = TRUE then v = EVAL(S_i)
    endfor
return (v)
end.
```

Fig. 1

```
procedure TEST (S,v,o)
    /* Invoked with o equal to either > or < */
    /* Returns TRUE if V(S)ov is true, otherwise
        returns FALSE*/
If S is terminal then if (V(S)ov) then return (TRUE) else return (FALSE)
else /* S_1,S_2, . . . ,S_n are the sons of S */
    for i = 1 to n do
        if TEST(S_i,v,o) = TRUE
            then if S is MAX and o is > then return (TRUE)
            else if S is MIN and o is < then return (TRUE)
        else if S is MAX and o is < then return (FALSE)
            else if S is MIN and o is > then return (FALSE)
    endfor
    if S is MAX then if o is > then return (FALSE) else return (TRUE)
    else if o is > then return (TRUE)
            else return (FALSE)
end.
```

Fig. 2

Pearl (1980a and 1980b) demonstrates a number of desirable theoretical and practical features of Scout and argues that it is potentially a useful tool in game-playing programs. Pearl has also suggested (personal communication, 1980) that parallel implementations of Scout are worthwhile investigating.

Under ideal circumstances, the minimum number of terminal nodes evaluated by sequential Scout while searching a uniform game-tree of depth D and branching factor N is

$$N^{(D+1)/2} + N^{(D-1)/2} - 1 \quad \text{if } D \text{ is odd}$$

and (1)

$$2N^{D/2} - 1 \quad \text{if } D \text{ is even.}$$

This is illustrated in Fig. 3 where the tree is perfectly ordered so that the best moves for both players are to the left. In such a tree, only those terminal nodes

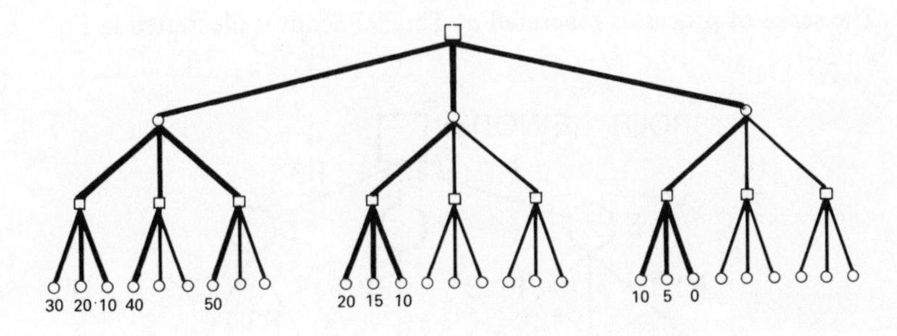

Fig. 3

shown with values attached to them must be examined in order to determine the minimax value of the root. This observation constitutes the basis for the authors' parallel implementation of Scout. Assuming that the tree is perfectly ordered, those nodes that *must* be evaluated are visited first concurrently. The subsequent stages are designed to reduce the search time and cost simultaneously by taking advantage of the parallelism inherent in the sequential version.

THE PARALLEL SCOUT ALGORITHM

The authors' objectives in designing Parallel Scout, the parallel version of Scout, are:

(a) to reduce the 'run time' of the search, and
(b) to increase the number of cutoffs or test exemptions, thereby decreasing the 'cost' of the search.

In the following Parallel Scout is described and it is shown how these objectives are met. A detailed algorithmic description is available from the authors.

First consider procedure EVAL (S): it examines all of the sons of S, evaluating the first son and testing all the others. This suggests that it should be possible to visit all the sons of S concurrently. A parallel implementation of procedure EVAL evaluates the first son of S while concurrently testing all the other sons. This is accomplished by letting the process which calls EVAL create an EVAL-process to examine the first son S_1, and TEST-processes to test $S_2, \ldots, S_n$. Clearly some synchronisation is required here to ensure that the evaluation of S_1 is complete before any attempt is made to compare the value of a terminal node with $V(S_1)$.

The run time of the search may be further reduced by implementing TEST(S) as a parallel procedure. This could be done by testing all the sons of S concurrently instead of one at a time. This approach is not taken as it obviously constitutes a brute force search of the game tree eliminating the purpose of the test function and defeating the objective of reducing the cost of the search.

The series of processes generated by Parallel Scout is illustrated in Fig. 4.

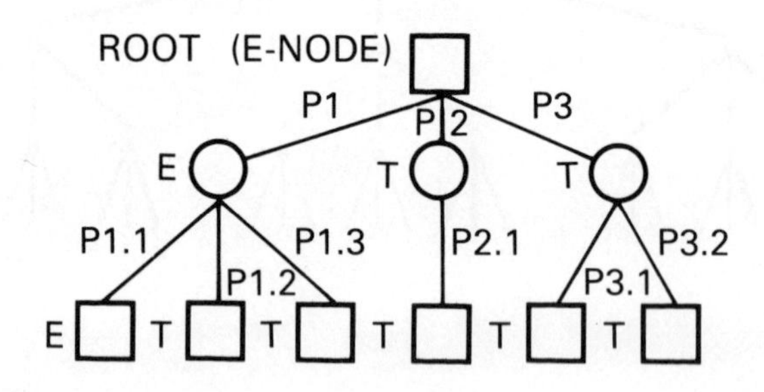

Fig. 4

A distinction is made among the sons of a node. A node that is evaluated by EVAL is called an E-node while a node that is tested by TEST is called a T-node. E-nodes and T-nodes are searched by E-processes and T-processes, respectively. A T-node may become an E-node if it is not exempted by the test. The root is an E-node and therefore generates an E-process P_1 to evaluate its first son. The root also generates T-processes P_2 and P_3, to concurrently test all its other sons.

The effect of Parallel Scout on the number of cutoffs is now considered. First, Parallel Scout may miss cutoffs that would be performed by Scout, thus increasing the cost of the search. On the other hand, Parallel Scout may cut off subtrees that Scout would not. In both cases the underlying reasons for this behaviour can be traced to the differences in process speed and the restrictions of process synchronisation.

Figure 5 shows a tree in which a cutoff is missed by Parallel Scout but caught by (sequential) Scout. Clearly, the circled portion of the tree would be cut off by Scout due to a test of node 4 refuting the evaluation of that subtree. Here the test of node 4 is against the value $v = 5$ which was updated when node 3 was evaluated (because its test did not exempt it). In Parallel Scout tests of nodes 3 and 4 are

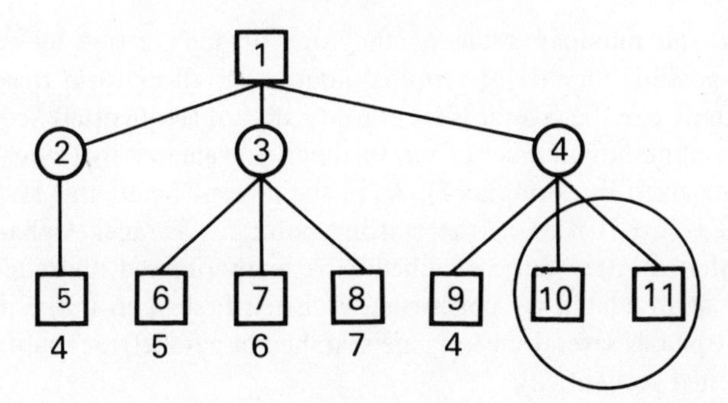

Fig. 5

performed concurrently (assuming a sufficient number of processors is available). Therefore, node 4 is not refuted in its test since it is compared to the temporary value of $\nu = 4$ from the evaluation of the first son of the root. In other words, the test of node 3 is not complete before the test of node 4.

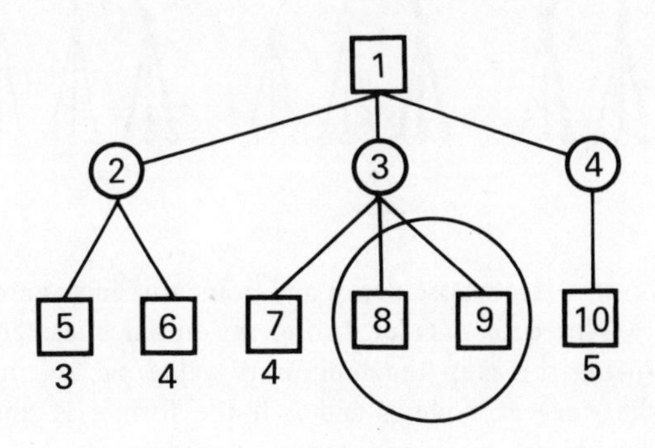

Fig. 6

In the tree of Fig. 6 Parallel Scout catches a cutoff that (sequential) Scout would miss. The circled portion is cutoff if the test and evaluation of node 4 finish before the test of node 3, causing a change in the test comparison value. The new test value exempts any further testing of the sons of node 3.

THE PARALLEL ALPHA-BETA ALGORITHM

The sequential Alpha-Beta algorithm is too well known to be reproduced here (see, for example, Jackson (1974) or Nilsson (1980)).

The parallel Alpha-Beta algorithm uses knowledge about the behaviour of the sequential version to increase the number of cutoffs and simultaneously reduce the search time. It is known (Nilsson, 1980) that (sequential) Alpha-Beta performs ideally when searching a tree like the one in Fig. 3. The algorithm determines the minimax value of the root of such a tree by evaluating the minimum possible number of terminal nodes over all uniform trees of the same size. This best case behaviour is identical to that of (sequential) Scout, described above. The minimum number of terminal nodes evaluated by (sequential) Alpha-Beta is thus given by formula (1). As in the case of Scout this lower bound on the search effort is used as the starting point for Parallel Alpha-Beta. Again, assuming that the tree to be searched is perfectly ordered, those terminal nodes that must be evaluated are concurrently visited first in an initial phase. During subsequent phases several subtrees are searched in parallel, each subtree, however, being searched sequentially.

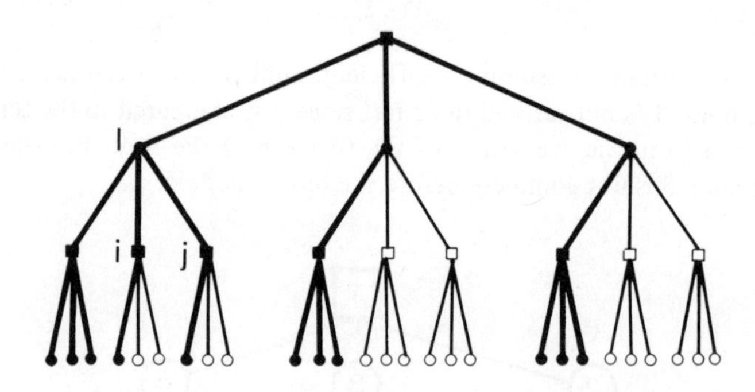

Fig. 7

Fig. 7 shows a uniform tree whose depth and branching factor are both equal to three. The paths explored in parallel during the initial phase are indicated by heavy lines. Following this step the temporary value backed up at node 1 is compared with the ones at nodes *i* and *j*; if the former is smaller, then the subtrees of *i* and *j* need not be considered at all. Otherwise these two subtrees, shown circled in Fig. 8, are searched in parallel (each sequentially) during the second phase.

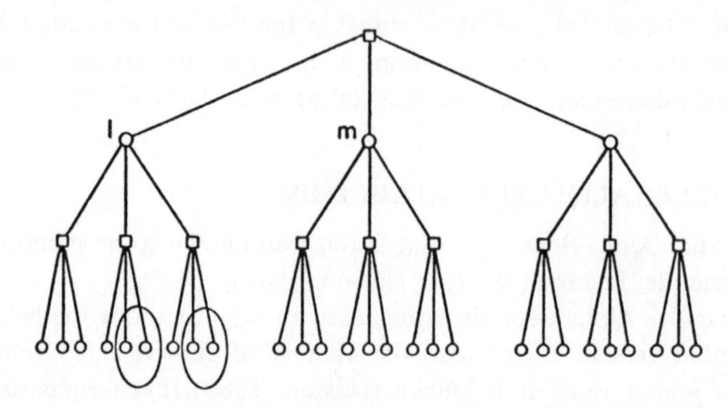

Fig. 8

When these two subtrees have been fully searched the final value backed up at node 1 is compared with the temporary score at node *m* for a cutoff. If this former is larger, the cutoff check is successful and the unexplored subtrees of *m* need not be considered. Otherwise, more subtrees, shown circled in Fig. 9, are searched in parallel (each sequentially) during the third phase and so on.

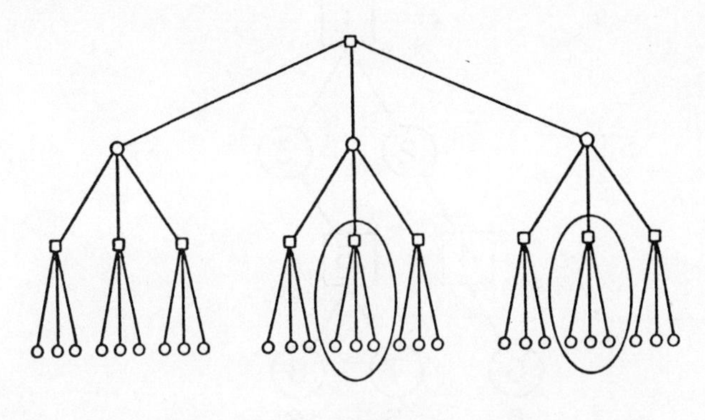

Fig. 9

It should be noted that deep cutoffs allowed by the sequential Alpha-Beta algorithm are not checked for in the parallel version. The result is an increased number of terminal nodes scored during the initial phase. This number, slightly larger than the strict minimum given by formula (1) is derived in Akl, Barnard and Doran (1980a). A full description of the algorithm along with theoretical and empirical analyses are provided in Akl, Barnard and Doran (1979, 1980a and 1980b).

BEST AND WORST CASE ANALYSES

Ideally, both Parallel Scout and Parallel Alpha-Beta will search a perfectly ordered tree. Parallel Scout would evaluate as many terminal nodes as its sequential version would, i.e. the number given by formula (1). Parallel Alpha-Beta would evaluate a few more nodes than its sequential version would, i.e. a number approximately equal (again) to the value given by formula (1). Thus, in the best case, Parallel Scout is more efficient than Parallel Alpha-Beta.

The situation is different at the other extreme. Although both Parallel Alpha-Beta and Parallel Scout end up evaluating all terminal nodes of the tree in the worst case, the former will examine each node exactly once, while the latter may have to examine certain nodes a number of times. This is due to tests not exempting a subtree from evaluation. Therefore, nodes that were examined during the test may be examined again during the evaluation. In fact, it is possible for a node at depth *d* in a subtree rooted at an *E*-node to be visited *d* times. A tree exemplifying this situation is shown in Fig. 10. Node 8 of the tree is visited three times: it is *tested* during the testing of node 3 and then *tested* and *evaluated* during the evaluation of node 3. It is concluded that Parallel Alpha-Beta has a better worst case behaviour than Parallel Scout.

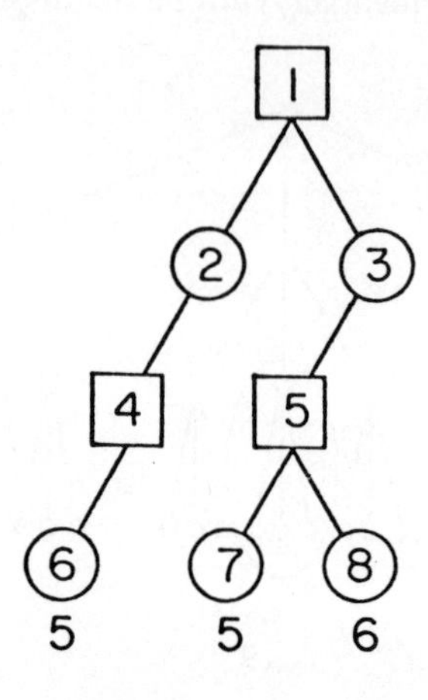

Fig. 10

EMPIRICAL ANALYSIS

In order to compare the typical performances of the two parallel algorithms in a practical setting a 'multiple-instruction stream multiple-data stream' (MIMD) machine was simulated on a sequential computer (the Burroughs B6700) using the simulation language GASP IV (Pritsker, 1974). Two versions of a checkers-playing program were run on the simulated machine: one using Parallel Scout, and the other using Parallel Alpha-Beta to search the game tree. Three criteria were used in the comparison: the running time of the search, the total number of nodes examined and the number of terminal nodes evaluated. These statistics were collected as follows. Several checkers game trees of maximum depth equal to 5 were generated and searched. The board configuration represented by each tree's root was either an opening, a mid-game or an ending position. (A board configuration was considered an *opening* when each player had made fewer than four moves. A position was an *ending* when there were no more than four pieces on the board and no more than seven moves left in the game.) The static evaluation function used to assign scores to terminal nodes was a simplified version of one given by Samuel (1959). The number of (simulated) processors used to search the tree was varied between 1 and 15.

The results of these experiments are shown by the curves in Figs. 11–13 where each curve point represents an average over three trees generated from opening and ending positions and five trees generated from mid-game positions.

DISCUSSION

The curves in Fig. 11 show that for Parallel Scout as for Parallel Alpha-Beta, a rapid reduction of the run time can be obtained by increasing the number of processors used to search the tree. It is also evident that a plateau is reached at about 5 or 6 processors beyond which the run time remains relatively constant as the number of processors increases. Similar observations can be made regarding the size of the tree examined. Figs. 12 and 13 show that the number of terminal nodes evaluated and the total number of nodes visited by both algorithms increases slightly with an increase in the number of processors used. This increase, however, also reaches a plateau after which there is little change.

By comparing the performance of the two algorithms it is obvious that Parallel Scout is slightly more efficient than Parallel Alpha-Beta when the initial board configurations are opening positions. For mid-game and ending positions,

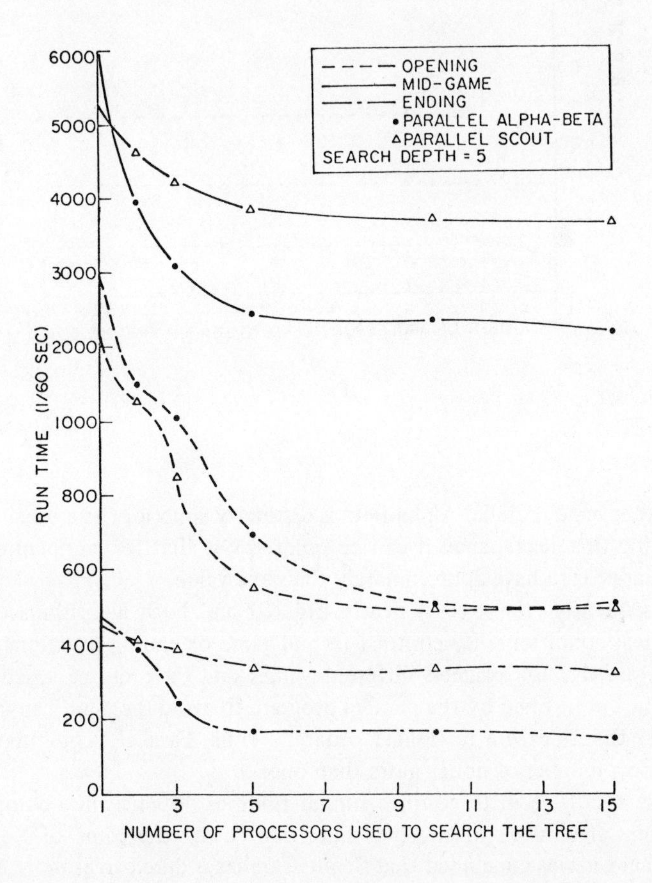

Fig. 11

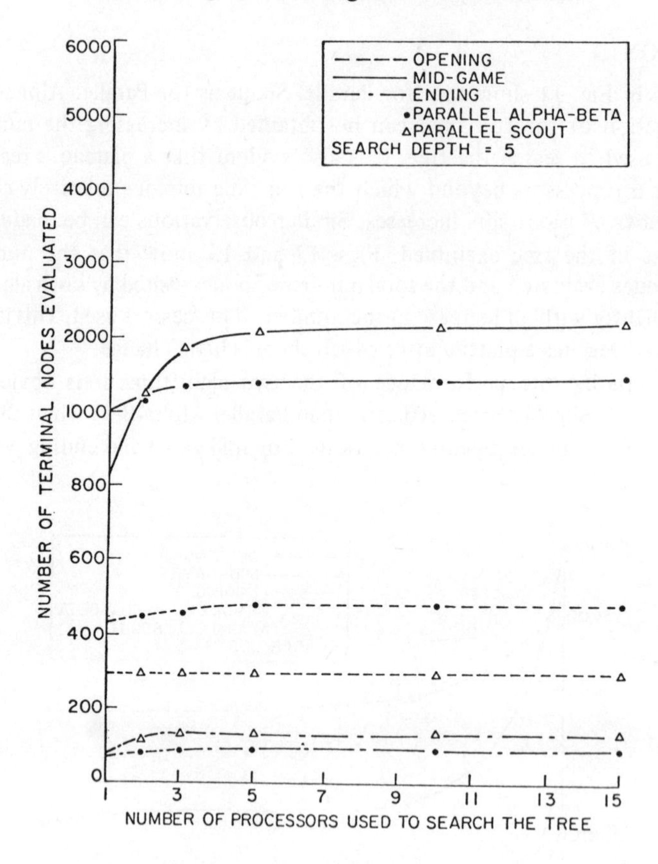

Fig. 12

on the other hand, Parallel Alpha-Beta is distinctly superior. As a possible way of interpreting this discrepancy it can be pointed out that for an opening position all nodes appear to have approximately the same value.

Consequently, the tree is nearly ordered and both algorithms operate in almost ideal conditions. By contrast in mid-game or ending situations, different positions are usually assigned different values and (as ordering based on static values is not performed by the parallel program to avoid the significant associated overhead) the trees are no longer ordered. Thus, Parallel Scout may have to re-examine a number of nodes more than once.

These results seem to confirm similar findings obtained in a comparison of the sequential versions of the two algorithms using the game of Kalah (Noe, 1980) where it was concluded that Scout searches ordered trees more efficiently than Alpha-Beta.

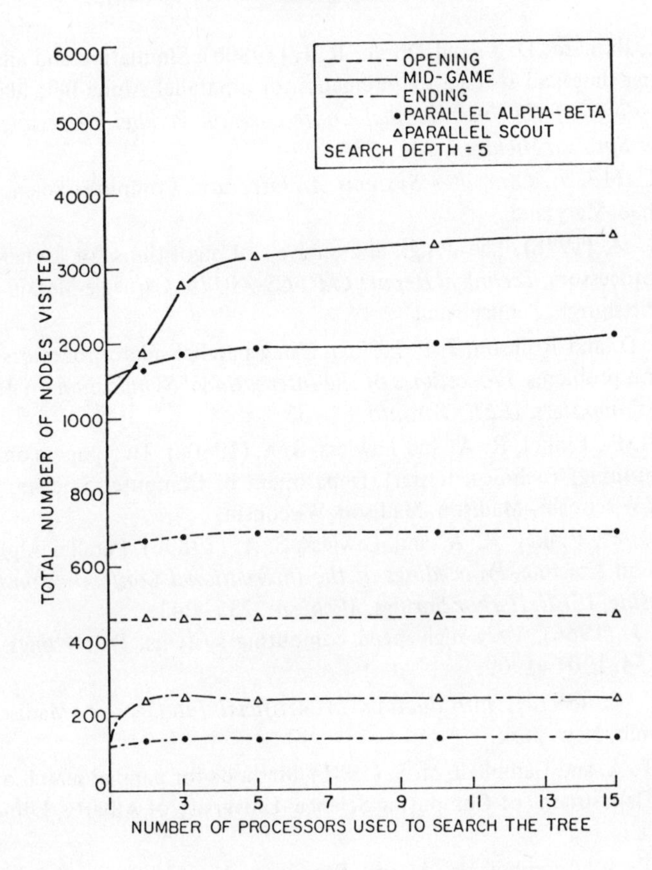

Fig. 13

ACKNOWLEDGEMENT

The authors are grateful to David Barnard for helpful discussions during the course of this research.

REFERENCES

Akl, S. G., Barnard, D. T. and Doran, R. J. (1979), Design, analysis and implementation of a parallel Alpha-Beta algorithm, *Technical Report No. 79–87*, Department of Computing and Information Science, Queen's University, Kingston, Ontario, November 1979 (revised April 1980).

Akl, S. G., Barnard, D. T. and Doran, R. J. (1980a), Searching game trees in parallel, *proceedings of the Third Biennial Conference of the Canadian Society for Computational Studies of Intelligence, Victoria, B. C.*, 224–231.

Akl, S. G., Barnard, D. T. and Doran, R. J. (1980b), Simulation and analysis in deriving time and storage requirements for a parallel Alpha-Beta algorithm, *Proceedings of the International Conference on Parallel Processing, IEEE, Harbor Springs, Michigan,* 231–234.

Baer, J.–L. (1980), *Computer Systems Architecture,* Computer Science Press, Potomac, Maryland.

Baudet, G. M. (1978), The design and analysis of algorithms for asynchronous multiprocessors, *Technical Report CMU-CS-78-116,* Carnegie-Mellon University, Pittsburgh, Pennsylvania.

Coraor, L. D. and Roinson, J. P. (1976), Using parallel microprocessors in tree decision problems, *Proceedings of the International Symposium on Mini and Micro Computers, IEEE, Toronto,* 51–55.

Fishburn, J. P., Finkel, R. A. and Lawless, S. A. (1980a), Two papers on Alpha-Beta pruning, Technical Report, Department of Computer Science, University of Wisconsin–Madison, Madison, Wisconsin.

Fishburn, J. P., Finkel, R. A. and Lawless, S. A. (1980b), Parallel Alpha-Beta search on Arachne, *Proceedings of the International Conference on Parallel Processing, IEEE, Harbor Springs, Michigan,* 235–243.

Flynn, M. J. (1966), Very high-speed computing systems, *Proceedings of the IEEE,* **54**, 1901–1909.

Jackson, P. C. (1974), *Introduction to Artificial Intelligence,* Madison and Lipscomb, New York.

Marsland, T. A. and Campbell, M. S. (1981), Methods for parallel search of game trees, Department of Computing Science, University of Alberta, Edmonton, Alberta.

Marsland, T. A., Campbell, M. S. and Rivera, A. L. (1980), Parallel search of game trees, *Technical Report TR80-7,* Department of Computing Science, University of Alberta, Edmonton, Alberta.

Nilsson, N. J. (1980), *Principles of Artificial Intelligence,* Tioga, Palo Alto.

Noe, T. D. (1980), A comparison of the Alpha-Beta and Scout algorithms using the game of Kalah, *Technical Report UCLA-ENG-CSL-8017,* Cognitive Systems Laboratory, School of Engineering and Applied Science, University of California, Los Angeles, California.

Pearl, J. (1980a), Asymptotic properties of minimax trees and game-searching procedures. *Artificial Intelligence,* **14**, 113–138.

Pearl, J. (1980b), Scout: A simple game-searching algorithm with proven optimal properties, Cognitive Systems Laboratory, School of Engineering and Applied Science, University of California, Los Angeles, California.

Pritsker, A. A. B. (1974), *The GASP IV Simulation Language,* John Wiley, Toronto.

Samuel, A. L. (1959), Some studies in machine learning using the game of checkers, *IBM Journal of Research and Development,* **3**, 211–229.

Stockman, G. C. (1979), A minimax algorithm better than Alpha-Beta?, *Artificial Intelligence*, **12**, 179–196.

Stone, H. S. (ed.) (1980), *Introduction to Computer Architecture*, SRA, Toronto.

Index